Glyn &Williams

Loaned
temperarily to
E. Finch. M.G. & BAR.

MECHANICS AND APPLIED HEAT

MECHANICS
AND APPLIED HEAT

A TEXTBOOK FOR ENGINEERS

BY

S. H. MOORFIELD

M.Sc. (Manch.), A.M.I.Mech.E.

FORMERLY HEAD OF THE MECHANICAL ENGINEERING DEPARTMENT,
WIGAN AND DISTRICT MINING AND TECHNICAL COLLEGE

AND

H. H. WINSTANLEY

B.Sc. (Lond. 1st Class Hons.), M.I.Mech.E.

LECTURER IN MECHANICAL ENGINEERING,
WIGAN AND DISTRICT MINING AND TECHNICAL COLLEGE

LONDON
EDWARD ARNOLD (PUBLISHERS) LTD.

Printed in Great Britain by
Butler & Tanner Ltd., Frome and London

PREFACE

This book has been written with the object of producing in one volume a course in engineering science which will prepare a student for his entry upon the final year of the Ordinary National Certificate Course.

To give the essential principles in direct and logical form has been the aim throughout; hence, descriptive matter and detailed experimental instructions have been omitted as far as possible. It is thought that this method best meets the needs of the part time student, who can thus make use of a textbook instead of using his limited and valuable time in taking extensive lecture notes. Detailed knowledge of experiments and apparatus is best obtained by actual contact; descriptive matter can be supplied by suitable illustrations indicated by the teacher, and familiarity with engine and other details should be obtained by correlating the work of the engineering drawing classes.

In the case of first year senior students it will be necessary for the teacher to decide what parts of the book are to be read to suit his particular syllabus. The second year student will generally require a thorough knowledge of all the subject-matter. The division of the examples at the ends of the chapters into two sections, where possible, will, however, be of some assistance. When the examples are taken from examination papers, those in section A are from the first year papers of the examining bodies mentioned, whilst those in section B are from the corresponding second year papers.

In attaining the above objects, carefully chosen worked examples have been freely used, and they must be regarded as an essential integral part of the text. Without them, the logical sequence would often be broken.

It is believed, too, that it will be a boon to students to be able to obtain at the beginning of their first year course, for a comparatively small outlay, a book which will cover all their requirements in the subject concerned until they enter upon the more diversified work required for the Ordinary National Certificate Examination.

The increasing use of electrical appliances has made it necessary, in the opinion of many people, for all engineers to have
some knowledge of the principles of electricity. Consequently,
a number of colleges and examining bodies have included some
electrotechnics in the first year senior courses for both mechanical
and electrical engineering students. The treatment here given
has been designed for such students.

In order to fix some definite limit to the treatment, the syllabus
of the Union of Lancashire and Cheshire Institutes has been
followed. No doubt this will meet the needs approximately of
many other courses with a similar aim.

The thanks of the authors are due to the Union of Lancashire
and Cheshire Institutes, the Union of Educational Institutions,
and the Northern Counties Technical Examinations Council for
permission to use examination questions, also to Messrs. Stirling
Boiler Co., Ltd., who supplied the drawing and full data from
which fig. 136 and the description have been prepared, to Messrs.
Galloways, Ltd., for loan of drawings from which figs. 134, 137,
138, 139 and 140 have been obtained, to Messrs. Crosby Valve
and Engineering Co., Ltd., for loan of blocks in connection with
figs. 143, 144 and 145, and to Messrs. National Gas Engine Co.,
Ltd., for drawings from which figs. 142, 142(a) and 180 are copied.
Finally we are indebted to the Publishers, Messrs. Edward
Arnold & Co., from whose publication of Callendar's Steam Tables
that at the end of this book has been compiled.

S. H. MOORFIELD
H. H. WINSTANLEY

Technical College,
   Wigan.
      May, 1934.

PREFACE TO SECOND EDITION

The main object of revising this book is to effect such changes, especially in the chapters dealing with heat, as have become necessary on account of a general tendency to discontinue the use of the pound-centigrade heat unit. The British Thermal Unit is now chiefly used in the text and examples, but the gramme-calorie is included since it is required by electrical engineering students.

As the above changes involve so much re-setting, the opportunity has been taken to make a few additions and alterations in the hope that some of the principles may be better elucidated.

The work has been greatly facilitated by the kindness of the Union of Lancashire and Cheshire Institutes, the Union of Educational Institutions and the Northern Counties Technical Examinations Council in granting permission to alter the units in their examination questions which have been used as examples hitherto, and to use questions set in recent years.

Thanks are also tendered to the City and Guilds of London Institute for kindly giving permission to include questions set for the Preliminary Grade in Machine Design.

It is hoped that the modifications now made will justify a continuance of the favour with which the first edition has been received.

S. H. MOORFIELD
H. H. WINSTANLEY

WIGAN.
September, 1947.

CONTENTS

MECHANICS AND APPLIED HEAT

CONTENTS

CONTENTS

MECHANICS
AND APPLIED HEAT

CHAPTER I

FORCE AND ITS EFFECTS

Engineering Science is a subject which deals with those parts of scientific knowledge which are essential to the intelligent understanding of the activities of the engineer. It also usually indicates some of the most important problems met with in engineering practice. We begin with the study of mechanics which treats of *force* and *motion*.

1. Force. Force is one of those things in life about which we all know something as a result of daily experience. We cannot say what it is, nor do we need to do so. We can, however, say much about what it does, that is, we can learn about its effects. Force causes bodies to move ; it also stretches, bends, breaks and compresses things. Force is always in evidence around us, especially that force which tends to make bodies fall downwards.

2. Gravity and Weight. The force which causes bodies to fall is known as gravity. All bodies of a material nature are attracted to one another. The more material there is in two bodies, and the nearer they are together, the greater is their attraction for each other. The earth is, to us, a very great body and all other bodies near its surface or upon its surface are drawn strongly towards it. This is on account of the force of gravity, and the force of gravity on a body is called its *weight*. Gravity is important to the engineer in many ways, but first of all it serves to give us a unit for measuring forces.

3. Unit of Force. When we wish to measure any force, we must have a known force to which others can be compared. This known force is called the *unit of force*.

The unit of force used by engineers in Britain, and also in some other countries, is the *pound*, and is written 1 lb.

The *Unit of Force*, known as the pound, is the force of gravity on a legal standard piece of metal.

The student will see that this unit is the weight of the piece of metal, or is one pound weight. A force, therefore, which is ten times as great as the unit force would be described as 10 lb. weight, or simply 10 lb. The student should note that all forces are not due to gravity.

4. The Spring. Let us now consider in some detail the effect of force on a spring.

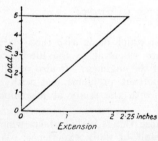

Extension

FIG. 1.

A spring was attached at its upper end to a fixed support and then a series of weights were hung on the lower end. The table below gives the weights or forces applied, the total stretch corresponding to those forces, and the increase in the stretch on each addition of load. Also, in fig. 1, a graph is plotted showing the stretch or extension on the horizontal scale and the force or load on the vertical scale.

Force	Stretch	Increase
0	0	—
1 lb.	0·45 in.	0·45
2 „	0·89 „	0·44
3 „	1·35 „	0·46
4 „	1·80 „	0·45
5 „	2·25 „	0·45

The following features will be noticed:

(*a*) The increases in extension for each additional pound of force are practically equal.

(*b*) The graph is very nearly a straight line.

When two quantities are so related that they both start from zero, and equal increases in one of them will produce equal increases in the other, they are said to be *proportional*. Again, when two quantities are proportional their graph will be a straight line.

EXAMPLE. A spring stretches 2·25 in. when a load of 5 lb. is applied· What should its extension be with a load of 3·5 lb. ?

With load of 5   lb., extension = 2·25 in.

$$\text{,,} \quad \text{,,} \quad \text{,,} \quad 1 \quad \text{,,} \qquad \text{,,} \qquad = \frac{2\cdot25}{5} = 0\cdot45 \text{ in.}$$

$$\text{,,} \quad \text{,,} \quad \text{,,} \quad 3\cdot5 \quad \text{,,} \qquad \text{,,} \qquad = 0\cdot45 \times 3\cdot5 = 1\cdot575 \text{ in.}$$

This result may be checked on the graph (fig. 1). The student should notice that this method of calculation is only correct when the load and extension are proportional.

In a spring the increase in extension per unit increase in force is called the *stiffness of the spring*. This also applies to compression spring.

5. Stretched Wire. Next let us consider the behaviour of a wire when a pull is applied to it. Results are given below of an experiment which was made on a mild steel wire. It was clamped at its upper end and weights were hung on its lower end. By means of a scale and vernier the stretch of the wire was measured. The diameter of the wire was 0·041 in. and its length 106 in.

Load on wire (lb.) . .	0	10	20	30	40	50	60
Stretch of wire (in.) . .	0	0·04	0·08	0·12	0·16	0·22	0·43
Increase per 10 lb. . .	0	0·04	0·04	0·04	0·04	0·06	0·21

The graph, plotting the extensions and loads, is shown in fig. 2.

Here we may notice the following points :

(a) The increases in extension for every additional 10 lb. are equal up to 40 lb.

(b) The graph is a straight line up to a load of 40 lb.

(c) Above 40 lb. the increases in extension are *not* equal, and the graph curves.

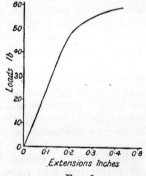

FIG. 2.

Thus the extension of the wire is proportional to the load up to a certain point, but beyond that point this relation ceases. This behaviour seems to be common to most substances and especially the metals which we use in engineering. More will be said of this later.

In this experiment, the wire has acted like the spring until the force of 40 lb. was passed.

EXAMPLE. A wire when pulled by a force of 40 lb. stretches 0·16 in. If, up to this point, extension and load are proportional, what extension might be expected at 24 lb. ?

Extension per pound $= \dfrac{0·16}{40} = 0·004$ in.

Extension for 24 lb. $= 0·004 \times 24 = 0·096$ in.

6. Measurement of Force. The fact that a spring stretches so regularly when a force is applied to it makes it suitable for measuring forces. If one end of the spring is fixed in a frame which carries a scale, whilst the other end carries a pointer moving over the scale, the latter may be so marked or graduated as to read directly the force on the spring. The student should examine an ordinary spring-balance which is the kind of apparatus just mentioned.

7. Tension and Compression. The forces applied to the spring and wire were pulling forces. A pulling force is called a *tensile force*, or simply *tension*.

All forces, however, are not in the nature of a pull. Some forces push on the bodies upon which they act. Such forces are called *compressive forces*, because they compress the bodies on which they act. A compressive force may be applied to a spring with resulting compression or shortening of the spring. Experiment shows that a spring under compression behaves similarly to one under tension in so far that the shortening or compression of the spring is proportional to the force applied.

8. Stress. It has been said in art. 1 that one of the effects of force is to break bodies. When a force tends to break a body, that is, when different portions of it are trying to come apart, the body is said to be in a state of *stress*. Thus the spring and wire of our experiments were in a state of stress. A beam which bends also has stress within it. Thus force produces stress when it acts upon bodies. Forces may be applied externally as we apply them to springs, wires and beams. Sometimes forces are only internal as when a casting cools irregularly. These forces also produce stress and may even break the casting.

We are chiefly concerned with those stresses produced by externally applied forces only. For the present we shall neglect all others.

9. Intensity of Stress. It is necessary for many reasons to have some method of representing stresses numerically. It is obvious that the stress will depend upon the magnitude of the force applied. A little thought will also show that the size of the body will affect the " tendency to break," that is, the stress.

We therefore express a stress in terms of force per unit area. This is called *intensity of stress*.

In the case of tension and compression the area of section is calculated or measured on the plane at right angles to the direction of the force.

EXAMPLE. A bar of steel is of square section $1\frac{1}{2}$ in. by $1\frac{1}{2}$ in. A pull of 7,000 lb. is applied to the bar. Find the intensity of the tensile stress.

Area of section of bar $= (1\frac{1}{2} \times 1\frac{1}{2})$ sq. in.

$$= 2\frac{1}{4} \quad\text{,, ,,}$$

Intensity of stress = force per unit area

$$= 7,000 \div 2\frac{1}{4} = \frac{7,000 \times 4}{9}$$

$$= 3,110 \text{ lb. per sq. in.}$$

EXAMPLE. The wire in art. 5 was 0·041 in. in diameter. Find the intensity of stress under the load of 40 lb.

Area of section of wire $= 0·7854 \times (0·041)^2$

$$= 0·00132 \text{ sq. in.}$$

Intensity of stress $= \dfrac{40}{0·00132} = 30,300$ lb. per sq. in.

Note that the length of the bar has no bearing upon the result.

Fig. 3 shows the arrangement in the former of the two examples just worked. Note that the pull is in the direction of the length of the bar and that the area of the section is perpendicular to the pull. The area is shaded in fig. 3.

The answers of both examples are given in pounds per square inch. It is always necessary in stating a stress to give the units of force and area used.

For engineering purposes we often give stresses in tons per square inch to avoid using big numbers.

EXAMPLE. Give the results of the previous examples in tons per square inch.

FIG. 3.

$3,110$ lb. per sq. in. $= \dfrac{3,110}{2,240} = 1·388$ tons per sq. in.

$30,300$ lb. per sq. in. $= \dfrac{30,300}{2,240} = 13·53$ tons per sq. in.

If, in the first example, the bar of steel had had a push applied to it, the intensity of stress would have been calculated in the same way. The stress would then have been *compressive stress*, whereas both examples are cases of *tensile stress*.

10. Pressure. There are many cases where we prefer to speak of a " push force " as a pressure. Thus we should say that a weight, resting on a table, exerts a pressure upon it. We also speak of liquids and gases as exerting pressure on the surfaces of the vessels which contain them. In the cases of liquids and gases we are nearly always concerned with compressive or push forces because liquids can only withstand a little tension and gases none.

Pressure is very similar to stress, and intensity of pressure to intensity of stress. The pressure within liquids and gases is, in fact, the stress within them.

We may define intensity of pressure as the force upon a unit area of surface. Thus a steam pressure of 180 lb. per sq. in. means that the steam presses with a force of 180 lb. on one square inch of any surface placed in it.

Further matters relating to pressure in liquids and gases will be found in the sections dealing with hydraulics and heat.

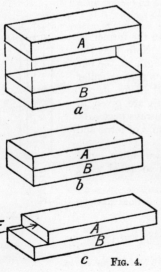

Fig. 4.

For the sake of brevity we generally speak of stress instead of intensity of stress and pressure instead of intensity of pressure. The context will usually prevent any confusion.

11. Shear Stress. There is one other form that stress may take, a form which is usually the most difficult to understand. Let us suppose that we have two blocks of wood, A and B. Suppose the lower surface of A and the upper surface of B to be coated with liquid glue. If the glued surfaces are brought together as at (*b*) and then a force F applied as in (*c*), the upper block A will slide over B, provided B is fixed. Here we should say that *shear* had taken place along the glued surface. Now let the block A be replaced as in (*b*) and left for the glue to harden. If a force F is again applied, no sliding would take place, but now a shear stress would be set up in the hardened glue. The shear stress would have an intensity equal to F divided by the area of A in contact with B.

EXAMPLE. Two blocks of wood each measuring 9 in. by 3 in. are glued together. A force of 108 lb. is applied to the upper block, tending to shear it off the lower block, which is fixed. Find the shear stress at the glued joint.

Area of surface on which shear occurs = $9 \times 3 = 27$ sq. in.

Shear stress = $\dfrac{108}{27} = 4$ lb. per sq. in.

The joint between the blocks need not be central, but may be in any position as shown in fig. 5. The shear stress on the joint would be the same as before. Again, if no joint has been made at all, the stress will still be there in the solid block, and it will occur in surfaces parallel to the applied force F.

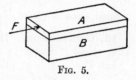

FIG. 5.

EXAMPLE. A piece of steel bar whose section is 4 in. × 2 in. is built securely into a block of concrete. A transverse force of 18 tons is applied to the steel. Find the shear stress in the steel.

Area of section parallel to force = $(4 \times 2) = 8$ sq. in.

Shear stress = $\dfrac{18}{8} = 2\tfrac{1}{4}$ tons per sq. in.

Note that the length of steel bar has nothing to do with the result, and also that the shear stress is the same on all sections parallel to the force.

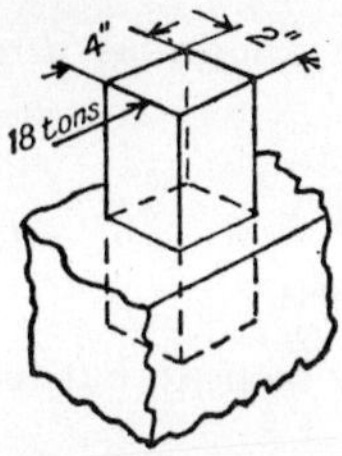

FIG. 6.

12. Cases of Shear. There are many examples of shear stress in engineering. Fig. 7 shows a riveted joint where two plates are fastened together by a rivet. When a force F pulls on the plates the rivet tends to shear off as shown at (*b*).

Fig. 8 shows a pin through a knuckle-joint. In this case the pin tends to shear on two surfaces and is said to be in double shear.

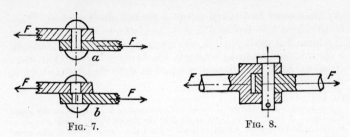

FIG. 7.   FIG. 8.

EXAMPLE. If, in fig. 8, the force F is 12 tons and the diameter of the pin is $1\frac{1}{2}$ in., calculate the stress in the pin.

Area of section of pin $= 0.7854 \times \dfrac{3}{2} \times \dfrac{3}{2} = 1.77$ sq. in.

Effective area resisting shear $= 1.77 \times 2 = 3.54$ sq. in. (There are two areas.)

Shear stress in pin $= \dfrac{12}{3.54} = 3.39$ tons per sq. in.

13. Conclusions. The student should now be able to see that stress is found by calculating a force per unit of area.

Let P = a pull or push force on a bar.

  ,,   A = area of section of bar measured at right angles to force P,

then stress $= \dfrac{P}{A} = p$ where p is the tensile or compressive stress.

Tensile and compressive stresses are also known as *direct stresses*.

Let F = a transverse force applied to a bar.

  ,,   A = area of section parallel to force F,

then stress $= \dfrac{F}{A} = f$ where f is the shear stress.

In the above formulæ any unit of force may be used, but tons and pounds are the commonest.

The unit for all dimensions is generally the inch, but occasionally the foot is used.

EXAMPLES I

1. In a test on a copper wire the following results were observed:

Load	.	.	0	5	10	15	20	25 lb.
Extension	.	.	0	0.02	0.04	0.06	0.10	0.21 in.

Plot these results and state at what load the extension ceases to be proportional to it.

2. The diameter of the copper wire in the last question was 0·048 in. Calculate the tensile stress under the load of 15 lb.

3. A spring is found to stretch $3\frac{1}{2}$ in. under a load of $12\frac{1}{2}$ lb. If this spring is to be used in making a spring balance, state the length of a division on the balance representing 1 lb.

4. A steel bar is $1\frac{1}{4}$ in. diameter and sustains a pull of 11 tons. Calculate the tensile stress in the bar.

5. A certain kind of cast iron breaks at a stress of 12 tons per sq. in. If a bar of this iron is 1 in. diameter, what pull will break it?

6. A stone column is 18 in. diameter and supports a weight of 10 tons. Find the compressive stress in the stone in pounds per square inch.

7. If concrete may be safely loaded to a stress of 80 lb. per sq. in. in compression, find the safe load which may be applied to a block of it which is 6 in. square.

8. A rivet $\frac{3}{4}$-in. diameter has a shearing force of 2 tons acting upon it. Calculate the shear stress.

9. A gudgeon pin in an engine crosshead is 3 in. diameter and is in double shear. If the safe stress for the pin is $1\frac{1}{2}$ tons per sq. in., calculate the safe force in lb. which may be applied to it.

10. A wire 0·04 in. in diameter and $9\frac{1}{2}$ ft. long was subjected to tensile loading, and the following results were obtained :

Load in lb. .	.	5	10	15	20	25	30
Extension in inches		0·0150	0·0302	0·0453	0·0595	0·0755	0·0907

Plot the load extension curve, and calculate (a) the stress in lb. per sq. in. when the wire supports a load of 18 lb.; and (b) the extension per inch length due to a load of 18 lb. U.E.I.

11. An iron wire 0·048 in. diameter and 10 in. long was subjected to a gradually increasing tensile load, and the magnitude of the loads, with the corresponding extensions of the wire, were as follows :

Load (lb.)	.	20	40	60	80	100	120	140	160
Extension (in.)		0·004	0·009	0·013	0·018	0·022	0·027	0·033	0·043

Draw the load extension diagram to the following scales : load, 1 in. to 20 lb.; extension, 1 in. to 0·01 in.

Find, for a load of 50 lb. (a) the force per unit area, and (b) the extension per unit length. U.L.C.I.

12. An ordinary helical spring measures 10 in. long when a force of 72 lb. acts upon it and $8\frac{1}{2}$ in. long when a force of 90 lb. acts upon it. What is the force required to make its length 9 in. and what is the length of the spring when no force acts upon it? C.G.L.I.

CHAPTER II

STRAIN AND ELASTICITY

14. Strain. It has now been seen that under the action of force bodies extend or compress or, in the case of shear, change their shape. Substances which suffer this deformation are said to be strained.

15. Measure of Strain. The total strain which is suffered depends upon the size of the body and also upon the force which acts, hence we are concerned with the relation between these quantities.

In order to compare amounts of strain we express it as the ratio between the deformation and the original size of the body.

Thus, when a piece of substance is stretched we define strain as :

$$\frac{\text{extension of the body}}{\text{original length of the body}}.$$

Thus, in the experiment of art. 5, when the load was 40 lb., the extension of the wire was 0·16 in. on an original length of 106 in. Hence in this case

$$\text{strain} = \frac{\text{extension}}{\text{original length}} = \frac{0\cdot16}{106} = 0\cdot00151.$$

The student should notice that this result may be regarded in two ways, either as a mere ratio and therefore just a number, or as the amount of strain in inches per inch of original length and therefore a dimension. Both ideas are sometimes useful.

In a similar way, when a body is compressed,

$$\text{strain} = \frac{\text{decrease in length}}{\text{original length}}.$$

16. Relation of Stress and Strain. As an example, in art. 9, the stress in the wire during the experiment of art. 5 was worked out for one of the loads, and in art. 15 the strain for that load was calculated. In the table given below these results are shown for each load up to 40 lb.

Load on wire (lb.) .	0	10	20	30	40
Stress (lb./sq. in.) .	0	7,575	15,150	22,725	30,300
Strain (in.) . .	0	0·000375	0·000750	0·001125	0·00151
Ratio $= \dfrac{\text{stress}}{\text{strain}}$.		20,200,000	20,200,000	20,200,000	20,200,000

The student will note from these values that the stresses and strains increase in the same proportion, or we may say that the strain is *proportional to the stress*.

A material which exhibits this property is said to be *elastic*.

If the body is perfectly elastic, all strain will disappear when the stress is removed. If the strain does not disappear on removal of all the load, the body is said to have taken a *permanent set*. If a piece of material is found to have a permanent set when all stress has been removed, the material has been stressed beyond the *elastic limit*.

The *elastic limit* is therefore the maximum stress which can be applied to a material without producing permanent set.

Hooke's Law. This law states that, within the elastic limit, the strain is proportional to the stress which produces it.

The above law is not absolutely true for any material, but is nearly so for many engineering materials.

From Hooke's Law it follows that the ratio of stress to strain will be constant. In the table given above for the wire, it will be noticed that this ratio is 20,200,000.

Young's Modulus of Elasticity is the name given to the ratio $\dfrac{\text{stress}}{\text{strain}}$. It is sometimes called the *modulus of direct elasticity*.

17. Algebraic Statement. We may now express the facts of the last two articles in algebraic symbols.

Let $l =$ length of an unstressed bar (original length).

$p =$ stress applied to the bar.

$x =$ total extension (or compression) of the bar.

$e =$ strain.

$E =$ Young's modulus of elasticity.

Then strain $= e = \dfrac{x}{l}$.

Modulus of elasticity $= \dfrac{\text{stress}}{\text{strain}} = E = \dfrac{p}{e}$.

The modulus of elasticity is here given as a ratio, but if $e = 1$, that is, unit strain, then $p = E$. Hence we may define the modulus as that stress which produces unit strain. Thus, in the above case of the wire, the modulus of elasticity is a stress of 20,200,000 lb. per sq. in.

We have seen (art. 13) that $p = \dfrac{P}{A}$,

also that $e = \dfrac{x}{l}$

therefore $E = \dfrac{p}{e} = \dfrac{P}{A}\,\dfrac{l}{x}$

and $x = \dfrac{P}{A} \cdot \dfrac{l}{E}$.

In applying the above formulæ it is necessary to use the correct units.

Length, l, may be in feet, inches, centimetres or any other suitable unit, but x must then be in the same unit. P may be in pounds, tons or other unit of force ; but p must be expressed in the same unit.

For example, if l is in inches and P in tons, then x is in inches, A in square inches, p in tons per square inch and E in tons per square inch.

For engineering purposes in this country it is usually most convenient to use the inch and ton, or the inch and pound where these formulæ are concerned.

EXAMPLE. A bar of copper is subject to a stress of 6,480 lb. per sq. in. and the strain is found to be 0·00054. Calculate the modulus of elasticity.

$$E = \frac{stress}{strain} = \frac{6,480}{0·00054} = 12,000,000 \text{ lb. per sq. in.}$$

EXAMPLE. A steel bar has an area of section of $1\frac{1}{2}$ sq. in. and an applied load of 6 tons. The length of bar is 5 ft. and the modulus of elasticity 13,000 tons per sq. in. Determine the extension of the bar.

$$\text{Stress} = p = \frac{P}{A} = \frac{6}{1·5} = 4 \text{ tons per sq. in.}$$

$$\text{Strain} = e = \frac{p}{E} = \frac{4}{13,000}.$$

$$\text{Extension} = x = l \times e = 5 \times 12 \times \frac{4}{13,000}$$

$$= \frac{60 \times 4}{13,000} = \frac{240}{13,000} = 0·0185 \text{ in.}$$

The formula $x = \frac{P}{A} \cdot \frac{l}{E}$ may also be used.

Note. If the stress is stated per square inch the length must be in inches.

EXAMPLE. A wire 96 in. long and 0·064 in. diameter has a load of 60 lb. suspended by it. The extension is found to be 0·0597 in. ; calculate the modulus of elasticity.

$$\text{Area of section of wire} = 0·7854 \times 0·064 \times 0·064$$
$$= 0·00321 \text{ sq. in.}$$

$$\text{Stress in wire} = \frac{60}{0·00321} = 18,700 \text{ lb. per sq. in.}$$

$$\text{Strain} = \frac{0·0597}{96} = 0·000622.$$

$$\text{Modulus of elasticity} = \frac{stress}{strain} = \frac{18,700}{0·000622} = 30,100,000 \text{ lb. per sq. in.}$$

18. Shear Strain. In the last chapter we dealt with shear stress. Such stress produces its own type of strain. Fig. 9 shows a block of rubber glued to a fixed surface such as a table. To the surface of the rubber a strip of metal is secured. The diagram A shows the block, which is rectangular, before any stress is applied. At B the same block is shown when a force F is applied

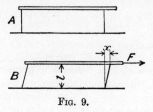

Fig. 9.

to the strip of metal, thus producing shear stress. A change of shape takes place as shown and the amount of deformation is marked as the dimension x.

In this case the strain $= \dfrac{x}{l}$ as before.

It should be noted that l is measured, not in the direction of the force, but at right angles to it.

An experiment was carried out with a rubber block such as that described. Various forces (F) were applied and the corresponding values of x were measured. The results given below were obtained.

On plotting values of F and x it is noticed that a straight-line graph is given very nearly.

F (lb.).				0	28	56	84	112
x (in.)				0	0·037	0·075	0·110	0·150
Increase in x					0·037	0·038	0·035	0·040

The dimensions of the rubber block measured perpendicular to l were 18 in. by $1\frac{1}{2}$ in., and length l was 5 in.

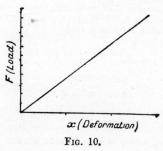

Fig. 10.

The area, therefore, was $18 \times 1\frac{1}{2} = 27$ sq. in.

If the student will work out values of stress $\left(\dfrac{F}{area}\right)$ and strain $\left(\dfrac{x}{l}\right)$, he will see from the results that stress and strain are proportional when shear stress occurs, just as in the case of direct stress.

Rubber has been chosen because it gives values of x which can be measured without complicated measuring devices. We know, however, as a result of experiment that many common engineering materials behave like rubber under shear stress.

Hence, Hooke's Law holds for shear stress and strain.

There is also a modulus of elasticity for shear strain which is named the *modulus of rigidity*.

The modulus of rigidity $= \dfrac{\text{shear stress}}{\text{shear strain}}.$

Let f = shear stress.
$\quad \phi$ = shear strain.
$\quad N$ = modulus of rigidity.

Then $\phi = \dfrac{x}{l}$ and $N = \dfrac{f}{\phi}.$

Also, since $f = \dfrac{F}{A}$ (art. 13)

$$N = \frac{F}{A} \cdot \frac{l}{x}$$

hence $x = \dfrac{F}{A} \cdot \dfrac{l}{N}.$

EXAMPLE. A piece of copper, 6 in. long, has a section 2 in. by 4 in. The modulus of rigidity is 2,100 tons per sq. in. Find the deformation (x) produced by a shearing force of 6 tons.

Shear stress $= \dfrac{F}{A} = \dfrac{6}{4 \times 2} = 0.75$ tons per sq. in.

Strain $(\phi) = \dfrac{f}{N} = \dfrac{0.75}{2,100} = 0.0003571.$

Deformation $(x) = \phi l = 0.0003571 \times 6 = 0.0021426$ in.

EXAMPLE. Taking the load of 112 lb. and the deformation 0.15 in. for the rubber block, calculate the modulus of rigidity for rubber. Length of block $(l) = 5$ in.

Area of section of rubber $= 18 \times 1\frac{1}{2} = 27$ sq. in.

Shear stress $= \dfrac{112}{27} = 4\cdot148$ lb. per sq. in.

Shear strain $= \dfrac{0\cdot15}{5} = 0\cdot03$.

Modulus of rigidity $= \dfrac{\text{shear stress}}{\text{shear strain}} = \dfrac{4\cdot148}{0\cdot03} = 138\cdot3$ lb. per sq. in.

19. A Typical Test. The engineer has the choice of a great variety of materials to meet an even greater variety of needs. The properties of materials must therefore be known by him before he can make a wise selection. The curve, fig. 11, shows how the strain on a bar of mild steel varied when a slowly increasing pull was applied to it. From O to A the curve is practically straight. At A the stress was 43,840 lb. per sq. in. During this range, O to A, we may regard Hooke's Law as sufficiently true for most practical purposes. Moreover, the strain represented at A is only 0·00139 in. To measure such small strains requires the use of an instrument called an extensometer. At A the material then stretched perceptibly without increasing the pull until point B was reached on the graph. At B the strain was 0·021 in., an amount which can be seen quite distinctly on a bar a

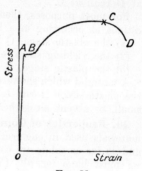

Fig. 11.

few inches long. At A, the material is said to *yield* and the stress, 43,840 lb. per sq. in., is said to be the *yield stress*. On increasing the pull, the mild steel bar elongates rapidly and the stretching can usually be seen to take place. This is known as the *plastic* stage and the steel shows plasticity until it finally breaks at D. Before D is reached, however, it is possible to find a point C where maximum load occurs.

It is found that a ductile material which had an original shape as in fig. 12 (*a*) reaches a load when a distinct plastic contraction as shown at R, fig. 12(*b*), occurs. Due to this phenomenon it is possible to reduce the pull and finally break the bar with a smaller load at D (fig. 11) than it had previously supported at C. The stress at C was 63,000 lb. and at D 53,600 lb. per sq. in. The stress at C is called the *ultimate stress* and is most used for practical work.

The curve of fig. 11 shows the stress as calculated on the original area of section of the bar. As the bar, however, stretches, its section becomes smaller and so the actual stress is more than

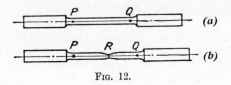

FIG. 12.

that shown. If the actual stress is calculated we find it is higher at D than at C.

For most purposes, then, we may regard three distinct conditions as occurring in a bar of mild steel broken by tension.

(1) the elastic stage, O to A.
(2) the yielding stage, or yield point, A to B.
(3) the plastic stage, B to D.

A material which shows a definite amount of elongation during the plastic stage is said to be *ductile*. If the plasticity is very small, or absent altogether, we say the material is *brittle*.

20. Properties of Common Materials. Practically all the materials used in engineering show some amount of elasticity, and as far as solids are concerned it is chiefly metals to which we must have regard. Cast iron, steel, wrought iron, brass, gun-metal, phosphor bronze, copper, aluminium, tin and lead are all more or less elastic.

Cast iron and hardened steel would show no yield under stress and are not plastic ; they are both brittle.

Copper is generally very ductile and gold is probably the most ductile metal in common use. Both are more ductile than mild steel.

Wrought iron has very similar properties to mild steel but has a smaller ultimate stress.

Aluminium is ductile, but the amount of ductility varies with the method of manufacture. Brass, gun-metal and phosphor bronze, being alloys, show various properties according to composition, but are all ductile, though generally less so than mild steel.

If the student has opportunity to see samples of the various metals under test, it is the best means to an understanding of their properties. Ductile materials are necessary where sudden loads have to be encountered, also where the metal must be worked in a cold condition such as being bent, pressed or dished into shape.

21. Factor of Safety. For many reasons it would be unwise in practice to allow stresses approaching the ultimate stress in parts of machines or structures. In fact, even if the stress were only allowed to exceed the yield stress in a ductile material, the machine part would become permanently deformed. Generally, this could not be permitted.

The stress which is made the basis of calculation of sizes is called the *working stress*, and it is much less than the ultimate or breaking stress. This gives rise to a margin of safety whose amount depends on circumstances.

The working stress is obtained by dividing the ultimate stress by a number called the *factor of safety*.

$$\text{Thus working stress} = \frac{\text{ultimate stress}}{\text{factor of safety}}$$

$$\text{or the factor of safety} = \frac{\text{ultimate stress}}{\text{working stress}}.$$

The value of the factor of safety depends chiefly upon whether the load is a dead load or a live load. A load which cannot vary, such as a stationary weight resting on a beam, is a dead load. A moving weight, such as a vehicle or a crowd of people, would be a live load. Variable forces, such as those acting on the piston rod of a steam engine, are live loads. For live loads higher factors of safety must be chosen than for dead loads. In the case of live loads it is liability to sudden shock which matters. Other things which are taken into account in fixing factors of safety are, danger of corrosion, possibility of abuse, existence of forces which cannot be accurately estimated, etc.

EXAMPLE. A tension member in a bridge girder is calculated to be subjected to a force of 22 tons. It is to be made of mild steel whose ultimate stress is 28 tons per sq. in. Allowing a factor of safety of 6, find the area of section required for the member.

$$\text{Working stress} = \frac{\text{ultimate stress}}{\text{factor of safety}} = \frac{28}{6} = 4 \cdot 67 \text{ tons per sq. in.}$$

$$\text{Area of section of member} = \frac{22}{4 \cdot 67} = 4 \cdot 71 \text{ sq. in.}$$

C

EXAMPLES II

SECTION A

1. What do you understand by the terms : Stress, Strain, and Modulus of Elasticity ?   A tie-rod 100 ft. long and 2 sq. in. sectional area is stretched $\frac{3}{16}$ in. under a load of 32,000 lb.   What are the stress, strain, and modulus of elasticity ?   U.E.I.

2. State Hooke's Law, i.e. state the relationship between the intensity of stress and the intensity of strain.

A hollow column, 10 in. internal diameter, metal 1 in. thick, supports an axial load of 80 tons.   What is the average compressive stress in the material ?   U.E.I.

3. In a tensile test on a wire 5 ft. long and 0·0125 sq. in. cross-sectional area, it was found that the wire stretched 0·0032 in. under a load of 10 lb. Calculate the stress in lb. per square inch, the strain, and the modulus of direct elasticity of the material of the wire in lb. per square inch.   U.E.I.

4. A bar of wrought iron is 12 ft. long and $\frac{1}{4}$ sq. in. in section.   Find the force required to stretch it half an inch ($E = 29,000,000$ lb. per sq. in.).
                                                                      N.C.T.E.C.

5. Gradually increasing tensile loads up to the elastic limit are applied to a wire 0·064 in. diameter, 200 in. long, and the corresponding extensions measured.   At a point on the load extension graph the load is 100 lb. and the extension 0·21 in.   Calculate the modulus of elasticity of the material of the wire.   N.C.T.E.C.

6. The following data were recorded during an experiment in tension with a 0·035-in. diameter wire having a length of 110 in.

Load (lb.) .	.	0	10	12	14	16	18	
Extension (in.) .	0·0	0·041	0·046	0·056	0·064	0·074		
Load (lb.) .		20	22	24	26	28	30	32
Extension (in.) .	0·082	0·093	0·105	0·131	0·161	0·191	0·231	

Plot the load extension diagram and describe its characteristic features. Also estimate the stress at the elastic limit of the material in tons per square inch.   U.L.C.I.

7. Give the meaning of the terms " elastic " and " non-elastic " deformation.   Illustrate your answer by the behaviour of an iron or steel wire when loaded to destruction.

A steel wire 10 ft. long and $\frac{1}{10}$-in. diameter stretched 0·152 in. when loaded with 300 lb.   Find the ratio of the load per square inch to the extension per inch length.   U.L.C.I.

SECTION B

8. A rod 12 in. long is $1\frac{1}{2}$ in. diameter over a length of 10 in. and 1 in. diameter over the remaining 2 in. of its length.   The smaller portion is subjected to a tensile stress of 9 tons per sq. in.   What is the stress intensity in the larger portion ?   How much will an 8-in. length of the larger portion stretch under the load if the modulus of direct elasticity of the material is 13,500 tons per sq. in.   U.E.I.

9. State Hooke's Law.   A rod $1\frac{1}{2}$ in. diameter and 10 ft. long is subjected to a tensile stress of 5 tons per sq. in.   What is the load on the rod in tons,

and what extension is produced by the load ? The modulus of direct elasticity of the material is 30×10^6 lb. per sq. in.   U.E.I.

10. A hollow cylindrical column 10 ft. long is 10 in. external diameter and 8 in. internal diameter. How much will it shorten under an axial load of 60 tons ? $E = 8,000$ tons per sq. in.   N.C.T.E.C.

11. A bar of steel, 4 in. by ¾-in. section, carries a tensile load of 36 tons. Calculate the extension on a length of 3 ft. Modulus of Elasticity = 29,500,000 lb. per sq. in.   N.C.T.E.C.

12. A block of steel is subjected to a shear stress of 5 tons per sq. in. Before the stress is applied a square is marked very accurately on the side of the block. Calculate how much the angle of the square will change due to the stress. $N = 5,200$ tons per sq. in.

13. A bar of steel 12 in. long by 2 in. by ½ in. is riveted to a similar bar of copper so as to make a single bar 12 in. by 2 in. by 1 in. A load of 8 tons is then applied to the combined bar so that both steel and copper extend equally. Find the total extension and the stresses in the steel and copper respectively. E for steel = 13,000 tons per sq. in. E. for copper = 5,200 tons per sq. in.

14. A tube of 0·5 in. outer diameter and 0·375 in. inner diameter is subjected to a tensile force of 0·5 ton and its length is then 40 ft. 5·1 in. The force is then increased to 1 ton and the length is then 40 ft. 5·15 in. What is the value of Young's Modulus of Elasticity for this material ?
          C.G.L.I.

15. Assuming that 16,000 lb. per sq. in. is the maximum stress which may be permitted on a metal alloy, calculate the pull which may be applied to a wire 0·125 in. diameter. What would be the extension on 1,000 ft. of the wire under that load ? Assume $E = 22,000,000$ in lb.-in. units.
          C.G.L.I.

16. A piece of rubber is 0·3 of an inch square in section. When a pull of 18 lb. is applied to the rubber it is 26 in. long and when the pull is increased to 24 lb. it is 28 in. long. Find the modulus of elasticity of the rubber.
          C.G.L.I.

CHAPTER III

EQUILIBRIUM OF FORCES

22. Representation of Forces. In this chapter we deal with the relation of forces to one another and not with the effects of force. It has no doubt been observed by the student that a force has a direction. In fact, if we wish to move a body by force we should usually apply the force in the direction in which we want the motion to occur.

Suppose a stake is driven in the ground at A and a rope AB is attached to it. A pull may be applied by means of the rope in any direction we choose. The pull or force on the stake may be stated by saying how many pounds pull there are in the rope, but we do not know the force completely until we are told the direction of the rope.

Thus the force may be 50 lb. (*its magnitude*), acting from A to B (*its sense*), in a direction making an angle of 30° with a fixed direction AC.

We see that a force has *magnitude*, which we state in pounds, tons or other suitable unit, *direction* which can be denoted in various ways, and *sense*.

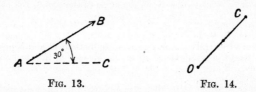

Fig. 13.   Fig. 14.

We find it convenient to represent a force by means of a straight line whose length represents the force to some scale. Thus OC may be a line 2 in. long and represent a force of 2 lb.

The direction of the line would also show the direction of the force. If it acts from O to C it has one sense, but if it acts from C to O it has the opposite sense.

By choosing a scale of 8 lb. to one inch, such a line may represent a force of 16 lb.

Such a line as OC is called a *vector*. A vector can always be used to represent a quantity which has both magnitude and direction. Quantities which have no direction cannot be shown by a vector ; such quantities are a sum of money, a number of wagons, etc.

23. Combining Forces. Suppose a stake at A is acted upon by two forces, shown at AB and AC, both acting along the same line and to the right. It needs no argument to convince anyone

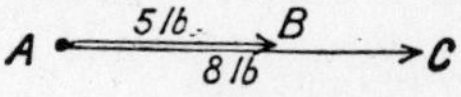

$$A \xrightarrow[\;8\,lb\;]{\;5\,lb.\;} B \longrightarrow C$$

Fig. 15.

that the total force is the sum of the separate forces. Thus if AB is a force of 5 lb. and AC one of 8 lb. the total is $5 + 8 = 13$ lb.

If AC, the force of 8 lb., acted to the right and AB = 5 lb. acted to the left, then the combined effect would be $8 - 5 = 3$ lb. acting to the right.

When we have found *one* force which gives the same result as two or more separate forces, it is called the *resultant*. Thus 13 lb. and 3 lb. are the resultants in the two cases respectively.

24. General Case. Let two forces such as AB and AC act so that there is an angle between them. Simple addition or subtraction will not then give us the resultant and we must now examine this case.

Join three pieces of cord together at a point O. To the other end of each cord attach a spring balance, and let each balance be fixed to a peg in a board or table so that there is a pull on each cord which the balances will indicate. The three forces in the cords will obviously be balanced, and the force in any one of them will be equal, and opposite in sense, to the resultant of the other two. Thus, the forces along OP and OQ are balanced by the single force along OR. If OR were not there, but a peg, driven into the board, were acted on by OP and OQ, the pull on the peg would be equal to the pull along OR, but opposite in sense.

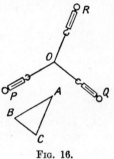

FIG. 16.

The force along OR is called the *equilibrant* of the other two forces. The equilibrant is always equal to the resultant, but opposite to it in sense. Also the three forces are said to be in *equilibrium*. When all are acting, they produce no result.

Now draw a triangle making AB parallel to OP, BC parallel to OQ and CA parallel to OR.

Measure the lengths of AB, BC and CA. The student will find that

$$\frac{\text{length AB}}{\text{force in OP}} = \frac{\text{length BC}}{\text{force in OQ}} = \frac{\text{length CA}}{\text{force in OR}},$$

or, what is the same thing, that

$$\frac{\text{AB}}{\text{BC}} = \frac{\text{force in OP}}{\text{force in OQ}} \text{ and } \frac{\text{BC}}{\text{CA}} = \frac{\text{force in OQ}}{\text{force in OR}}.$$

The directions of OP, OQ and OR, and the forces in them, may be varied as we please, but we shall always find the above relationships to be true.

Hence we conclude that when three forces are in equilibrium they are parallel and proportional to the sides of a triangle.

Again, if there are two forces acting at a point, and vectors representing them be drawn parallel to their directions, in proper order, so as to form two sides of a triangle, the third side will give their resultant. The triangle ABC is known as the *triangle of forces* or the *force triangle*.

25. Concurrency. Instead of joining the cords at a point,

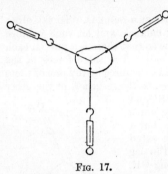

FIG. 17.

let them now be attached to different points on a light piece of cardboard or metal; a thin sheet of aluminium will answer admirably. It will be found that the directions of the cords are such that they are *concurrent* or *meet in one point*. The importance of this fact cannot be over-emphasized. Except when they are parallel, three forces which are in equilibrium *must pass through one point*.

The use of this fact is often essential to the solving of important problems.

26. Triangle of Forces. The principles involved in the last two articles may be briefly stated as follows : If three forces (not parallel) are in equilibrium they must

(1) pass through one point,
(2) be parallel and proportional to the sides of a triangle taken in order.

This is known as the Principle of the Triangle of Forces.

27. Bow's Notation. A system of lettering the diagram which shows the arrangement of a number of forces and also the corresponding triangle of forces has been generally adopted. It is known as Bow's Notation, and when its rules are adhered to, it makes the work simpler and less liable to error. In fig. 18 a line with arrowhead shows the direction and sense of a force, and instead of placing letters at its ends the capital letters A and B are placed one on each side of it. The line is now read as AB or BA. The vector representing the force AB is *ab*, the corresponding small letters. This vector *ab* must

FIG. 18.

(1) represent the magnitude of the force to some chosen scale,
(2) be parallel to the line of action of the force,
(3) be lettered so that when the force is called AB the letters
    a to *b* indicate the sense of the force, that is, *a* to *b* will
    follow the arrowhead.

In (3) the force may be named BA, but then the vector must
be *ba*, that is, *b* and *a* would be reversed in position. The significance of these rules will appear in the given examples.

EXAMPLE. Two forces of 8 and 12 lb. respectively act as shown in the
diagram with an angle of 60° between them. Find the equilibrant and
resultant.

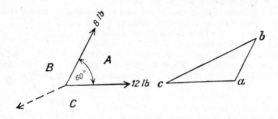

FIG. 19.

In fig. 19 the diagram showing the arrangement of the forces CA and AB
is called the *space diagram* and the triangle *cab*, the *vector diagram*.

In solving the problem, first decide whether the letters in the spaces are
to be taken in clockwise or anti-clockwise order. In the solution given,
they are taken anti-clockwise.

Draw *ca* parallel to CA, making it represent 12 lb. to some suitable scale.
From *a*, draw *ab*, using the same scale, to represent 8 lb. and parallel to AB.
Then, on measuring *bc* to the same scale again, we obtain the value of the
equilibrant. This will be found to be 17·44 lb.

Points to be noted are : (1) Force CA acts towards the right and the
letters *ca* read in the same sense. (2) We have taken CA in a counter-
clockwise order and hence we must continue in that order when we come
to AB. (3) The vector *ab* reads in the sense in which the force acts and
must be drawn in that way. (4) The equilibrant is given by *bc*, read in
that order, and denoting that the force acts parallel to *bc* with its sense
from *b* to *c* as shown by the dotted line. (5) To obtain the resultant we
read *cb* and the resultant has the same value as the equilibrant, *but is
opposite to it in sense.*

EXAMPLE. Three forces, acting as shown on the point O, are in
equilibrium. The force AB is 8 lb., find the magnitudes of the other two.

We will decide to take the letters A, B and C in the clockwise direction.
Draw *ab* parallel to AB, making it 8 units in length. BC should be taken
next, and notice that it pushes on O. Draw a line from *b* parallel to BC.

The length of *bc* is as yet unknown.   Now draw a line from *a* parallel to CA, intersecting *bc* in *c*.   Thus point *c* is found.   Measure *bc* and *ca* to find

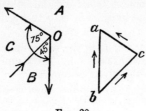

FIG. 20.

the magnitudes of the forces BC and CA.   These should be 7·16 lb. and 5·85 lb. respectively.   Notice again that *ab*, *bc* and *ca* all read in the directions and senses in which the forces act.

EXAMPLE.   Fig. 21 shows a jib crane in outline.   The jib OM is hinged at M and is supported by a rope (or tie) ON.   A weight of 12 cwt. hangs from the end of the jib and the angles are as indicated in the figure.   Find the forces in the jib and tie.

This is a practical application of the previous example.   Letter the spaces ABC as before.   Draw a line *ab*, making it 12 units in length.   We have taken A and B clockwise and must thus continue in that direction. The letters *ab* must read downwards since the weight acts downwards.   From *b*, draw a line parallel to BC, and from *a* draw one parallel to CA.   These meet in *c*.   The vector *bc*, when measured, gives the force in the jib, and since we took B and C in the order B to C we read *bc* in that order.   The force, then, acts in a sense from *b* to *c* and thus pushes on the point O. The jib is, therefore, in compression and such a member is called a *strut*.   The force in the tie is given by *ca* in that sense, and thus pulls on O. Measuring, we find force in jib = 23·2 cwt., force in tie = 16·9 cwt.

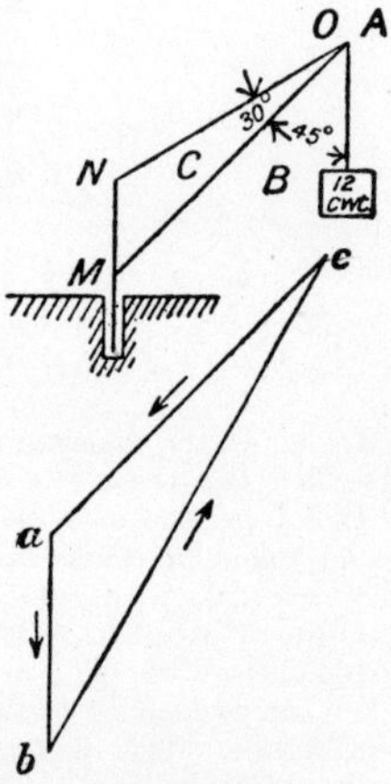

From the three preceding examples the significance of the words " taken in order " in art. 26(2) can be observed.

EXAMPLE.   The force on the piston-rod of a steam engine is 14 tons.   The crosshead moves between guide bars.   When the connecting-rod makes an angle of 20° with the guide bars, find the force in the connecting-rod and that on the guide.

FIG. 21.

Sometimes, as in this case, it is not apparent in what directions the forces are acting.   The force in the piston-rod will obviously act along its centre line.   There will be a force along the connecting-rod.

A third force is needed for equilibrium, and it is supplied by the reaction of the guide on the crosshead.   That is, the guide holds up the crosshead by exerting a force upon it.   As the friction is being neglected the reaction is perpendicular to the guide.   The diagrams may be drawn to scale as in fig. 22.   The clockwise order has been adopted.   On measuring the diagram we find *bc* = force in connecting-rod = 14·9 tons

$$ca = \text{reaction of guide} \qquad = 5·09 \text{ tons.}$$

Note.—If there were a pull on the piston-rod, all the forces would be reversed and the reaction would be exerted by the upper guide. The student should work out this case for himself. The numerical results will be unaltered.

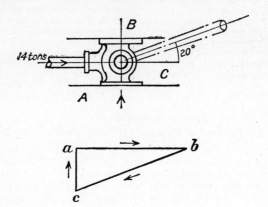

FIG. 22.

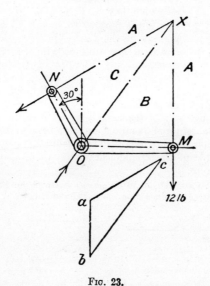

FIG. 23.

EXAMPLE. A cranked lever MON, fig. 23, turns about the point O. At M a force of 12 lb. acts at right angles to OM. A force acts at N perpendicularly to ON and just keeps the lever in balance. Find the force which must be applied at N to produce a balance, and also the force on the pivot at O. The angle MON = 120°. OM = 12 in. ON = 8 in.

This example shows the importance of the fact that the three forces in equilibrium must meet in a point. The direction of the force on the pivot would be unknown, except that we know that it must pass through X, where the forces through M and N intersect. Thus OX is the line of action of the force on the pivot. Letter the spaces ABC and, working clockwise round X, note that the force at M acts downwards, so that *ab* reads downwards ; *bc* and *ca* are drawn parallel to BC and CA. The forces act as indicated in the diagram. Measuring *ab*, *bc* and *ca* we find :

$$\text{force at N} \qquad = ca = 18 \text{ lb.}$$
$$\text{force on pivot} = bc = 26\cdot1 \text{ lb.}$$

28. Resolution of Forces. Having seen how to find one force which is equivalent to two given forces, that is, to find their resultant, we now have to consider the reverse operation.

If we are given *one* force and succeed in finding *two* forces equivalent to it, we are said to *resolve* the force into two *components*. Suppose we are given a force AB whose vector is *ab*, on *ab* we can construct a triangle *abc*. Obviously, there can be two forces parallel and proportional to *ac* and *cb* which have AB as their resultant. The two forces parallel to *ac* and *cb* are the *components* of the force AB.

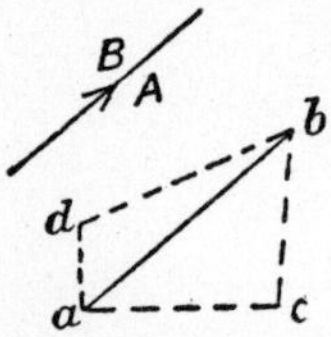

Again, the student will see that we can construct any number of triangles on *ab*, such, for instance, as *adb*. Therefore, it is possible to find an unlimited number of pairs of components of the force AB. As a result, it is necessary, when resolving a force, to say in what directions the required components act, or else to give some other indication which components we require.

FIG. 24.

The principle of the triangle of forces, then, also enables us to resolve forces.

EXAMPLE. A force, AB, of 16 lb. acts as shown in fig. 25. Resolve it into two component forces acting along BC and CA.

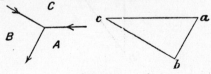

FIG. 25.

Letter the diagram ABC in accordance with Bow's Notation. Draw *ab* parallel to AB, making it 16 units in length.

From *b* draw a line parallel to BC, and from *a* draw a line parallel to CA. The triangle *abc* results.

Measuring the triangle *abc* we find cb = force CB = 27·7 lb.

$$ac = \text{,,} \quad AC = 32 \text{ lb.}$$

These forces are the components of AB. Note that AB is the resultant of BC and CA so that *ac* and *cb* read in the opposite order round the triangle to that of *ab*.

EXAMPLE. A connecting-rod and crank are in the positions as shown in the diagram. The force along the connecting-rod is 2,500 lb. Resolve this force into two components, one along the crank, and the other perpendicular to it.

Letter the spaces ABC. Set off *ab* parallel to AB and 2,500 units in length. Construct the triangle *abc* with *bc* and *ca* parallel to BC and CA respectively. The components are *ac* and *cb*, reading them round the triangle in the opposite order to *ab*.

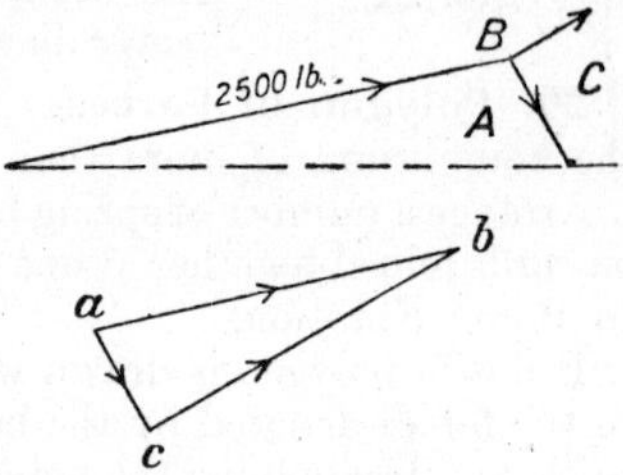

FIG. 26.

The component AC =   760 lb.
     ,,   ,,   BC = 2,389 lb.

EXAMPLE. A weight of 40 lb. is placed on a plane inclined at 30° to the horizontal. Find the total pressure of the weight on the plane and the force with which it tends to slide down the plane.

The solution of this problem lies in resolving the weight, i.e. the force of gravity, which always acts vertically downwards, into two components.

The pressure is perpendicular to the plane and the sliding tendency is parallel to the plane.

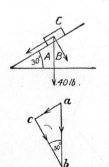

Lettering the diagram as usual, we obtain the triangle *abc* by drawing *ab* parallel to AB, making *ab* read downwards since the weight acts downwards. The components read *ac* and *cb*. On measuring the triangle we find :

Force down the plane = ac = 20 lb.
Pressure on   ,,   ,,   = cb = 34·6 lb.

The student who knows sufficient trigonometry may here note that the angle $abc = 30°$ and therefore $ac = ab \sin 30° = 40 \times 0·5 = 20$ lb. and $cb = ab \cos 30° = 40 \times 0·866 = 34·64$ lb.

Very often we need to resolve a force in two directions at right angles, and when that is the case, one component is always obtained by multiplying the force by the

FIG. 27.

cosine of an angle, and the other by multiplying the force by the sine of the same angle.

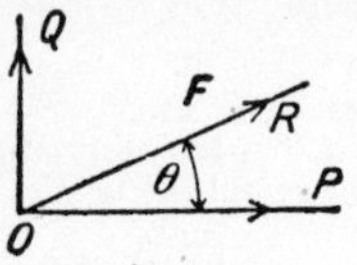

Thus the force, say F, in OR may be resolved horizontally along OP and vertically along OQ as follows :

Component along $OP = F \cos \theta$.
   ,,   ,, $OQ = F \sin \theta$.

The student should draw the appropriate vector diagram to verify his calculation.

FIG. 28.

29. Polygon of Forces. It is often necessary to consider the equilibrium of more than three forces acting on a body.

Arrange a number of spring balances pulling, as shown in fig. 29, on cords joined together at one point. Letter the figure according to Bow's Notation.

If now a polygon is drawn with sides parallel and proportional to the forces denoted by the balances, the polygon will be found to close. In applying the notation, exactly the same rules should be followed as in the case of three forces. Thus *ab* reads upwards because AB is an upward force. *bc, cd, de* and *ea* denote the senses of the forces in BC, CD, DE and EA respectively. Note that the clockwise order has been followed. We conclude, therefore, that if a number of forces pass through one point and are parallel and proportional to the sides of a polygon, then the forces are in equilibrium.

The student should here note very carefully that we have specified forces passing through one point. In this book we confine ourselves to such cases, but it is possible for *more than three forces* to be in equilibrium when they do *not meet in a point*. For the treatment of this case of non-concurrent forces, the student must refer to more advanced books on applied mechanics.

Suppose that on drawing vectors

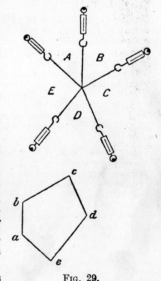

FIG. 29.

parallel and proportional to a number of forces, the figure does not close, then the vector which closes the polygon is the *equilibrant* of the given forces. Taken in the opposite sense it is the *resultant*.

It is not necessary to revert to the experimental method to reach the above conclusions, which follow from a knowledge of the triangle of forces. If points *a* and *c* were joined in the vector diagram, then *abc* would be a vector diagram in which *ac* would give the resultant of forces AB and BC. They could then be replaced by this resultant and, by joining *c* and *d*, the triangle *acd* would be obtained in which *ad* would represent the resultant of forces AB, BC and CD. Replacing these forces by their resultant, only this resultant and the two forces DE and EA remain, and *ade* would be the vector triangle for them. Hence the equilibrium as shown by the polygon would be established. The figure *abcde* is the polygon of forces.

EXAMPLE. Forces act on a point O as in fig. 30. The forces along OP, OQ and OR are 5, 7 and 6 lb. respectively. Find the forces along OS and OT so that equilibrium may exist.

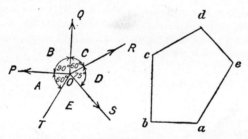

FIG. 30.

Letter the spaces A, B, C, D and E. Set off vectors *ab*, *bc*, *cd*, making them 5, 7 and 6 units in length respectively. From *d*, draw *de* parallel to DE and from *a*, draw *ae* parallel to AE. Then *de* and *ea* are the required forces, and equal 5 lb. and 7·46 lb. respectively.

Note that A, B, C, etc., have been taken in the clockwise direction and that once having chosen that direction we adhere to it.

It is not always necessary to take the forces in the order in which we come to them, but there is no advantage in doing otherwise. It generally avoids confusion if we take them in rotation.

EXAMPLE. Three electric wires attached to the top of a pole have the following pulls and directions. (*a*) 500 lb. due north, (*b*) 480 lb. due east, (*c*) 540 lb. south-east. Find the direction and magnitude of the resultant pull on the pole.

The arrangement is shown in plan in fig. 31. Lettering A, B, C, etc., we draw ab, bc and cd in the force polygon, each representing its corresponding force to scale.

Join ad, which gives the required resultant to scale. Notice that it acts

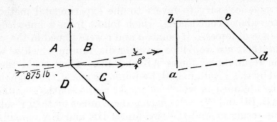

FIG. 31.

from a to d. The equilibrant would act from d to a. The resultant is a force, shown at AD, of 875 lb. at 8° to the direction of BC. The student should understand that this is the total force tending to bend the pole. When a resultant force is asked for as in this case, the answer is only complete when its magnitude, direction and sense are all given.

30. Further Examples. In this article, two examples on the triangle of forces of a more difficult nature are worked.

EXAMPLE. A ladder, weighing 108 lb. and being 25 ft. long, rests against a wall where friction is negligible. The centre of gravity of the ladder is 10 ft. from the lower end, which is 10 ft. from the foot of the wall. Find the reactions of the wall and ground upon the ladder.

The forces acting on the ladder are three :

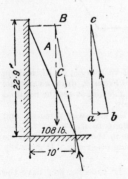

FIG. 32.

(1) The reaction of the wall, which is perpendicular to it, because there is no friction.

(2) The weight of the ladder acting vertically downwards through its centre of gravity.

(3) The reaction of the ground on the ladder. This force is unknown in direction until the other two are known, but since the three forces, to be in equilibrium, must act through one point, the reaction at the ground must pass through the point of intersection of CA and AB. It must also pass through the foot of the ladder and thus its direction is found.

Draw the diagram of wall and ladder to scale to act as the space diagram, and having found the directions of the forces draw the vector triangle abc.

On measuring, it will be found that:

reaction of wall   = 18·9 lb.
reaction of ground = 110 lb.

EXAMPLE. A closed trap-door in a floor measures 3 ft. by 2 ft. and weighs 40 lb. It is hinged along a 2-ft. edge and a rope, inclined at 60° to the door, is attached to the opposite edge. The centre of gravity of the door is 15 in. from the hinged edge. Find the pull in the rope and the force on the hinges when the door is just on the point of opening.

Draw the trap-door and rope to scale.

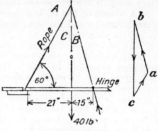

FIG. 33.

The forces acting are:
(1) Force of gravity vertically at 15 in. from the hinge.
(2) Force in rope.
(3) Force on the hinges. As the three forces must meet in a point, this force passes through the point of intersection of (1) and (2), also it passes through the hinge.

Draw the vector diagram *abc*, and measure up, when we find:

Force in rope   = 19·2 lb.
    ,,   on hinges = 25·4 lb.

EXAMPLES III

SECTION A

1. A length of shafting weighing 18 cwt. has to be lifted by a crane. The rope sling used is so attached that each half makes an angle of 60° with the shaft. Find the force in each half of the sling.

2. If, in example 1, the angles had been 30°, what would the force then be?

3. A rope 7 ft. long is attached at one end to a hook in a horizontal beam. The other end is fastened to another hook on the beam 5 ft. from the former. A weight of 50 lb. is fastened to the rope, 3 ft. from one end. What is the force in each section of the rope?

4. Two electric wires are attached to the top of a standard. The pull in one wire is 240 lb. and in the other 280 lb. The angle between the directions of the wires is 60°. Find the resultant pull on the standard in direction and magnitude.

5. A carriage mounted on wheels which may be assumed to be frictionless rests on a plane inclined at 30° to the horizontal. If the carriage weighs 8 lb., find by graphical construction the force required to keep it in equilibrium—
(*a*) when the force is applied horizontally,
(*b*) when the force is applied in a direction parallel to the plane.

U.L.C.I.

6. The base of a machine exerts a thrust of 5 tons, inclined at an angle of 10° to the vertical, upon its horizontal bedplate. Determine the vertical

and horizontal components of the thrust and state what the component
forces tend to do.   U.L.C.I.

7. A weight of 10 lb. is suspended by a string AB from a fixed point A.
A horizontal force F acts on the weight at B and moves it into such a
position that the angle between the horizontal force F and the string is
120°.   Find the magnitude of F.   U.L.C.I.

8. (a) Find the horizontal and vertical components of a force of 150 lb.
acting towards the left at 60° downwards from the horizontal.

(b) A weight of 100 lb. is supported by two cords, one inclined at 45°
to the horizontal and the other horizontal.   Find, in any way you please,
the pull in each cord.   N.C.T.E.C.

9. The jib and tie of a simple crane make 45° and 15° respectively with
the horizontal, the angle between the two being 30°.   Find the force in
each when a load of 10 tons is suspended from the hook.   N.C.T.E.C.

10. Show how to resolve a force into two components acting in given
directions.

A barge is towed along a canal by two men, one on each bank.   The
rope to the left bank is inclined at 30° to the bank and the pull is 60 lb.
If the rope to the right bank is inclined at 45° to the bank, find the pull
in it if the barge continues on a straight course down mid-canal without
any steering.   N.C.T.E.C.

11. The piston of a horizontal steam engine is 12 in. diameter and the
piston-rod is $1\frac{1}{2}$ in. diameter.   The effective steam pressure on the piston-
rod side of the piston is 100 lb. per sq. in.   Calculate the total pull in the
piston-rod.   The connecting-rod of the engine is 5 ft. long and the crank
arm 1 ft. long.   Find, by means of a scale drawing, the pull in the connecting-
rod and the normal reaction between the crosshead and the guide bar when
the crank arm is 60° from the inner dead centre, the piston moving away
from the crank shaft.   U.E.I.

12. A body weighing 20 lb. rests on a plane inclined at 30° to the horizontal.   Neglecting friction, find graphically the force which will maintain
equilibrium when :
(a) it acts horizontally ;
(b) it acts upwards at 45° to the horizontal.
The two angles are measured anti-clockwise from the horizontal.
                                                                      U.E.I.

13. A cranked lever ABC is pivoted at B, with the arm BC horizontal.
BC is 6 in. long, and is acted upon by a vertical downward force of 12 lb.
at C.   The angle CBA is 150° and the arm AB is 8 in. long.   A horizontal
force of P lb. acts at A and maintains balance.   Find the magnitude of P.
Find also the magnitude and direction of the reaction at the pivot.   U.E.I.

Section B

14. A ladder 14 ft. long rests against a line of shafting 10 ft. from the
workshop floor.   The centre of gravity of the ladder is 6 ft. from its lower
end and the inclination to the horizontal is 70°.   Find the reaction of the
shaft and floor upon the ladder if it weighs 45 lb.   Assume no friction
between ladder and shaft.

15. A cranked lever of which one arm OM is 15 in. long and the other
ON 12 in. long has an angle of 135° between the arms.   A force of 40 lb.
acts at M which intersects the force acting on N at a point P.   The angle

OMP $= 60°$ and angle ONP $= 45°$. Find the force at N, and the direction and magnitude of the force on the pivot O.

16. A pole AB, 30 ft. long, is hinged at A, and a chain attached to B keeps the end B 20 ft. above the level of A. The chain at B is at right angles to the pole. Find the pull in the chain and the magnitude and direction of the reaction of the hinge at A when a load of 1 ton is suspended from the middle of the pole.   U.L.C.I.

17. The dimensions of an ordinary crane are as follows : crane post 8 ft. high, tie-bar 12 ft. long, jib 17 ft. long. Determine the forces in the tie-bar and jib when a load of 5 tons is suspended by a rope passing over a pulley at the end of the jib, the other part of the rope being led to the winch in a direction parallel to the tie-bar.   U.L.C.I.

18. The following forces act on a body : 2 lb. north, $3\frac{1}{2}$ lb. north-east, 5 lb. 30° south of east, 7 lb. west. Find the resultant in magnitude and direction.   N.C.T.E.C.

19. Five bars of a steel roof frame, all in one plane, meet at a point ; one is a horizontal tie-bar carrying a tension of 40 tons ; the next is a tie-bar inclined at 60° to the horizontal and sustaining a pull of 30 tons ; the next (in continuous order) is vertical and runs upwards from the joint, and carries a thrust of 5 tons ; and the remaining two bars in the same order radiate at angles of 135° and 210° to the first bar. Find graphically the stresses in the last two bars, and state whether they are in tension or compression.   N.C.T.E.C.

20. A rectangular trap-door ABCD of uniform section is hinged along the edge AB and is held in a position inclined at 30° to the ground by a cord attached to the middle of the edge CD. This cord is inclined at 45° to the partly opened door. Find graphically the pull in the cord and the magnitude and direction of the reaction at the hinge. The weight of the door is 50 lb., AB = CD = 6 ft. and BC = AD = 4 ft.   U.E.I.

21. A ladder rests with one end on rough horizontal ground, the other end resting against a smooth vertical wall. Show by means of a diagram the forces acting on the ladder. Denote carefully the directions of the forces and describe the forces, e.g. weight, etc.

If the length of the ladder is 60 ft. and its centre of gravity is 25 ft. from the end resting on the ground, find by means of a scale drawing, the reaction between the ladder and the wall when the foot of the ladder is 30 ft. from the wall. The weight of the ladder is 100 lb.   U.E.I.

22. Four forces act from a point A. The first is of magnitude 15 lb. and acts towards the north-west, the second is of 10 lb. and acts towards the north-east, the third is of 10 lb. and acts towards the north and the fourth is of 12 lb. and acts towards the east. Find the magnitude and direction of a fifth force which will balance the system and keep the point A at rest.
                                                          C.G.L.I.

23. A circular shaft is 10 ft. above the workshop floor and a bar of steel 16 ft. long, of uniform section, is left leaning against the shaft at an angle of 60° with the floor. The weight of the bar is 50 lb. Find the force between the shaft and bar if the friction between them is negligible.
                                                          C.G.L.I.

24. A bell-crank lever has two arms, AC and CB, the fulcrum being at C. The angle ACB $= 150°$; the arm AC is 2 ft. long and CB 6 ft. long. The arm CB is horizontal. A weight of 60 lb. is suspended from B and a horizontal pull is applied to A. By means of a triangle of forces, find the force on the fulcrum and also the force applied to A.   C.G.L.I.

CHAPTER IV

MOMENTS OF FORCES

31. Turning Effect. One of the effects of force is to produce turning movement. Even when no turning actually occurs a force often *tends* to produce rotation. Turning effect and tendency to produce rotation are sometimes popularly called *leverage*, but in mechanical terms we speak of the *moment* of a force. Common observation of a force applied, say, to a door or a crow-bar soon shows us that the turning tendency of a given force depends upon the point where it is applied. Apply a force near to the hinge of a heavy door and it is moved with difficulty ; apply the force as far away as possible from the hinge and the door moves with ease. Experience tells us that a crow-bar is most effective when the available force is applied at the extreme end.

The value of the moment of a force about a chosen point is

FIG. 34.

the product of the force and the perpendicular distance of the point from the line of action of the force. Thus (fig. 34) a force F has a moment about $O = F \times OA$.

It should be noticed that the moment of the force involves two things, the force and the point of reference. The force F would have a different moment if O were chosen differently. In practice, the point of reference, O, is often determined by circumstances as in the hinge of a door. In solving problems the point may be chosen as a rule to give the most ready solution.

32. Kinds of Moment. Moments of forces fall into two classes according to whether they tend to produce clockwise motion or anti-clockwise motion. A moment may be given an algebraic sign depending upon its class. There is no universal rule, but the anti-clockwise direction may be regarded as positive and the clockwise as negative.

33. Equilibrium of Moments. Arrange a piece of cardboard or similar material so that any number of forces act upon it such as P, Q, R, S. The forces may be applied by spring balances or by weights passing over pulleys. When at rest choose any point O. Let OA be the perpendicular distance of

O from the force **P**. Let OB be the perpendicular distance of
O from Q, and so on.

Then the sum of the anti-clockwise moments will be

$$P \times OA + R \times OC.$$

Also the sum of the clockwise moments will be

$$Q \times OB + S \times OD.$$

On measuring and calculating, the sum of the anti-clockwise
moments will be found equal to the sum of the clockwise ones.

If we conduct a number of such experiments, we find that
whatever the forces, and wherever O is chosen, this relation is
true so long as the cardboard is allowed to come to rest before
measurements are taken. In the above experiment the weight
of the sheet of cardboard has been ignored. If the forces
P, Q, R and S are made large compared with the weight of the
cardboard, the result will not be seriously affected. After dealing
with centres of gravity later
in the chapter, it will be seen
how this weight may be taken
into account, either by choosing the point O at the centre
of gravity, or by considering
the weight as an additional
force.

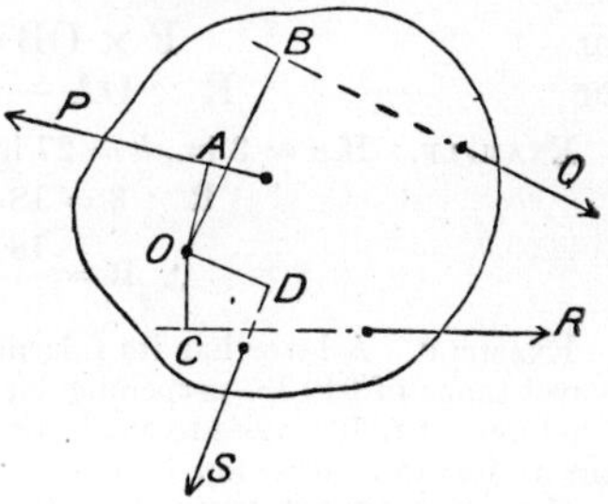

FIG. 35.

Such experiments justify us
in stating the *Principle of
Moments*, which is very important.

*If a body is at rest under
the action of a number of forces, then the algebraic sum of all
their moments about any point is zero.*

The student must clearly understand what is meant by
" algebraic sum," as against " arithmetic sum." The algebraic
sum takes account of the sign.

In the above case of moments on the body, we have algebraic
sum $= P \times OA - Q \times OB + R \times OC - S \times OD = 0$.

The anti-clockwise moments have the positive sign and the
clockwise moments the negative sign.

34. Units. In obtaining the moment of a force we multiply
a force by a distance. Thus, in fig. 34, if F = 24 lb. and OA
= 5 ft. we have

Moment of force F about O $= F \times OA = 24 \times 5 = 120.$

The result is said to be in *pound-feet*, or the moment of **F** about O is 120 lb.-ft.

If OA had been in inches the result would be stated in pound-inches. Thus OA = 5 ft. = 60 in., therefore, moment of **F** about O = 24 × 60
= 1,440 lb.-in.

Although the numbers 120 and 1,440 are different, the moment is the same. The *units* of moment are different.

35. Levers. A simple but very useful application of moments occurs in calculations dealing with levers.

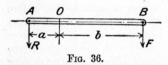

FIG. 36.

Fig. 36 shows a lever turning about a point O. O is called the *fulcrum* of the lever. A force F, acting at right angles to the lever, is balanced by a resistance R at right angles to the lever. The moments must therefore be equal and opposite,

or $$F \times OB = R \times OA$$
or $$R \times OA - F \times OB = 0.$$

EXAMPLE. If $a = 3$ in., $b = 27$ in., and $F = 18$ lb., find the value of R.

$$R \times 3 = 18 \times 27$$

$$\therefore R = \frac{18 \times 27}{3} = 162 \text{ lb.}$$

EXAMPLE. A lever has its fulcrum at one end O. At A, 4 in. from O, a resistance of 840 lb. perpendicular to the lever is to be overcome. Find the force, at right angles to the lever and 32 in. from O, which will overcome the resistance. (See fig. 37.)

Here F must act upwards if the 840 lb. act downwards.

We may state our moments thus :

$$32F - 840 \times 4 = 0$$
$$\therefore 32F = 840 \times 4 = 3,360$$

$$\therefore F = \frac{3,360}{32} = 105 \text{ lb.}$$

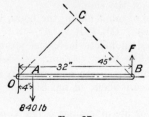

FIG. 37.

EXAMPLE. If, in fig. 37, the force acts at 45° to the lever as shown dotted, what will be the value of F to overcome the resistance at A ?

It must never be forgotten, that in taking the moment of a force, perpendicular distance is involved. The moment of F about the fulcrum will now be F × OC.

$$\therefore \ F \times OC - 840 \times 4 = 0$$
$$\therefore \ F = \frac{3,360}{OC}.$$

Drawing to scale and measuring we find OC = 22·6 in.

$$\therefore \ F = \frac{3,360}{22·6} = 148·5 \ lb.$$

EXAMPLE. In the case of the cranked lever of fig. 23, find the force at N by the method of moments.

Taking moments about O we have

Force at N × ON = Force at M × OM.

ON and OM are both perpendicular distances.

$$\therefore \ Force \ at \ N \times 8 = 12 \times 12 = 144$$
$$\therefore \ Force \ at \ N = \frac{144}{8} = 18 \ lb.$$

This result agrees with that found by an entirely different method in art. 27.

EXAMPLE. A simple winch is used to draw water from a well. The drum of the winch is 4 in. diameter and the handle is 15 in. long. Find the force, applied to the end of the handle, which will raise a weight of 18 lb. from the well.

The moment of the weight = weight × radius of drum
$$= 18 \times 2 = 36 \ lb.\text{-}in.$$
Moment of force on the handle = F × 15 lb.-in.

$$\therefore \ 15F = 36$$

$$F = \frac{36}{15} = 2·4 \ lb.$$

36. Parallel Forces.

The principle of moments may be used to consider the relation between parallel forces which are in equilibrium.

Let three parallel forces P, Q and R act on a body so as to keep it in equilibrium. Draw a line AB perpendicular to the forces. Let the perpendicular distance between P and R = x and that between Q and R = y.

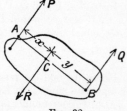

FIG. 38.

Now by the principle of moments, the turning effect on the

body must be zero about any point whatever, since the body is in equilibrium.

Select A as the point for taking moments.

Then $Q(x + y) - R \times x = 0$.

(P has no moment about A because the perpendicular distance is zero.)

Now take moments about B. Then

$$R \times y - P(x + y) = 0$$

Therefore, $Ry - P(x + y) = Q(x + y) - Rx$

$$Rx + Ry = P(x + y) + Q(x + y)$$
$$R(x + y) = P(x + y) + Q(x + y)$$
$$\therefore R = P + Q.$$

Thus we see that one of the forces must equal the sum of the other two.

If we now select the point C on the force R and take moments, we have

$$Qy - Px = 0$$
$$\therefore Qy = Px$$
$$\therefore \frac{P}{Q} = \frac{y}{x},$$

from which we see that point C on R divides the distance AB in the ratio $\frac{P}{Q}$. Notice that P and y are the numerators, and Q and x the denominators, y being the length remote from P and x the length remote from Q.

As in the case of non-parallel forces R is called the *equilibrant* of P and Q.

A force acting opposite to R would be the *resultant* of P and Q; it would have the same value and act along the same line as the equilibrant.

Instead of P and Q, P and R might have been the given forces. In that case, Q would be the equilibrant of P and R; also a force equal and opposite to Q would be the resultant.

Now, since $P + Q = R$
$$Q = R - P.$$

Hence, to find the resultant of two parallel forces which point in opposite directions it is necessary to subtract them.

Also, taking moments about B, we get

$$R \times y = P \times (x + y)$$
$$\therefore \frac{R}{P} = \frac{x + y}{y}.$$

We express this result by saying that B divides AC externally in the ratio R to P.

EXAMPLE. A light wooden rod whose weight may be neglected is supported by two spring balances 42 in. apart. The balances register pulls of 6 lb. and 8 lb. respectively when a weight W is hung on the beam. Find the value of W and the point where it hangs.

$$W = \text{sum of the two upward pulls} = (6 + 8) \text{ lb.}$$
$$= 14 \text{ lb.}$$

Also
$$\frac{AC}{CB} = \frac{6}{8} \quad \therefore \quad AC = \frac{3}{4}CB.$$

$$AC + CB = \frac{3}{4}CB + CB = 42 \text{ in.}$$

$$\frac{7}{4}CB = 42 \text{ ,,}$$

$$CB = \frac{4 \times 42}{7} = 24 \text{ in.}$$

$$AC = 42 - 24 = 18 \text{ in.}$$

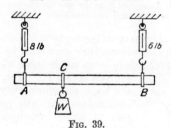

FIG. 39.

Having found W, a more convenient way of finding the position of C is as follows :

Take moments about A.

Then
$$W \times AC = 6 \times AB.$$
$$14 \times AC = 6 \times 42$$
$$AC = \frac{6 \times 42}{14} = 18 \text{ in., as before.}$$

This example is based on an experiment suitable for proving the relation between three parallel forces.

EXAMPLE. A light rod is suspended from two spring balances, A and B 24 in. apart. At C, 9 in. from A, a weight of 18 lb. is hung. Find the reading of each spring balance.

The arrangement is similar to that of fig. 39.

Taking moments about A we have

$$\text{Reading of B} \times 24 = 18 \times 9 = 162 \text{ lb.-in.}$$

$$\therefore \text{ Reading of B} = \frac{162}{24} = 6\frac{3}{4} \text{ lb.}$$

Taking moments about B we have

Reading of A $\times$ 24 = 18 $\times$ (24 − 9)

= 18 $\times$ 15 = 270 lb.-in.

$\therefore$ Reading of A = $\dfrac{270}{24}$ = 11¼ lb.

As a check the student may note that 6¾ + 11¼ = 18. Or after finding reading at A,

Reading at B = 18 − reading at A

= 18 − 6¾ = 11¼ lb.

EXAMPLE. In the lever of fig. 37, if the resistance is 840 lb. and the force F is a vertical force of 105 lb., find the force on the fulcrum.

Take moments about B.

Then, force at fulcrum $\times$ 32 = 840 $\times$ (32 − 4) = 840 $\times$ 28

$\therefore$ Force at fulcrum = $\dfrac{840 \times 28}{32}$ = 735 lb.

Notice that force at fulcrum = 840 − 105 = 735 lb. If we regard it as the upward reaction on the lever, the force at the fulcrum is the *equilibrant* of the other two. If we regard it as the downward pressure exerted by the lever on the fulcrum it is then the *resultant*.

37. Couples. If two *equal* forces, both of value P, are parallel and act in opposite directions, their resultant, by the last article, is P − P = 0. Thus, there is no single force which can replace

FIG. 40.

the two forces P. Yet, it is clear that the body on which they act is not in equilibrium but will rotate. Such a pair of equal and opposite forces is called a *couple*.

They produce a pure turning moment, or pure torque, and the moment = P $\times$ a.

a is called the *arm* of the couple and P $\times$ a is called the *value* or *moment* of the couple.

A couple can only be balanced by another couple of equal moment, and it can act anywhere on the body in the same plane as the original couple. Thus two equal parallel forces of value F, at a perpendicular distance x, and acting in opposite directions, will balance the couple P $\times$ a, if F $\times$ x = P $\times$ a.

EXAMPLE. What is a couple ?

A steel sliding door weighs 84 lb. and runs on two small wheels 21 in. apart. The vertical line through the centre of gravity of the door passes midway between the wheels. To push the door a horizontal force of 12 lb. is needed. When this force is applied 36 in. above the wheels find the vertical load on each wheel.   C.G.L.I. (1945)

Two equal parallel forces of opposite sense constitute a couple.
The applied force of 12 lb. and the frictional resistance at the wheels form a couple.

$$\text{Value of couple} = 12 \times 36 = 432 \text{ lb.-in.}$$

This couple is balanced by an increased reaction on the leading wheel and an equal decrease on the trailing wheel. Let this increase $= F$.

$$\text{Then } F \times 21 = 432 = \text{value of both couples}$$

$$\therefore F = \frac{432}{21} = 20 \cdot 57 \text{ lb.}$$

Load on each wheel when at rest $= \dfrac{84}{2} = 42$ lb.

$$\therefore \text{Required load on leading wheel} = 42 + 20 \cdot 57 = 62 \cdot 57 \text{ lb.}$$
$$\text{,, \quad ,, \quad ,, \quad trailing \quad ,, \quad } = 42 - 20 \cdot 57 = 21 \cdot 43 \text{ lb.}$$

38. General Case of Parallel Forces. When more than three parallel forces act on a body we can still solve the problems which arise by means of the moments of the forces.

EXAMPLE. A rod AB, 40 in. long, is supported by a spring balance at A and another 30 in. from A. Weights of 3, 5, 4 and 2 lb. are suspended from the rod at distances 6, 15, 24 and 40 in. respectively. Find the force recorded on each spring balance.

The student may, if there is an opportunity, do this by experiment and check the results.

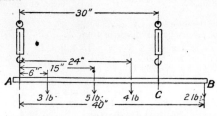

FIG. 41.

$$\text{Let } R_1 = \text{reading of balance at A}$$
$$\text{,, \quad } R_2 = \text{,, \quad ,, \quad ,, \quad ,, \quad C}$$

Take moments about A. Then R_2, which is an upward pull on the rod at C, will give an anti-clockwise moment, whilst all the weights will give clockwise moments

$$R_2 \times 30 = 3 \times 6 + 5 \times 15 + 4 \times 24 + 2 \times 40$$
$$= 18 + 75 + 96 + 80$$
$$= 269 \text{ lb.-in.}$$

$$\therefore R_2 = \frac{269}{30} = 8 \cdot 97 \text{ lb.}$$

Notice that we took moments about a point on the line of action of an unknown force. This is not necessary, but it simplifies the mathematics. Now take moments about C.

Clockwise moments are $\quad R_1 \times 30 + 2 \times (40 - 30)$
$$= R_1 \times 30 + 2 \times 10$$
Anti-clockwise moments are $4 \times 6 + 5 \times 15 + 3 \times 24$
$\therefore\ R_1 \times 30 + 2 \times 10 = 4 \times 6 + 5 \times 15 + 3 \times 24$
$$30R_1 + 20 = 24 + 75 + 72$$
$$30R_1 = 24 + 75 + 72 - 20 = 151$$

$$R_1 = \frac{151}{30} = 5{\cdot}03 \text{ lb.}$$

Note that $R_1 + R_2 = 8{\cdot}97 + 5{\cdot}03 = 14$ lb.
Also sum of weights $= 3 + 5 + 4 + 2 = 14$ lb.

If, instead of being supported by spring balances, the rod in this example had rested on two fixed supports, R_1 and R_2 would have been the reactions at those supports.

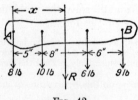

EXAMPLE. Parallel forces of 8 lb. 10 lb., 6 lb. and 9 lb. act on a body. The perpendicular distances between them are 5 in., 8 in. and 6 in. respectively. Find a single force which will be equivalent to the given forces, i.e. find their resultant, and also where it acts.

Take moments about A, a point in the line of action of one of the forces.

FIG. 42.

Let R = the resultant
,, x = its perpendicular distance from A.
Then $\qquad Rx = 10 \times 5 + 6 \times 13 + 9 \times 19$
$$= 50 + 78 + 171$$
$$= 299 \text{ lb.-in.}$$

Now take moments about B, a point in another force.
Then $\qquad R(19 - x) = 6 \times 6 + 10 \times 14 + 8 \times 19$
$$19R - Rx = 36 + 140 + 152$$
$$= 328 \text{ lb.-in.}$$
But $\qquad Rx = 299 \text{ lb.-in.}$
$\therefore\ 19R - 299 = 328 \text{ lb.-in.}$
$\therefore\ 19R = 627 \text{ lb.-in.}$
$R = 33$ lb. = the sum of all the forces.

To find x.
$$Rx = 299 \text{ lb.-in.}$$
$\therefore\ 33x = 299 \text{ lb.-in.}$
$\therefore\ x = 9{\cdot}07 \text{ in.}$

The above method is too laborious for ordinary purposes, but it has been adopted here to show that the resultant force is the sum of all the forces. It is, in fact, the algebraic sum. That means that forces in one direction must be called positive and opposite ones negative. The addition is then carried out as for algebraic quantities.

In solving the problem the student should proceed as follows:

$$R = 8 + 10 + 6 + 9 = 33 \text{ lb.}$$

To find x. Take moments about A in one of the forces.

$$Rx = 10 \times 5 + 6 \times 13 + 9 \times 19$$
$$= 50 + 78 + 171$$
$$= 299 \text{ lb.-in.}$$

But $R = 33$ lb.

$$\therefore 33x = 299 \text{ lb.-in.}$$
$$x = 9 \cdot 07 \text{ in.}$$

39. Centre of Gravity. The last problem has an important application in finding the centre of gravity of a body. In engineering, we are constantly considering the force due to the earth's attraction or gravity (see chap. I). This attraction does not act as one large force on a mass of material, but rather as a multitude of very small forces. It acts, in fact, separately on every particle of the mass of a body. All these small forces act towards the earth's centre and are thus not quite parallel, but the earth's centre is so far away that in the case of bodies small enough to be moved, we may regard them as parallel. It would be very inconvenient if we always had to think of all the small parallel forces due to gravity. Hence, it is usual to find their resultant and the point where it acts. This point is called the *Centre of Gravity.* There is always a point such that, whichever way a body is placed, this resultant force of gravity acts through the point. The student should note that this resultant force is the weight of the body.

EXAMPLE. Two weights of 10 lb. and 16 lb. respectively are fastened to a thin steel rod whose weight is negligible. The centres of the weights are 13 in. apart. Find the centre of gravity of the arrangement.

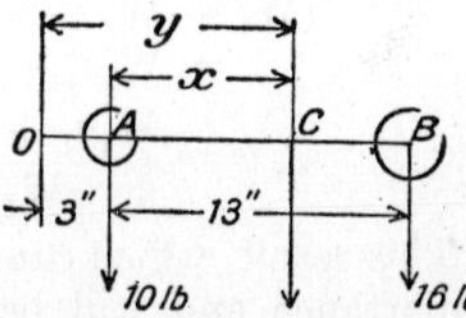

FIG. 43.

Gravity acts vertically downwards on both weights and we require to find the position of the point through which the resultant acts. (Note the use of principles demonstrated in earlier exercises).

The resultant $= 10 + 16 = 26$ lb.

Now take moments about A and let $x =$ distance from A of the point on AB where the C. of G. lies.

Then $26 \times x = 16 \times 13$

$$\therefore x = \frac{16 \times 13}{26} = 8 \text{ in.}$$

Thus C, 8 in. from A, is the C. of G.

It is not necessary to take moments only about A or B. It is often convenient in finding centres of gravity to take them about some other point.

Let O be a point on BA produced and 3 in. to the left of A, then taking moments about O

$$26 \times y = 10 \times 3 + 16 \times (13 + 3)$$
$$= 30 + 256$$
$$\therefore y = \frac{30 + 256}{26} = \frac{286}{26} = 11 \text{ in.}$$

This is evidently the same point as before.

If the two weights were equal then it is easily seen that the point C would be midway between A and B.

Another important point to observe is that the weights will balance about C as a fulcrum because $10 \times 8 = 16 \times (13 - 8) = 16 \times 5$.

If a knife-edge were placed at C or if the arrangement were suspended by a string fastened at C, the weights would balance with AB horizontal.

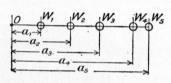

FIG. 44.

40. General Case of Calculation of Centre of Gravity. Let a number of weights, W_1, W_2, W_3, W_4, etc., be attached to a rod at distances a_1, a_2, a_3, a_4, etc., respectively from a point O on the rod. We require to find the distance of the C. of G. of this system of weights from O. The student will find this problem similar to the second example of art. 38.

Let $x =$ the distance of the C. of G. from O.

Then taking moments about O

$$(W_1 + W_2 + W_3 + W_4 + W_5) \times x$$
$$= W_1 a_1 + W_2 a_2 + W_3 a_3 + W_4 a_4 + W_5 a_5$$
$$\therefore x = \frac{W_1 a_1 + W_2 a_2 + W_3 a_3 + W_4 a_4 + W_5 a_5}{W_1 + W_2 + W_3 + W_4 + W_5}.$$

This result, which can be stated in many ways, is of very great importance and will be required many times in the study of engineering problems.

It may be stated briefly by saying that the distance of the C. of G. of a body from a point of reference is the total moment of the weight of that body about the point divided by the total weight.

41. Special Cases of Centre of Gravity. It is desirable to know the position of the C. of G. of many bodies of shapes commonly met with.

Thin rod. Let us consider a thin uniform rod AB (fig. 45). Divide it into an even number of equal parts (fig. 45) with corre-

sponding portions numbered 1, 1 ; 2, 2 ; 3, 3 ; etc. Since the
sections 1, 1, are equal, their C. of G. will be midway between
them, i.e. at C. Also the C. of G.
of sections 2, 2, will be at C;
similarly for 3, 3, the C. of G.
will be at C ; and so on for the
whole of the rod. Hence we

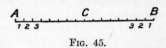

FIG. 45.

conclude that the C. of G. of a thin uniform rod is its
middle point.

The meaning of this result is that in problems where the weight
of a uniform rod is involved we may take it as a single weight
at its centre.

Rectangular sheet. Let us consider a sheet of iron, or some
other substance, ABCD (fig. 46). Take a narrow strip of it
along AB. The strip is like a thin rod and its C. of G. is at its
middle point E. Any other strip parallel to AB has its C. of G.
at the middle point. If the whole rectangle be divided into
strips parallel to AB then all their C. of G. lie on EF. Hence
the C. of G. of the whole is on EF. By dividing into strips
parallel to AD we can show that the C. of G. of the rectangle lies
on KH. Hence, the C. of G. of the whole is at G, the point
where EF and KH intersect. It should be noticed that this is
also the point where the diagonals intersect.

Triangular sheet. A triangular sheet may be treated in the
same way. Take strips parallel to AB (fig. 46). Then their

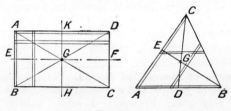

FIG. 46.

centres of gravity lie on CD where D is the middle point of AB.
Also, strips taken parallel to AC show the C. of G. to lie on BE
where E is the middle point of AC. Thus the C. of G. of the
triangle is at G, the point common to CD and BE. By drawing
or by geometry the student may prove that $DG = \frac{1}{3}CD$.

By similar methods, other shapes may be treated, as, for
instance, the circle, whose C. of G. is at the centre.

42. Centre of Area. The rectangular, triangular and circular plates in the last article have been imagined to possess weight, but their centres of gravity were found without using the idea of weight. We may, in fact, think of them only as areas without weight. In that case, the points found are called their *centres of area* or *centroids*. When the area of a surface is multiplied by the distance of its centroid from some axis the product is called the *moment of area* about that axis.

43. Experimental Method for finding Centre of Gravity. Many centres of gravity can be readily found by experiment and some can be found in no other way. Take a thin sheet of any shape and suspend it by a cord, firstly attaching it to point A

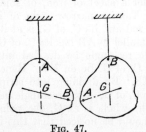

FIG. 47.

and secondly to B. In each case, if the line of the cord be produced, the point of intersection, G, is the centre of gravity. This is because the pull in the cord must be equal and opposite to the force of gravity. They are thus in the same straight line and the C. of G. must lie on this line. Whilst this experimental method will give the true C. of G. of the thin sheet, care must be taken if this method is being used for the purpose of finding the centre of area of some figure. It is then essential that the material should be homogeneous and of uniform thickness. For example, a sheet of cardboard which is very damp over a part of its area would be valueless for finding the centre of area. By this method the results of art. 41 may be tested.

44. Centre of Gravity of Solids. Solid bodies also have their centres of gravity, but a general treatment is beyond the scope of this book. Symmetrical solids usually present no difficulty. The centre of gravity of a sphere is at its geometrical centre and the same applies to the cube. The square prism and the right circular cylinder have their centres of gravity at the middle point of the line joining the centres of opposite faces.

Pyramids of all kinds, including the cone, have their centres of gravity on the line joining the apex to the centre of area of the base and one-quarter of its length from the base.

45. Typical Examples. A number of examples follow.

EXAMPLE. Find the centre of area of the figure shown in fig. 48. PN = 8 in., AB = 6 in., EK = 8 in. The width is everywhere 1 in.

In this case we do not regard weights, but treat areas as if they were weights. If the figure represents a sheet of material, then weight will be proportional to area and the result will be the same.

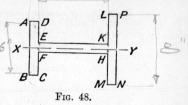

FIG. 48.

Divide the area into three as follows :

ABCD = 6 × 1 = 6 sq. in.   Centre of area ½ in. from AB
EFHK = 8 × 1 = 8 ,, ,,   ,,   ,,   ,, 5 ,, ,, ,,
LMNP = 8 × 1 = 8 ,, ,,   ,,   ,,   ,, 9½ ,, ,, ,,

Total area = 22 sq. in.

Let x = distance of centre of area from AB.   Take moments about AB.

$$22 \times x = 6 \times \tfrac{1}{2} + 8 \times 5 + 8 \times 9\tfrac{1}{2}$$
$$22x = 3 + 40 + 76$$
$$= 119 = \text{moment of area about axis AB}$$
$$x = \frac{119}{22} = 5\tfrac{9}{22} \text{ in.}$$

Thus the centre of area is on XY, because the figure is symmetrical about XY, and is $5\tfrac{9}{22}$ in. from AB.

EXAMPLE. Find the centre of area of the L-shaped section shown. AB = 12 in., BC = 8 in., AF = 1¼ in., DC = 1½ in.

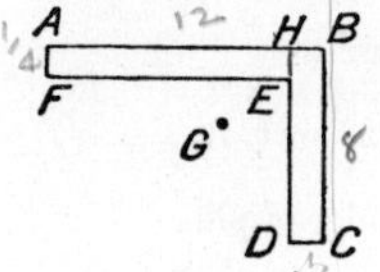

There is no axis about which the figure is symmetrical. We must therefore find the position of the C. of A. (centre of area) by taking moments twice. The student should carefully note the method as it often has to be adopted, particularly in the design of structures. Divide the figure into two areas as follows :

FIG. 49.

AFEH = 10½ × 1¼ = 13⅛ sq. in.   C. of A. 5¼ in. from AF
BCDH = 8 × 1½   = 12 ,, ,,   ,,   11¼ ,, ,, ,,
Total area = 25⅛ ,, ,,

Take moments about AF, and let C. of A. be x in. from AF.

$$25\tfrac{1}{8} \times x = 13\tfrac{1}{8} \times 5\tfrac{1}{4} + 12 \times 11\tfrac{1}{4}$$
$$25\tfrac{1}{8}x = 68\cdot9 + 135 = 203\cdot9$$
$$x = \frac{203\cdot9}{25\cdot12} = 8\cdot12 \text{ in.}$$

Take moments about AB, and let C. of A. be y in. from AB.

In AFEH, C. of A. is ⅝ in. from AB
BCDH   ,,   ,, 4 ,,   ,,   ,,
$$25\tfrac{1}{8}y = 13\tfrac{1}{8} \times \tfrac{5}{8} + 12 \times 4$$
$$= 8\cdot21 + 48 = 56\cdot21$$
$$y = 2\cdot24 \text{ in.}$$

Thus the centre of area is 8·12 in. from AF and 2·24 in. from AB, i.e. at G. The student will notice that it lies outside the figure.

EXAMPLE. A circular plate 18 in. diameter has a hole 6 in. diameter cut in it. Find the centre of area of the remaining plate. Distance between centres of plate and hole in 5 in. The plate is of uniform thickness.

$$\text{Area of plate} = 0\cdot7854 \times 18^2$$
$$= 254\cdot5 \text{ sq. in.}$$
$$\text{Area of hole} = 0\cdot7854 \times 5^2$$
$$= 19\cdot6 \text{ sq. in.}$$
$$\text{Remaining area} = 254\cdot5 - 19\cdot6 = 234\cdot9 \text{ sq. in.}$$

The figure is symmetrical about AB, hence the C. of A. lies on it. Take moments about A. Then

$$234\cdot9 \times x = 254\cdot5 \times 9 - 19\cdot6 \times 14 \quad \text{(Note minus sign.)}$$
$$234\cdot9x = 2{,}290\cdot5 - 274\cdot4 = 2016\cdot1$$
$$x = 8\cdot59 \text{ in.}$$

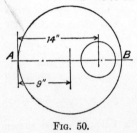

FIG. 50.

EXAMPLE. A large engine connecting-rod weighs 6 cwt. and measures 8 ft. from centre to centre of crank-pin and gudgeon-pin. The big end rests on a knife-edge directly below the centre of the crank-pin hole, whilst the knife-edge is supported by a weighing machine which registers 3·5 cwt. The other end of the rod is supported by a knife-edge at the gudgeon-pin centre. Find the distance of the C. of G. of the connecting-rod from the centre of the gudgeon-pin.

Moment of rod about gudgeon-pin $= 6x$
„ „ reaction of weighing machine $= 3\cdot5 \times 8$
$$= 28 \text{ cwt.-ft.}$$
$$\therefore 6x = 28$$
$$x = 4\tfrac{2}{3} \text{ ft.} = \text{distance of C. of G. from gudgeon-pin.}$$

EXAMPLES IV

SECTION A

1. Explain clearly the meaning of the term "Moment of a force about a point," and give the units in which it is commonly expressed. A tapered rod, 16 in. long, rests horizontally on two pegs, 9 in. apart, with the centre of the rod midway between them. The greatest weights that can be suspended in succession from the two ends without disturbing equilibrium are 4 lb. and 5 lb. Find the weight of the rod and the position of its centre of gravity.   U.E.I.

2. A horizontal beam of uniform section and 18 ft. long rests on supports at its ends. The beam weighs 540 lb. and carries a load of 2 tons at a point 4 ft. from one end and a load of 1 ton at a point 5 ft. from the other end. Find the reactions of the supports.   U.L.C.I.

3. A rod of uniform section, 6 ft. long and weighing 20 lb., rests on a fulcrum at one end and is supported in a horizontal position by a vertical force F acting at the other end. Determine the magnitude of F when the rod supports a weight of 40 lb. at a point 2 ft. from the fulcrum. Also find the pressure on the fulcrum.   U.L.C.I.

4. A heavy bar of uniform section is 12 ft. long. Find the position of its centre of gravity (*a*) when it is straight, (*b*) when it is bent into a right angle having legs each 6 ft. in length. U.L.C.I.

5. A beam rests on supports 20 ft. apart. If a load of 500 lb. is placed at 5 ft. from a support, determine where another load of 900 lb. must be placed so that each support will carry one-half of the total load. N.C.T.E.C.

6. Give three examples of the use of simple levers in everyday life. Explain how the relation between effort and load is calculated. N.C.T.E.C.

7. A four-wheeled truck crosses a girder, 36 ft. long, supported at the ends. The front axle supports a load of 4 tons, the rear axle a load of 3 tons, and the axles are 8 ft. apart. Determine the reactions of the supports when the truck is at the centre of the span. N.C.T.E.C.

8. A horizontal beam 12 ft. long weighs 0·5 ton and is pivoted 4 ft. from one end. Its centre of gravity lies in the longer part 1 ft. from the fulcrum. A load of 140 lb. acting downwards is applied 6 ft. from the fulcrum in the longer part. Find where a load of 560 lb. must be placed in order to keep the beam balanced. What is then the total load on the fulcrum ? U.L.C.I.

Section B

9. A metal cylinder, 4 in. diameter and 8 in. long, has a hole bored in it which is 2 in. diameter and 6 in. long, the hole having the same axis as the cylinder. Find the position of the centre of gravity of the bored cylinder. N.C.T.E.C.

10. A disc, 12 in. diameter, has a hole, 4 in. diameter, whose centre is 3 in. from the centre of the disc. Find the position of the centre of gravity. N.C.T.E.C.

11. Show how you would calculate the position of the centre of gravity of a number of given weights which lie in given positions in a plane.

Weights of 2, 3, 1, 4 oz. respectively are placed at the corners of a square, taken in order ; find the position of their C. of G. if the side of the square is 3 in. N.C.T.E.C.

12. A steel cube of 4-in. edge has a steel rod 1 in. diameter fitted perpendicularly into the middle of one face so that it projects 10 in. Find the C. of G. of the combination measured from the end of the rod. N.C.T.E.C.

13. A figure of the form of the letter E measures 14 in. vertically. The overall width at the top and bottom is 9 in., whilst the central limb is 1 in. shorter than the others. Find the centre of area, if the width is everywhere 1 in.

14. A casting for a tapered pillar is 15 ft. long. On being placed with its ends resting on weighbridges, one records 4 cwt. and the other 5½ cwt. Find the centre of gravity of the pillar.

15. A rod 36 in. long rests on supports 20 in. apart, and overhangs the left-hand support by 6 in. It carries loads of 4, 8, 12 and 5 lb. at distances of 0, 12, 24 and 36 in. respectively from the left-hand end. Find the reactions of the supports.

16. A casting for a certain bedplate is 12 ft. long. The C. of G. is 7½ ft. from one end. At 2½ ft. from the C. of G. and 2 ft. from the end of the casting a crane hook is attached. Find the pull necessary just to raise one end of the casting. Weight of casting = 2½ tons.

17. A beam is 3 ft. long. Weights of 8, 6, 4 and 2 lb. are placed respectively at distances of 1 ft. apart along the beam. The weight of the beam

E

is 6 lb. At what point along the beam would you have a support so that the beam would remain horizontal ?   C.G.L.I.

18. A square metal plate of 12 in. sides and of uniform thickness weighs 20 lb. If it is placed on a knife edge, the position of which is parallel to one edge and 3 in. from that edge, what force must be applied at the opposite edge to keep the plate horizontal ?   C.G.L.I.

19. A rectangular block of metal is 10 in. long and its cross-section is a square of 2 in. side. The block is put in a lathe and half of its length is turned down to 1·5 in. diameter. Calculate the position of the C. of G. of the new shape.   C.G.L.I.

20. A plank of wood, the cross-section of which is 8 in. by 3 in., is 6 ft. long and is hinged at its lower end. Find the point of application and the value of the smallest force which can hold the plank at an angle of 30° to the horizontal. Assume the density of wood to be 45 lb. per cu. ft.
                                                                        C.G.L.I.

21. A steel bar AB, of uniform section, is 48 in. long and is placed on a horizontal floor. A weight of 42 lb. is laid on the bar 30 in. from A. A rope is attached to the end B and the angle between the bar and the rope is 120°. The pull in the rope which just raises the end B from the floor is 59·2 lb. Calculate the weight of the bar.   C.G.L.I.

22. A horizontal beam AB is 40 ft. long, A being the left-hand end of the beam. Loads are placed on the beam as follows :—5 tons at 7 ft., 13 tons at 13 ft., 9 tons at 24 ft. and 3 tons at 40 ft. from A. The beam rests on supports at A and C. At what distance is C from A if the reactions of the two supports are equal ?   C.G.L.I.

CHAPTER V

APPLICATIONS

46. Safety Valve. This chapter will be devoted to some practical applications of the work of the preceding chapters.

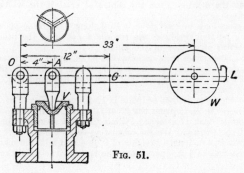

Fig. 51.

EXAMPLE. In the lever safety valve of fig. 51, a valve V is ground to a good fit on a valve seat. It is held down against the steam pressure by a lever OL acting through a contact at A and loaded by the weight W. Taking the valve to be 2 in. diameter and 6 oz. in weight, the length OA $= 4$ in. and OL $= 33$ in., find the weight W so that steam may blow off at 180 lb. per sq. in. pressure. The lever weighs 5 lb. and its C. of G. is 12 in. from O.

$$\text{Upward force of steam on valve} = 0.7854 \times 2^2 \times 180$$
$$= 565 \text{ lb.}$$

$$\text{Upward force on lever at A} = 565 - \text{weight of valve}$$
$$= 565 - 0.375 = 564.625 \text{ lb.}$$

Taking moments about O

$$33W + 5 \times 12 = 564.6 \times 4 = 2,258.5 \text{ lb.-in.}$$
$$33W = 2,258.5 - 60 = 2,198.5$$
$$W = 66.6 \text{ lb.}$$

EXAMPLE. A valve is loaded by the compression of a spring instead of a lever. The valve is 1·5 in. diameter and its weight may be neglected. Find the initial force of compression of the spring for steam to blow off at 160 lb. per sq. in. If the spring compresses 1 in. for every 50 lb. of load, find the steam pressure when the valve lifts $\frac{3}{8}$ in.

$$\text{Force exerted by steam on the valve} = 0.7854 \times 1.5^2 \times 160$$
$$= 282 \text{ lb.}$$

This is the initial force required.
Additional force when valve lifts $\frac{3}{8}$ in.

$$= \tfrac{3}{8} \times 50 = 18.7 \text{ lb.}$$
$$\therefore \text{ Force to be exerted by steam} = (282 + 18.7) \text{ lb.}$$
$$= 300.7 \text{ lb.}$$
$$\therefore \text{ Steam pressure} = \frac{\text{Force on valve}}{\text{Area of valve}} = \frac{300.7}{0.7854 \times 1.5^2}$$
$$= 170 \text{ lb. per sq. in.}$$

47. Compound Levers. A lever is used when, by exerting a force at one point, we wish to produce a much larger force at some other point. To produce even bigger forces one must increase the length of the lever. So as to avoid unreasonably long levers we may use compound levers. The possible arrangements are numerous, but the following example illustrates the principle.

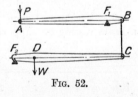

FIG. 52.

EXAMPLE. Two levers are connected by a link BC as shown and are pivoted at fulcra F_1 and F_2. The following are lengths: AB $= 40$ in., $BF_1 = 3$ in., $CF_2 = 35$ in. and $DF_2 = 3$ in. If the effort at P $= 24$ lb., find the weight W which will be lifted. Take moments about F_1, then

$$\text{Force in BC} \times BF_1 = P \times AF_1$$
$$\therefore \text{ Force in BC} = \frac{P \times AF_1}{BF_1} = \frac{24 \times 37}{3} = 296 \text{ lb.}$$

Take moments about F_2, then

$$\text{Weight } W \times DF_2 = \text{Force in } BC \times CF_2$$

$$\therefore \text{ Weight } W = \frac{296 \times 35}{3} = 3,450 \text{ lb.}$$

Note that this compound lever is solved by applying the simple lever principle twice. The process may be continued for three or more levers.

48. Crank Effort. A crank is used to produce rotary motion from linear motion. It is necessary to know how to calculate the turning moment, turning effort or torque on the crank-shaft.

EXAMPLE. The force in a connecting-rod is 3,600 lb. Length of crank = 14 in. Length of connecting-rod = 60 in. Find the turning effort on the crank-shaft when the crank has turned 30° from the inner dead centre. Give the answer in lb.-in. and lb.-ft.

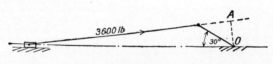

FIG. 53.

Set off the crank and connecting-rod to scale. We require to find the moment of the force in the connecting-rod about O.

Moment of force about O = Force × perpendicular distance of O.

Measure on the drawing the length OA to scale; in this case the result is: OA = 8·4 in.

$$\therefore \text{ Turning moment} = 3,600 \times 8\cdot4 = 30,200 \text{ lb.-in.}$$

or, $$\text{Turning moment} = 3,600 \times \frac{8\cdot4}{12} = 2,520 \text{ lb.-ft.}$$

49. Shearing Force and Bending Moment. Consider a beam resting on supports with loads W_1 and W_2 resting upon

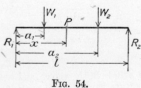

FIG. 54.

it in the positions shown in fig. 54. We have seen in the last chapter how to find the reactions R_1 and R_2 by taking moments. Let us take a point P distant x from the left-hand support. We can find the moments of R_1 and W_1 about the point P; they are R_1x and $W_1(x - a_1)$. As they operate in opposite directions the total moment at P

$$= W_1(x - a_1) - R_1x.$$

This result is merely the algebraic sum of the two moments concerned.

The moment about a point such as P is of very great importance, because this moment tends to bend the beam at that point. Hence it is called the *Bending Moment*. Each point along the beam has its own bending moment which may be calculated as above, by taking the moments of the forces *on one side* of the point. If the student took a numerical case and found the bending moment at P by calculating the moments of R_2 and W_2 about P, he would find the moment to be exactly as before, but of opposite sign. This is to be expected, because the moments at any point must be equal and opposite, if no actual rotation is to occur, i.e. if the beam is in equilibrium.

Now let us consider the direct effect of the forces R_1 and W_1 on the beam at P. In chapter I we saw that a force acting at right angles to the axis of a piece of material produces a shearing stress at right angles to that axis. Thus at P there is shear stress due to R_1; but W_1 is also setting up shear stress and it is in opposition to that of R_1. Hence

$$\text{Total shear force at } P = R_1 - W_1.$$

This is the algebraic sum of the forces R_1 and W_1, since, if we call an upward force positive, we should call the downward one negative or vice versa.

If we consider the shearing force from the other side of P the result will be the same but opposite in sign, viz.

$R_2 - W_2$, because $(R_1 - W_1) = -(R_2 - W_2)$ since
$R_1 + R_2 = W_1 + W_2$.

Our conclusions may be expressed as follows:

The *Bending Moment* at any section in a beam is the algebraic sum of the moments of the forces *on one side* of the section.

The *Shearing Force* at any section in a beam is the algebraic sum of all the forces *on one side* of the section.

EXAMPLE. A beam 25 ft. long rests on supports at its ends. It carries loads of 2, 6 and 4 tons at 4, 15 and 20 ft. from the left-hand support respectively. Find the bending moment and shearing force at the middle point of the beam. Also draw the bending moment and shearing force diagrams.

It is first necessary to find the reactions of the supports.

Take moments about A, fig. 55.

$25R_2 = 2 \times 4 + 6 \times 15 + 4 \times 20$
$\quad = 8 + 90 + 80 = 178$
$R_2 = 7 \cdot 12$ tons
$R_1 = 2 + 6 + 4 - 7 \cdot 12 = 4 \cdot 88$ tons.

B.M. at middle point
= Moment of R_1 about middle point — moment of 2 ton force
= $R_1 \times 12\cdot5 - 2 \times (12\cdot5 - 4)$
= $4\cdot88 \times 12\cdot5 - 2 \times 8\cdot5$
= $61 - 17 = 44$ ton-ft.
S.F. at middle point
= sum of forces to left of middle point
= $R_1 - 2 = 4\cdot88 - 2$
= $2\cdot88$ tons.

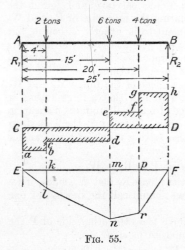

FIG. 55.

If the student will solve the problem working from the right instead of the left hand, he will find the values agree.

To draw the S.F. diagram. Starting at the left-hand end, the S.F. is the upward force R_1 = $4\cdot88$ tons, until we reach the 2-ton load. Choosing a scale for the beam and the S.F., draw *ab* making $Ca = 4\cdot88$ tons to scale. On passing the 2-ton load the S.F. drops by 2 tons and is = $4\cdot88 - 2 = 2\cdot88$ tons. The diagram continues at a depth of $2\cdot88$ to *d*. The S.F. on passing the 6-ton load = $4\cdot88 - 2 - 6 = -3\cdot12$ tons, and has thus changed sign. Draw *de* so that *e* is $3\cdot12$ tons above the line CD. The S.F. changes at the 4-ton load to $4\cdot88 - 2 - 6 - 4 = -7\cdot12$ tons. The line *gh* is drawn denoting that value, which, it should be noted, = R_2.

To draw the B.M. diagram. This may be done by calculating the B.M. for a large number of points and plotting them. In the case of loads acting at a point, however, this is not necessary.

Consider the B.M. at a point distant *x* from A between the 2- and 6-ton load; then

$$\text{B.M.} = R_1 \times x - 2(x - 4) = 4\cdot88x - 2x + 8 = 2\cdot88\ x + 8.$$

This is the equation to a straight line, hence the B.M. curve is a straight line between the loads 2 and 6 tons.

This is true for each section. We, therefore, find the B.M. under each load and, setting off to scale, join by straight lines.

Set off EF, representing the beam to scale.

B.M. at E = $R_1 \times 0 = 0$
B.M. at 2-ton load = $R_1 \times 4 = 4\cdot88 \times 4 = 19\cdot52$ ton-ft.
B.M. „ 6 „   „   = $R_1 \times 15 - 2(15 - 4) = 4\cdot88 \times 15 - 2 \times 11$
                  = $73\cdot2 - 22 = 51\cdot2$ ton-ft.
B.M. „ 4 „   „   = $4\cdot88 \times 20 - 2 \times 16 - 6 \times 5$
                  = $97\cdot6 - 32 - 30 = 35\cdot6$ ton-ft.
B.M. at F = $4\cdot88 \times 25 - 2 \times 21 - 6 \times 10 - 4 \times 5$
          = $122 - 42 - 60 - 20 = 0.$

Choosing a scale of ton-ft. set off $kl = 19.52$, $mn = 51.2$, $pr = 35.6$. Join ElnrF, which gives the curve of bending moments.

EXAMPLE. A cantilever is 12 ft. long and carries a load of 4 tons at the free end, and another of 6 tons 5 ft. from it. Calculate the shearing force and bending moment at the fixed end.

A cantilever is a beam firmly clamped at one end, but unsupported at the other end.

The student should draw a sketch.

$$\text{S.F. at fixed end} = 4 + 6 = 10 \text{ tons.}$$
$$\begin{aligned}\text{B.M. } \text{,, } \text{ ,, } \text{ ,, } &= 4 \times 12 + 6 \times (12 - 5)\\ &= 4 \times 12 + 6 \times 7\\ &= 48 + 42 = 90 \text{ ton-ft.}\end{aligned}$$

50. Structures. For combining lightness and strength we build up rigid frameworks to carry roofs, loads on bridges, etc. They consist of suitable members which we regard as being freely hinged at each end. This ensures that the force in each member is either a simple push or a simple pull. Those members subject to a push are called *struts*, and those subject to a pull are called *ties*.

In practice, the ends of the members are seldom hinged, though for calculation purposes we so regard them. Usually they are firmly riveted, but experience suggests that we are safe in regarding them as hinged when designing.

51. The Simple Truss. A simple form of roof truss takes the shape of a triangle which may be isosceles or not. It rests on supports with reactions at R_1 and R_2. Given the load W, which is applied at the apex, we can find the forces in AB and

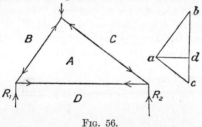

FIG. 56.

CA by a triangle of forces. Having found the force in AB, we can draw another triangle to find the forces in AD and DB, and so on for each point.

In the present case such methods would give three separate triangles. It is more convenient and saves labour if we apply the method of Bow's Notation, because the three triangles will fit together. Letter the spaces in and around the truss, which must be set out to scale. We commence with a point where we know at least one force and where *not more than two are unknown*. The only suitable point in the present case is the apex.

In drawing the force diagram we must observe certain rules.

(1) The letters must be taken in the same order around all the joints of the frame.

(2) A point where only two forces are unknown must be taken at each step.

(3) Each vector must be lettered in the sense of the force, when the force and its sense are known.

In fig. 56 the clockwise order has been chosen. W is the known force, so we set off *bc* representing W to scale and making *bc* read downwards because force W acts downwards. From *c* draw *ca* parallel to CA and from *b* draw *ab* parallel to AB. We may now consider the forces acting on the point R_1. We know the force in BA and it is already on the force diagram. Going clockwise round the point R_1 we have *ba* parallel to BA. Draw from *a* a line *ad* parallel to AD. *db* must be parallel to DB and is already in the diagram. Proceeding now to the other point of support R_2, we find, going clockwise, that all the vectors have been drawn, *ac* parallel to AC, *cd* parallel to CD and *da* parallel to DA.

To discover ties and struts we must consider the sense of the forces at each point. W is known to be downward and reads *bc*. Force in CA reads *ca* and thus pushes on the apex. Force in AB reads *ab* and also pushes on the apex. Coming now to the left-hand support, BA pushes on the point R_1 and its vector reads *ba*. Force in AD reads *ad* and so pulls on the joint. Force DB reads *db* and is upwards; this force is the reaction of the support.

We have thus found

a push in AB which is a strut
a push in CA   ,,   ,, ,,   ,,
a pull in AD   ,,   ,, ,, tie.

Measuring *ab*, *ca*, and *ad* to scale, we get the forces in the members. In addition, the reactions at R_1 and R_2 are given by *db* and *cb* respectively.

It is important to realize that, in solving this and subsequent problems, the forces acting on the pin of the pin-joint are being considered. It is that which accounts for the arrows on each of the members of the frame pointing in opposite directions, for

it is obvious that if a member pulls on the pin-joint at one end
it must also pull on the joint at the other end.   Similarly a push
on one end necessitates a push on the other end.

52. Braced Roof Truss.   This may be treated as a numerical
example, the principles used being exactly as in the last article.

EXAMPLE.   A roof truss of form shown in fig. 57 carries two loads of
8 cwt. and 10 cwt.   The span is 16 ft. and the vertical rise to the apex
is 7 ft.   The 8-cwt. load is 4 ft. horizontally from the left-hand support
and the 10-cwt. load is 6 ft. farther to the right.   Find the load in each
member, discover struts and ties, and tabulate the results.

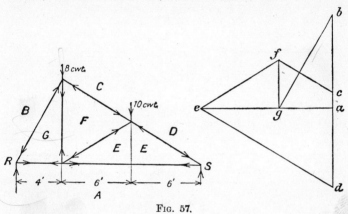

FIG. 57.

In this case we begin by calculating the reactions, as we cannot start at
the points of application of the loads, because there are three unknown
forces at each of these joints.   The method is that of the example in art. 49.
The fact that the loads are not applied at the level of R and S makes no
difference.

Take moments about R, then

$$\text{Force } DA \times 16 = 8 \times 4 + 10 \times 10$$
$$= 32 + 100 = 132 \text{ cwt.-ft.}$$

$$\therefore \text{ Force } DA = \frac{132}{16} = 8\cdot25 \text{ cwt.}$$

$$,, \quad AB = 10 + 8 - 8\cdot25 = 9\cdot75 \text{ cwt.}$$

We may now start the force polygon beginning with the forces at either
R or S.

The diagram has been drawn, taking the clockwise order.   Starting at
the joint R, set off *ab* upwards making it 9·75 to a suitable scale.   Draw
bg parallel to BG, and *ga* to GA.   We can now proceed to the apex where,
BG having been found, only two forces remain unknown.   GB is already
represented by *gb*; *bc* is set off to scale as 8 cwt.; draw *cf* parallel to

CF and *fg* parallel to FG. Each joint may be proceeded with, always observing the clockwise order. The student is advised to draw the diagram to a large scale, and not merely study it.

To find struts and ties, we commence with a force of known sense such as AB. Taking the triangle *abg* in that order, we have *ab*, a push on R, *bg*, a push on R and *ga*, a pull on R. The forces at the apex are represented by the polygon *bcfg*, and if the forces are read in that order, we find a push in CF and a pull in FG. Proceeding in the same way throughout the diagram we find the forces as indicated by the arrows. On measuring all the vectors, and tabulating, the following are the results:

Member	Struts	Ties
	cwt.	cwt.
BG	11·24	—
GA	—	5·62
GF	—	5·0
CF	6·48	—
FE	10·0	—
ED	16·5	—
EA	—	14·3

53. Overhung Frame. As another example the overhung structure shown with loads in fig. 58 is taken.

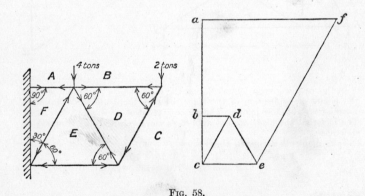

Fig. 58.

The clockwise direction is taken and the starting-point is BCD, the point of application of the 2-ton load.

The force diagram contains the following polygons in the order in which they must be drawn: *bcd*, *dce*, *abdef*, and arrows indicate the directions of the forces on each joint.

The following table shows the collected results:

Member	Struts	Ties
	tons	tons
CD	2·31	—
DB	—	1·16
CE	2·31	—
ED	—	2·31
EF	6·92	—
FA	—	5·77

EXAMPLES V

Section A

1. The rafters of a simple roof truss are inclined at 60° and 30° to the horizontal respectively. At the intersection of the rafters two forces act towards the joint : (a) a vertical downward load of 2,500 lb. ; (b) a load of 4,500 lb. perpendicular to the longer of the two rafters. Find graphically the resultant of the two forces, also the amount and nature of the forces in the two rafters due to the external loading. U.E.I.

2. What do you understand by the " moment of a force " ? How is its magnitude measured ?

In a horizontal steam engine the crank is 6 in. long and is inclined at 45° to the inner dead centre. For this crank position the connecting-rod is found to be inclined at 10° to the line of centres. If the thrust in the piston-rod is 4,000 lb., determine the thrust in the connecting-rod and the reaction between the crosshead and the guide. Find also the turning moment about the axis of the shaft. U.E.I.

3. A crank is 1 ft. long and its connecting-rod 4 ft. long, and the force along the axis of the latter is 10,000 lb. Resolve this force along the axis of the crank and perpendicular to it. The crank has turned 30° from its inner dead centre. Explain the effect each component will have on the crank. U.L.C.I.

4. A uniform beam 20 ft. long, supported at the ends, carries a distributed load, including its own weight, of $\frac{1}{2}$ ton per ft. run. A concentrated load of 2 tons rests 8 ft. from one end and another of 5 tons 3 ft. from the other end. Calculate the reactions of the supports. N.C.T.E.C.

5. In a lever safety valve the distance, fulcrum to valve, is 4 in., fulcrum to weight is 26 in., diameter of valve is $1\frac{3}{4}$ in. Find at what pressure steam will blow off with a weight of 20 lb. Neglect weight of valve, but take lever as being uniform and 5 lb. in weight.

Section B

6. A girder, 50 ft. span, supports three side wheels of a six-wheel motor lorry. The fore wheel is 10 ft. from the left-hand support and the distances between the axles, in order, are 12 and 4 ft., and the loads transmitted to the girder are, in order, $4\frac{1}{4}$, $3\frac{1}{2}$ and 4 tons respectively. Calculate (a) the reactions at the supports, (b) the bending moment at a section 12 ft. from the left-hand support, (c) the shearing force at the same point. U.E.I.

7. An electric motor weighing 4 tons is carried by two parallel beams which rest on supports 12 ft. apart. The centre line of the motor is at

a distance of 8 ft. from the left-hand support. Assuming the load to be a concentrated load, draw curves of bending moment and shearing force for one of the loaded beams, each beam carrying the same load.
U.E.I.

8. State the conditions to be fulfilled for a body to remain at rest under the action of three forces (a) when they are parallel, (b) when they are not parallel. A uniform bar, 10 ft. long and weighing 100 lb., is supported at two points 7 ft. apart, one support being 1 ft. from one end of the bar. Find the pressures on the supports.
U.E.I.

9. A wall crane is fastened to a vertical support at A and B, A being 6 ft. above B. The crane consists of two horizontal members AC and BD, 12 ft. and 6 ft. long respectively, and inclined members AD and CD such that ADC forms a triangle. A vertical load of 5 tons is suspended from the point C. Find graphically the amount and nature of the forces in the members AC, CD, DA and BD.
U.E.I.

10. A beam 20 ft. long is supported at its ends. It carries loads of 100, 240 and 350 lb. at points 5, 12 and 16 ft. respectively, from the left-hand support. Calculate the bending moments and shearing forces at the points of application of the loads and draw bending-moment and shearing-force diagrams. What is the area of the shearing-force diagram from the left-hand support to the point of application of the 100 lb. load ? What does this result suggest ?
U.E.I.

11. ABCD is a framework of four rods loosely jointed, AB and AD being each of length 4 ft. and BC and CD of length 2 ft. The hinge C is connected with A by means of a fine string of length 5 ft. Weights of 100 lb. each are attached to B and D, and the whole is suspended from A. Find the tension in AC.
U.E.I.

12. A pin-jointed framework is attached to a wall at points A and B 3 ft. apart. AC is horizontal and 3 ft. long. BD is horizontal and 6 ft. long. There are members joining BC and CD. Find the load in each member, distinguishing between ties and struts, when a load of 8 tons hangs from D.
U.L.C.I.

13. A cantilever, 10 ft. long, carries a load of 2 tons at the free end and a load of 3 tons distant 4 ft. from the free end. Calculate the maximum bending moment and draw the bending-moment diagram, stating the scales.
N.C.T.E.C.

14. A beam of 12 ft. span is simply supported at the ends and carries a load of $3\frac{1}{2}$ tons distant 39 in. from one end. Calculate the maximum bending moment on the beam and draw the bending-moment diagram.
N.C.T.E.C.

15. Sketch a compound lever consisting of two parallel levers. Such a contrivance is required to have a velocity ratio of 600 and the lever to which the load is applied has arms respectively 2 in. and 36 in. long. If the second lever has one arm $1\frac{1}{2}$ in. long, find the length of the other arm.
N.C.T.E.C.

16. An axle carries a load of 10 tons. The wheels are 5 ft., and the axle-boxes 4 ft. 4 in. apart. Sketch the B.M. diagram and calculate the maximum B.M.
N.C.T.E.C.

17. A connecting rod is 18 in. long and the crank 6 in. If the total force in the piston rod is 400 lb., what is the turning moment on the crankshaft when the crank is at 30° from the dead centre ?
C.G.L.I.

CHAPTER VI

WORK AND POWER

54. Meaning of Work. The term work is used in a very exact sense in mechanics, and not with the indefinite meaning often attached to it in common speech.

Work is done by a force which produces motion, and there must be motion in the direction of the line of action of the force. If a force acts on a body which remains stationary, then no work is done.

As examples, work is done when a crane lifts a weight, when a locomotive hauls a train and when a force stretches a spring. When work is done the force is overcoming some resistance to the motion. The crane lifts the weight against the resistance offered by the earth's attraction (or gravity). The friction resists the motion of the train, and the elasticity of the spring resists the stretching force. It is useful to remember this, because it is often easier to find the work done *against* the resistance, than *by* the force, and these two quantities are equal.

55. Units. In order to compare quantities of work we need some unit.

Unit work is done when a force of 1 lb. acts through a distance of 1 ft. This unit is called a *foot-pound* (ft.-lb.).

Thus 1 ft.-lb. of work is done when a pound weight is lifted vertically through 1 ft.

If 1 lb. is lifted through 50 ft. then 50 ft.-lb. of work are done. If 2,000 lb. are lifted through 1 ft. then 2,000 ft.-lb. of work are done. If 2,000 lb. are lifted through 50 ft., we do $2,000 \times 50 = 100,000$ ft.-lb. of work.

Although the foot-pound is the commonest unit used by engineers it is not the only one. A force of 1 ton acting through 1 in, would do 1 in.-ton of work.

Care must be taken not to confuse these units with those used for the moment of a force.

Moments are stated in pound-feet or ton-inches. Work is stated in foot-pounds or inch-tons, the order being reversed.

Another unit, used in science and also in electrical work, is the *erg*. One *erg* of work is done when a force of 1 *dyne* acts through 1 *centimetre*. The dyne is a very small force. 1 lb. = 445,000 dynes very nearly; hence the erg is a very small unit of work. Because the erg is very small, the *joule* is used and equals 10,000,000 ergs = 10^7 ergs.

EXAMPLE. A horse, exerting a pull of 200 lb., hauls its load 40 yd. Find the work done.

$$40 \text{ yd.} = 120 \text{ ft.}$$
$$\text{Work done} = 200 \times 120 = 24{,}000 \text{ ft.-lb.}$$

EXAMPLE. A magnetic force of 80 dynes moves a magnetic pole 20 cm. Find the work done.

$$\text{Work done} = 80 \times 20 = 1{,}600 \text{ ergs.}$$

In general, if a force F, acts upon a body which moves a distance d in the direction in which the force acts, then

$$\text{Work done} = \text{F}d.$$

EXAMPLE. A man turns the handle of a crane through 20 revolutions. applying a steady force of 24 lb. in the direction of the handle's motion, The length of the arm carrying the handle is 15 in. Calculate the work done by the man.

$$\text{Distance moved by handle} = \left(\frac{2\pi \times 15}{12} \times 20\right)\text{ft.} = 157 \cdot 1 \text{ ft.}$$
$$\text{Work done} = 24 \times 157 \cdot 1 = 3{,}770 \text{ ft.-lb.}$$

56. Work done by a Torque. Suppose a rope is coiled round a drum of radius R. Let a pull F be applied to the rope as it unwinds from the drum; then

$$\text{Work done} = \text{F} \times \text{distance moved}$$
$$= \text{F} \times \text{length of rope unwound.}$$

Let the drum make N revolutions, then

$$\text{Length of rope unwound} = 2\pi\text{R} \times \text{N}$$
$$\therefore \text{Work done} = \text{F} \times 2\pi\text{RN.}$$

(R is measured to the centre of the rope.)

This result is itself important, but it also leads to another very important one.

Rearranging the symbols, we have

$$\text{Work done} = \text{FR} \times 2\pi\text{N.}$$

Now $\text{F} \times \text{R}$ is the moment of the force F about the centre of the drum, that is, it is the *torque* or turning effort on the drum axle.

Again, since a complete revolution is equivalent to an angle of 2π radians, the expression $2\pi\text{N}$ is the angle, expressed in radians, through which the drum has turned. Therefore, we may say

$$\text{Work done} = \text{Torque} \times \text{Angle of rotation in radians.}$$

If T = torque in pound-feet, and θ = angle in radians, this result may be expressed :

$$\text{Work done} = T\theta \text{ ft.lb.}$$

This result is very frequently used.

EXAMPLE. An electric motor exerts a torque of 16·8 lb.-ft. It makes 2,800 r.p.m. Find the work done in one minute by the motor.
Angle turned through in one minute by the motor shaft
$$= (2\pi \times \text{number of revolutions) radians}$$
$$= 2 \times 3\cdot1416 \times 2,800 = 17,580 \text{ radians.}$$
Work done = torque $\times$ 17,580 = $(16\cdot8 \times 17,580)$ ft.-lb.
$$= 295,400 \text{ ft.-lb.}$$

EXAMPLE. A pulley, 27 in. diameter, is driven by a belt, and makes 210 r.p.m. It does 820,000 ft.-lb. of work in that time. Find the difference between the pulls on the tight and slack sides of the belt.
The difference between the pulls on the two sides of the belt
$$= \text{effective pull} = F.$$

Distance moved by belt in 1 min. = $2\pi RN$
$$= \left(2 \times 3\cdot1416 \times \frac{27}{2} \times 210\right) \text{ in.}$$
$$= 17,820 \text{ in.} = 1,485 \text{ ft.}$$
Work done per minute = $F \times 1,485 = 820,000$ ft.-lb.
$$\therefore F = \frac{820,000}{1,485} = 552 \text{ lb.}$$

57. Work Diagrams. If we plot a curve of force and distance moved in the direction of the force, we obtain a work diagram. It is usual to plot the distance horizontally and the force vertically. Such a line is shown in fig. 59 for a uniform force of 200 lb. acting through 40 ft. The work done in this case = $200 \times 40 = 8,000$ ft.-lb.

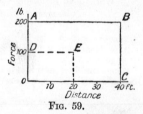

FIG. 59.

Now the height of the rectangle OABC is proportional to the force, and its length is proportional to the distance moved. Moreover, height OA $\times$ length OC = area of the rectangle. The area of the rectangle is therefore proportional to the work done by the force.

To find what area of diagram represents the work done, let us suppose that force is plotted to a scale of 100 lb. to 1 in. and distance to a scale of 20 ft. to 1 in. Then ODEF will be a unit of area = 1 sq. in. But OD also represents a uniform force of

100 lb., and OF represents a distance of 20 ft. through which the force acts. The work done = $100 \times 20 = 2,000$ ft.-lb.

Hence 1 sq. in. of diagram = 2,000 ft.-lb. of work.

Expressed algebraically we have:

Let F_s = force per inch of vertical scale

,, d_s = distance ,, ,, ,, horizontal ,,

Then work per square inch of diagram = $F_s \times d_s$.

Work diagrams are chiefly useful in dealing with cases where the force varies.

The following examples will illustrate.

EXAMPLE. A wire rope weighing 1·5 lb. per ft. hangs down a shaft. The length of rope is 200 ft. Find the work done in winding the rope on a drum at the top of the shaft.

Force required to lift full length of rope = $200 \times 1 \cdot 5 = 300$ lb.

Force ,, when 100 ft. have been raised = $100 \times 1 \cdot 5 = 150$ lb.

Force ,, when all the rope is raised = $0 \times 1 \cdot 5 = 0$.

Plot these values as in fig. 60. The three points lie on a straight line and if others were calculated they would also be found to lie on the straight line.

Suppose the scale of force to be 150 lb. to 1 in.

and ,, ,, ,, distance ,, 100 ft. to 1 in.

∴ Work scale = $150 \times 100 = 15,000$ ft.-lb. to 1 sq. in.

The length of the diagram is 2 in., and its height is 2 in., and as it is triangular in shape,

area of diagram = $\frac{1}{2} \times 2 \times 2 = 2$ sq. in.

∴ Work done in raising the rope

= area of diagram × work scale

= 2 × 15,000 = 30,000 ft.-lb.

Alternative method.

A problem such as this may be solved by using the diagram to find the average force.

When the force graph is a straight line, the average force is the mean of the initial and final values.

$$\text{Average force acting} = \frac{\text{initial force} + \text{final force}}{2}$$

$$= \frac{300 \text{ lb.} + 0 \text{ lb.}}{2} = 150 \text{ lb.}$$

∴ Work done = average force × distance

= $150 \times 200 = 30,000$ ft.-lb.

EXAMPLE. A spring is in compression under the action of a force of 75 lb. Additional force is applied with the following results:

Total force (lb.)	.	.	.	99	123	147	171
Compression (in.)	.	.	.	0·5	1·0	1·5	2·0

Find the work done in producing this additional compression of 2 in.

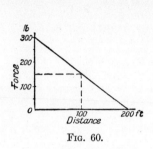

FIG. 60.

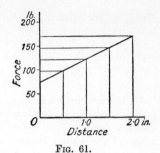

FIG. 61.

Plot the values to a force scale of 50 lb. to 1 in., and a distance scale of 0·5 in. to 1 in.

Work scale of diagram = 50 × 0·5 = 25 in.-lb. per sq. in.

Length of diagram = 4 in.

$$\text{Mean height of diagram} = \frac{1·5 \text{ in.} + 3·42 \text{ in.}}{2} = 2·46 \text{ in.}$$

Area of diagram = 2·46 × 4 = 9·84 sq. in.

∴ Work done = area of diagram × work scale
= 9·84 × 25 = 246 in.-lb.

Alternative method.

$$\text{Average force on spring} = \frac{75 + 171}{2} = 123 \text{ lb.}$$

Work done = average force × additional compression
= 123 lb. × 2 in. = 246 in.-lb.

The student will notice that the alternative method is shorter, but it is only when the diagram is a straight line that such a simple method of finding the average force is correct.

EXAMPLE. A cage, with its contents, weighs 2½ tons and is at the bottom of a shaft 540 ft. deep. The rope weighs 1·8 lb. per ft. Find the work done in raising the cage.

Weight of cage = (2½ × 2,240) lb. = 5,600 lb.
Weight of rope = (540 × 1·8) lb. = 972 lb.
Total wt. = 6,572 lb.
Pull on rope with cage at bottom = 6,572 lb.
„ „ „ „ „ „ top = 5,600 lb.

$$\text{Average pull on rope} = \frac{6,572 + 5,600}{2} = 6,086 \text{ lb.}$$

Work done = 6,086 × 540 = 3,286,440 ft.-lb.

EXAMPLE. A well, 8 ft. diameter, is 84 ft. deep. It is filled with water to a depth of 20 ft. Find the work done in pumping the well empty, given that 1 cu. ft. of water weighs 62·4 lb.

Sometimes, as in this case, it is easier to take the average distance moved. The top layer of water obviously must be pumped 20 ft. less than the bottom layer.

F

Mean height water must be pumped $= \dfrac{84 + 64}{2} = 74$ ft.

$$\begin{aligned}
\text{Total weight of water} &= \text{volume} \times \text{weight of 1 cu. ft.} \\
&= 0{\cdot}7854 \times 8 \times 8 \times 20 \times 62{\cdot}4 \\
&= 62{,}760 \text{ lb.}
\end{aligned}$$

$$\begin{aligned}
\text{Work done} &= \text{weight} \times \text{average distance} \\
&= 62{,}760 \times 74 = 4{,}644{,}240 \text{ ft.-lb.}
\end{aligned}$$

58. Irregular Variations. The force does not always vary in the simple way dealt with in the above examples. Fig. 62 shows a curve of force where the average force would *not* be the mean of the values OA and CB. In such cases, however, the principles are the same as before.

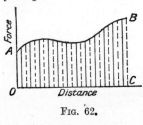

FIG. 62.

We first find the work scale. Next it is necessary to find the area OABC. This can be done by using an instrument called a planimeter, or by using the mid-ordinate rule. In the latter case, the area is divided into a number of strips of equal width as shown by dotted lines. The height at the middle of each strip (indicated by a full line) is then measured. Then

Area OABC = sum of middle heights × width of a strip.

∴ Work done = sum of middle heights × width of a strip
× work scale.

Or we may proceed as follows :

$$\text{Average force} = \frac{\text{sum of middle heights}}{\text{number of strips}} \times \text{force scale.}$$

∴ Work done = average force × total distance moved.

59. Closed Curves. Sometimes a body is acted upon by a force which does work upon it as it moves it through a certain distance. The body then returns to its starting-point and exerts a force against some resistance, thus doing work itself. The net amount of work done *on* the body is then the difference between the work done *on* the body during the outward journey, and the work done *by* the body on its return journey. A very important case of this type is that of the work done by the piston of a steam, petrol, or oil engine. Fig. 63 shows this kind of diagram. On the outward journey the variable force is shown by the curve ABC and the work done is represented by the area OABCE. On the return, the curve CDA shows the variable force, and the work done is represented by the area OADCE. The nett amount of work done is represented by area OABCE — area OADCE = area ABCDA.

The method of finding this amount of work consists in finding the area of the closed curve ABCDA and multiplying by the work scale.

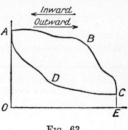

FIG. 63.

Such diagrams for engines are obtained by using an indicator, an instrument described later, in the section on Applied Heat. It records the pressure on the piston and the distance moved by the piston, to suitable scales.

EXAMPLE. A variable force is measured at a number of points and a curve, such as that of fig. 62, is plotted. The force scale is 250 lb. to 1 in. and the distance or space scale is 10 ft. to 1 in. There are ten mid-ordinates and their sum is 15·6 in. The length of the diagram is 6·7 in. Find the work done by the force.

Area under the curve = sum of mid-ordinates × width of strip.

$$= 15\cdot6 \times \frac{6\cdot7}{10} = 10\cdot452 \text{ sq. in.}$$

Work scale = 250 × 10 = 2,500 ft.-lb. per sq. in.
∴ Work done by variable force = 10·452 × 2,500
= 26,130 ft.-lb.

Another method.

Average force = average ordinate × force scale

$$= \frac{15\cdot6}{10} \times 250 = 390 \text{ lb.}$$

Distance moved = 6·7 × 10 = 67 ft.
Work done = 390 × 67 = 26,130 ft.-lb.

EXAMPLE. An indicator diagram such as that in fig. 63 is taken from a steam engine. The vertical scale indicates pressures on the piston and 1 in. on this scale corresponds to 120 lb. per sq. in. on the piston. The horizontal scale represents piston movements. The length of the diagram is 3·2 in. and the stroke of the engine is 26 in. If the mean height of the diagram is 1·4 in. and the piston diameter is 16 in., find the work done on one side of the piston when the diagram was taken.

The diagram records steam pressure, but by multiplying this by the piston area, we get force on the piston.

∴ Force scale of diagram = pressure scale × area of piston
= 120 × 0·7854 × 16 × 16
= 24,100 lb. per in.

$$\text{Distance scale} = \frac{26}{12 \times 3 \cdot 2} = 0 \cdot 677 \text{ ft. to 1 in.}$$

$$\therefore \text{ Work scale} = 24{,}100 \times 0 \cdot 677 = 16{,}300 \text{ ft.lb. per sq. in.}$$

Area of diagram = mean height × length
$$= 1 \cdot 4 \times 3 \cdot 2 = 4 \cdot 48 \text{ sq. in.}$$

$$\therefore \text{ Work done} = 4 \cdot 48 \times 16{,}300 = 73{,}000 \text{ ft.-lb.}$$

Another method.

Mean effective pressure on piston = mean height of diagram
$$\times \text{ pressure scale}$$
$$= 1 \cdot 4 \times 120 = 168 \text{ lb. per sq. in.}$$

Mean force on piston = $168 \times 0 \cdot 7854 \times 16 \times 16 = 33{,}800$ lb.

Work done = Force on piston × stroke in feet.

$$= 33{,}800 \times \frac{26}{12} = 73{,}000 \text{ ft.-lb.}$$

The student should note the term " mean effective pressure " (M.E.P.) which occurs often. It means the difference of the average pressures on one side of the piston during an outward stroke and return stroke.

60. Space Average. All the average forces treated here have been averages based on distance. Such an average is called a *space average.* If we plot forces on a time base, the time average thus obtained cannot serve for calculating work done except in special cases. The significance of the time average of a force is mentioned later (art. 105).

61. Power. In practice we are very much concerned not only with quantity of work done, but also with the rate at which it is done.

The rate of doing work is called the *power.*

Power is stated in foot-pounds per second or foot-pounds per minute.

Thus the power of a man is about 4,000 ft.-lb. per min. and that of a horse rather less than 33,000 ft.-lb. per min.

A power of 33,000 ft.-lb. per min. = 550 ft.-lb. per sec., because they are both the same rate. (550 × 60 = 33,000.)

To avoid using big numbers we use the *horse-power* as a unit of power and it equals 33,000 ft.-lb. per min.

Thus an engine of 5 H.P. is so described because it can do 33,000 × 5 = 165,000 ft.-lb. of work per min. It means the same thing to say that a 5-H.P. engine can do

$$550 \times 5 = 2{,}750 \text{ ft.-lb. per sec.}$$

In the centimetre-gram-second (C.G.S.) or metric system of units, one erg per second is the unit of power.

The *watt* is used because the erg per second is very small.
One watt = 10,000,000 ergs per sec. = 10^7 ergs per sec.
= one joule per sec. (art. 55).

In electricity, the rate of flow of electricity or current is measured in a unit called the *ampere*. The instrument used to measure this current is known as an ammeter.

The electrical potential or pressure is measured in *volts* by means of a voltmeter.

In a direct current circuit, when the current in amperes is multiplied by the potential in volts, we obtain the power of that circuit in watts, or

$$\text{volts} \times \text{amperes} = \text{watts}.$$

The watt is only a small unit of power, being less than 1 ft.-lb. per sec., hence a larger unit, the *kilowatt*, is in general use.

$$1 \text{ kilowatt} = 1,000 \text{ watts}.$$

If a kilowatt operates for one hour it does work known as a *kilowatt-hour*. This is the Board of Trade Unit.

$$
\begin{aligned}
1 \text{ kilowatt} &= 1,000 \text{ watts} \\
&= 1,000 \text{ joules per sec.} \\
&= (1,000 \times 60 \times 60) \text{ joules per hr.} \\
&= 3,600,000 \text{ joules per hr.}
\end{aligned}
$$

Hence, 1 kilowatt-hour = 3,600,000 joules.

Another very useful relationship is proved in a following example, viz.

$$1 \text{ horse-power} = 746 \text{ watts.}$$

This constant should be remembered.

EXAMPLE. A dynamo is supplied with driving power of 180 H.P. The efficiency of the dynamo is 94 per cent. How many (a) watts, (b) kilowatts does it generate? If the voltmeter reads 230 volts, what will be the ammeter reading?

$$
\begin{aligned}
180 \text{ H.P.} &= 180 \times 746 \text{ watts} \\
&= 134,280 \text{ watts.}
\end{aligned}
$$

$$\text{Output of dynamo} = \frac{134,280 \times 94}{100} = 126,200 \text{ watts}$$

$$= 126.2 \text{ kilowatts.}$$

$$\text{Volts} \times \text{amperes} = \text{watts}$$

$$\therefore \text{amperes} = \frac{\text{watts}}{\text{volts}} = \frac{126,200}{230} = 548$$

$$= \text{ammeter reading.}$$

EXAMPLE. A crane lifts a block of stone weighing 2,400 lb. at a speed of 3 ft. per sec. Find the power expended (a) in ft.-lb. per sec., (b) in horse-power.

(a) Work done per second = force × distance moved per second
$$\therefore \text{Power} = 2,400 \times 3 = 7,200 \text{ ft.-lb. per sec.}$$

(b)
$$\text{Horse-power} = \frac{7,200}{550} = 13 \cdot 06.$$

EXAMPLE. A locomotive hauls a train of 500 tons on a level track at a speed of 1 mile per min. The frictional resistance is 12 lb. per ton. Find the horse-power expended.

As the track is level no force is needed to overcome gravity. Only the frictional resistance has to be overcome.

Force to overcome friction = 500 × 12 = 6,000 lb.
Distance moved per minute = 1 mile = 5,280 ft.
Work done per minute = 6,000 × 5,280 = 31,680,000 ft.-lb.

$$\text{Horse-power} = \frac{31,680,000}{33,000} = 960.$$

EXAMPLE. A pulley, 3 ft. diameter, is driven at 160 r.p.m. by a belt whose pull on the tight side is 760 lb. and on the slack side 180 lb. Calculate the horse-power delivered to the pulley.

Effective pull of belt = 760 − 180 = 580 lb.
Torque exerted on pulley = 580 × radius of pulley

$$= 580 \times \frac{3}{2} = 870 \text{ lb.-ft.}$$

Angle turned through per minute = 160 × 2π = 1,005 radians.
Work done per minute = Torque × angle turned through per minute

$$= 870 \times 1,005 = 874,350 \text{ ft.-lb.}$$

$$\text{Horse-power} = \frac{874,350}{33,000} = 26 \cdot 5.$$

EXAMPLE. Find the power in watts equal to 1 H.P. Given 1 lb. 445,000 dynes and 1 ft. = 30·5 centimetres (cm.).

1 ft.-lb. = 1 ft. × 1 lb. = (30·5 × 445,000) ergs

$$= \frac{30 \cdot 5 \times 445,000}{10^7} \text{ joules}$$

$$= 1 \cdot 356 \text{ joules.}$$

33,000 ft.-lb. = (1·356 × 33,000) joules = 44,800 joules.

$$\therefore 1 \text{ H.P.} = 33,000 \text{ ft.-lb. per min.}$$
$$= 44,800 \text{ joules per min.}$$

$$= \frac{44,800}{60} \text{ joules per sec.}$$

$$= 746 \text{ watts.} \quad (1 \text{ joule per sec.} = 1 \text{ watt.})$$

EXAMPLE. An electric motor supplied with 10,000 watts converts 80 per cent. of this into useful power at its shaft. It runs at 1,800 r.p.m. Find the torque exerted on the shaft in pound-feet and pound-inches.

Power supplied = 10,000 watts.

$$\text{Power at shaft} = 10,000 \times \frac{80}{100} = 8,000 \text{ watts.}$$

$$\text{Horse-power at shaft} = \frac{8,000}{746} = 10\cdot71.$$

Work done per minute = $10\cdot71 \times 33,000 = 353,800$ ft.-**lb.**
Angle turned per minute = $1,800 \times 2\pi = 11,300$ radians.

$$\text{Torque on motor shaft} = \frac{353,800}{11,300} = 31\cdot3 \text{ lb.-ft.}$$

Torque on motor shaft = $31\cdot3 \times 12 = 375\cdot6$ lb.-**in**

62. Principle of Work. It was mentioned early in this chapter that work is done in overcoming some form of resistance. The principle of work tells us that the work done at the point where force is applied is equal to that done upon the resistance, or resistances, if there are more than one.

For example, work may be done in overcoming friction, as when a train is hauled along. Work may be done against gravity as when a train is hauled up an incline. Again, work may be done in hauling a train against friction and up an incline at the same time. In any case, the total work done will be the sum of the work done in overcoming every form of resistance.

The student will no doubt have the opportunity of investigating these facts in the laboratory by experiments on levers, the inclined plane, etc. We now proceed to illustrate the principle. Consider a lever such as that shown in fig. 36, page 36. Let OA = 3 in. and OB = 36 in. If a force of 12 lb. be applied at B we have seen how to find the resistance overcome at A, for

Resistance at A $\times$ 3 = 12 $\times$ 36
∴ Resistance at A = 144 lb.

Now suppose the force of 12 lb. depresses B through 1 in. Then, it is obvious that A will be raised through $\frac{1}{12}$ in.

Therefore work done by the force = $12 \times 1 = 12$ in.-lb. Also work done against resistance = $144 \times \frac{1}{12} = 12$ in.-lb.

These, it will be observed, are equal, and show that in this case our statement of the principle of work is borne out by the principle of moments. We now give a few examples which serve to illustrate the principle of work and its uses.

EXAMPLE. A garden roller weighing 2 cwt. is hauled up an inclined plank from one level to another 3·5 ft. higher. Neglecting friction, find the work done.

We do not know what force was applied to the garden roller nor how far it was hauled, but we know that gravitational resistance was overcome, and because of the principle of work we can say

work done on roller = work done against gravity
= weight of roller $\times$ vertical lift
= $2 \times 112 \times 3\cdot5 = 784$ ft.-lb.

The student may note that this answer is not affected by the path of the roller, when friction is neglected. It may have been straight or not, and the incline may have been steep or gradual.

EXAMPLE. A board 4 ft. long is inclined at 30° to the horizontal. A weight of 10 lb. is pulled, (a) by a force parallel to the board, (b) by a horizontal force, from the bottom to the top of the board.

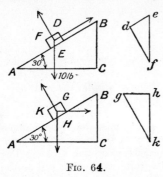

Find (1) the work done, (2) the force in case (a), (3) the force in case (b). Friction is neglected.

AB represents the board 4 ft. long. Either by drawing to scale or by trigonometry the student may find that

$$BC = 2 \text{ ft.}$$
$$\text{and } AC = 3.464 \text{ ft.}$$
$$\text{for } BC = AB \sin 30°$$
$$= 4 \times 0.5 = 2 \text{ ft.}$$
$$\text{and } AC = AB \cos 30°$$
$$= 4 \times 0.866 = 3.464 \text{ ft.}$$

FIG. 64.

(1) Work done on the weight = weight × vertical lift
$$= 10 \times 2 = 20 \text{ ft.-lb.}$$

(2) Force parallel to plane × length = work done.
$$\therefore \text{ Force DE} \times 4 = 20 \text{ ft.-lb.}$$

$$\therefore \text{ Force} = \frac{20}{4} = 5 \text{ lb.}$$

(3) Force (horizontal) × horizontal displacement = work done.
$$\therefore \text{ Force GH} \times 3.464 = 20 \text{ ft.-lb.}$$

$$\text{Force} = \frac{20}{3.464} = 5.78 \text{ lb.}$$

The last case is one which emphasizes the fact that the motion must be measured in the direction in which the force acts, when work is being calculated.

If the triangles of forces are drawn as shown in fig. 64, we see that the results are the same as those obtained by the principle of work.

Cases of agreement such as these give us confidence in the soundness of mechanical principles.

EXAMPLE. A train of 400 tons is hauled at 30 miles per hour (m.p.h.) up an incline of 1 in 75. The tractive or frictional resistance is 11·5 lb. per ton. Find the work done per minute and the horse-power expended on the train.

(An incline of 1 in 75, we take as meaning that there is a vertical rise of 1 ft. for every 75 ft. travelled up the plane. Sometimes the 75 ft. are taken horizontally, but the difference is negligible unless the gradient is a very steep one.)

$$\text{Distance moved in 1 min.} = 0\cdot5 \text{ mile} = 2,640 \text{ ft.}$$
$$\text{Vertical rise in 1 min.} = 2,640 \div 75 = 35\cdot2 \text{ ft.}$$
$$\text{Work done against gravity} = 400 \text{ tons} \times 2,240 \times 35\cdot2$$
$$= 31,500,000 \text{ ft.-lb. per min.}$$
$$\text{Work done against friction} = 400 \times 11\cdot5 \times 2,640$$
$$= 12,120,000 \text{ ft.-lb. per min.}$$
$$\text{Total work done per minute} = 31,500,000 + 12,120,000$$
$$= 43,620,000 \text{ ft.lb.}$$

$$\therefore \text{ Horse-power} = \frac{43,620,000}{33,000} = 1,320.$$

EXAMPLES VI

SECTION A

1. A body of weight 200 lb. is maintained at rest on a frictionless inclined plane of $25°$ slope by a force parallel to the plane. Determine the magnitude of this force and the reaction of the plane. N.C.T.E.C.

2. A crane lifts a load of 5 tons through 60 ft. in 45 sec. at a steady speed. Draw a diagram the area of which represents the work done and calculate the horse-power. N.C.T.E.C.

3. A train is hauled up an incline of 1 in 20 by a pull of 3 tons acting parallel to the slope. Calculate the work done when the train has been raised through a vertical distance of 60 ft. N.C.T.E.C.

4. A train weighing 300 tons has a tractive resistance of 16 lb. per ton when the speed is 40 miles per hour. Determine the horse-power required to haul the train at that speed on a level track. N.C.T.E.C.

5. A frictionless inclined plane is one mile long and has a slope of 1 in 100. Calculate the work done and the horse-power required if a load of one ton is pulled to the top in 30 min. at constant speed. N.C.T.E.C.

6. A man exerts a force of 30 lb. on the arm of a capstan at a distance of $10\cdot5$ ft. from the centre of rotation ; he works at the rate of 198,000 ft.-lb. per hr. How many times does the capstan turn in an hour ?

N.C.T.E.C.

7. The cutting stroke of a planing machine, which cuts in both directions, is 8 ft. The number of single strokes made per hour is 170, and the average resistance to cutting is 420 lb. Find the horse-power absorbed in cutting.

U.L.C.I.

8. 500 lb. of material contained in a cage are lifted from a shaft 600 ft. deep by means of a rope weighing $1\cdot2$ lb. per ft. of length. Show by means of a carefully drawn diagram the work done in lifting the cage to the surface of the shaft, stating the total amount of work done. If the cage is lifted to the surface in 5 min. at uniform speed, what horse-power has been exerted ? U.E.I.

9. An engine is used to drive a dynamo. It is observed that the readings of the ammeter and voltmeter are 24 amperes and 250 volts respectively. What is the output of the dynamo in watts ? If the efficiency of the dynamo is 86 per cent. what is the B.H.P. of the engine ?

10. You are required to find the B.H.P. of a small electric motor. Sketch neatly the form of brake you would use and explain the method of conducting the experiment (see fig. 151).

Using symbols to denote the observed quantities, explain how the B.H.P. would be calculated.   U.E.I.

11. A body is being acted upon by a variable lifting force. When the body is lifted S ft., the force P lb. is observed.

S	0	10	20	30	40	50	60	70
P	850	810	720	605	495	390	300	250

Find the average lifting force and the work done by P in lifting the body 70 ft.   U.E.I.

12. An electric tram car weighs 5 tons and the total resistance to motion is 12 lb. per ton. Find the horse-power required to draw the tram car at a uniform speed of 10 m.p.h. (a) on the level ; (b) up a slope of 1 in 35.
U.E.I.

13. A spiral spring is stretched through 1 in. by a force of 10 lb. Find the work done in stretching it through an additional 2 in. Draw the diagram of work done giving dimensions.   U.E.I.

14. A man weighing 140 lb. riding a bicycle weighing 30 lb. rides 100 yd. up a hill of gradient 1 in 20. How much work has he done in foot-pounds ? If he takes 24 sec. to do it, what average horse-power is he exerting ? Neglect friction and wind resistance.   U.L.C.I.

SECTION B

15. A belt pulley, 5 ft. diameter, rotates at 96 r.p.m. and transmits 75 H.P. Find the tensions in the belt, assuming the tension in the tight side to be 1·7 times that in the slack side.   N.C.T.E.C.

16. A locomotive capable of developing 800 H.P. draws a train of weight 400 tons. If the resistances to motion amount to 12 lb. per ton, calculate in miles per hour the greatest speed which can be maintained (a) along a level stretch of line, (b) up an incline of 1 in 100.   N.C.T.E.C.

17. A petrol engine develops 60 B.H.P. at 1,500 r.p.m. What is the mean turning moment exerted on the crank-shaft ?   N.C.T.E.C.

18. A 200-ton train is hauled at 30 m.p.h. up a slope of 1 in 100 against a frictional resistance of 15 lb. per ton. Calculate the tractive effort and power.   N.C.T.E.C.

19. A belt transmits 40 H.P. to a pulley 18 in. diameter running at 210 r.p.m. What is the difference of the tensions on the tight and slack sides ?   N.C.T.E.C.

20. A pulley 8 ft. in diameter transmits power by means of 10 cotton ropes, the effective driving force of each rope being 160 lb. Determine the horse-power transmitted when the pulley is running at a speed of 220 r.p.m.
U.L.C.I.

21. In measuring the flow of water in a certain stream by means of a V-notch weir it was found that 240,000 gallons of water passed through the weir per hour. The water has an available fall of 25 ft. and is used to drive a water wheel of 70 per cent. efficiency. Find the horse-power available at the wheel. The wheel drives a dynamo of 86 per cent. efficiency, find the output of the dynamo in watts. Neglecting all other losses, would this dynamo drive a machine requiring a current of 55 amperes at a voltage of 240 ?   U.E.I.

22. A belt is required to transmit 12 H.P. It passes over a pulley 2 ft. diameter which is rotating at 250 r.p.m. Find the effective pull in the belt. If the pull in the tight side of the belt is 2·1 times the pull in the slack side, find the maximum pull in the belt. If one square inch section of belt

will safely withstand a pull of 300 lb., what sectional area of belt will be required ?   U.E.I.

23. An electric tramcar, weighing 10 tons, is travelling at a steady speed of 10 m.p.h. up an incline of 1 in 50. The tractive resistances are equivalent to 12 lb. per ton weight of the car. The mechanical efficiency of the gearing is 85 per cent. and that of the motor 90 per cent. Find the horse-power supplied to the motor. If the voltage of the supply is 450, what current, in amperes, will the motor take ?   U.E.I.

24. An electric motor whose efficiency is 75 per cent., gives out 10 H.P. What is the power cost per hour, if 1 kilowatt-hour costs $1\frac{1}{2}$ pence ?   U.E.I.

25. The tension on the tight side of a belt is $2\frac{1}{2}$ times that on the slack side. It runs at 2,300 ft. per min. and gives 120 H.P. The belt has a section of 22 in. by $\frac{3}{8}$ in. The ultimate stress of the belt is 2,100 lb. per sq. in. Find the factor of safety.   U.E.I.

26. A rope passes round a capstan whose effective diameter is 15 in. The pull on the tight side of the rope is 236 lb. and on the slack side 16 lb. If the capstan makes 80 r.p.m., what horse-power is it absorbing ?
                                                                       C.G.L.I.

27. The mean turning moment on the crankshaft of a locomotive travelling at 60 m.p.h. is 8,700 lb.-ft. The driving wheels are 6 ft. diameter. What horse-power is being exerted ?   C.G.L.I.

CHAPTER VII

FRICTION

63. Force of Friction. When two bodies move over each other so that rubbing occurs a resisting force is set up. This force is due to friction and is called the *force of friction*, or the *frictional resistance*. In the case of liquids and gases the rubbing may be between different portions of the same material.

Let a board or metal plate AB, fig. 65, be levelled. Upon it place a block of wood, metal, or other suitable material. Let a spring balance be attached to the block so as to measure the pull F required to drag the block along. With apparatus such as this we can investigate the force of friction between the board and the block. Let a weight be placed on the block so that the total

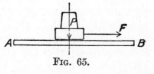

Fig. 65.

pressure exerted on the surface of the board is P. Now apply a pull to the spring balance and it will be found that no motion occurs until a certain force is reached. Notice the maximum reading of the spring balance at the instant that movement begins.

Now continue to exert just enough force to keep the block moving at a steady speed and again notice the reading on the balance. It will be found that the latter force is smaller than the former.

Repetition of this experiment leads us to conclude that the force of friction at the start is greater than the friction resisting continuous motion.

The force of friction at the start is called *static friction*. The smaller *running friction*, which we will call F, is what concerns us most.

64. Coefficient of Friction. Next, place different weights on the block so that P has different values, and, neglecting the static friction, find the values of F which just maintain uniform speed of the block. The values of F. and P may be plotted, when they will give a straight-line graph, or the values of the ratio $\dfrac{F}{P}$ may be calculated. In either case, it will be seen that $\dfrac{F}{P}$ is practically constant. Let us signify this ratio by μ (Greek letter " mu ").

Then

$$\mu = \frac{F}{P}.$$

This ratio is called the *coefficient of friction*.

Now take another block of the same material but with a different area of the face in contact with the board. Place such weights on the block as will give the same values of P as before. It will be found that corresponding values of F are the same. Hence, we conclude that the force of friction does not depend upon the area of the surfaces in contact.

Replace the last block with another of different material, or with a different type of surface. Using various weights so as to give different values of P, as before, find the corresponding forces F. They will be found to be different from those of the last experiment, but the ratio F/P will still be constant for this material. In other words we obtain a different value for μ, the co-efficient of friction.

If, while performing the above experiments, the student takes readings of F for different speeds of rubbing, he will find that the value of F is not affected, provided always, that when the reading is being taken the speed is uniform.

65. Laws of Friction. From experiments such as the above we find the following rules, known as the *laws of friction*, to be true for the speeds of rubbing that are possible with the apparatus suggested.

(1) The force of friction, or frictional resistance, is proportional to the total pressure between two surfaces.

(2) It depends upon the nature of the surfaces.

(3) It is independent of the area of contact.

(4) It does not depend upon the speed of rubbing.

The last of these laws is known to be untrue for high speeds.

EXAMPLE. A brake is applied to the rim of a flywheel with a total pressure of 864 lb. The coefficient of friction for the material which lines the brake block, on the metal of the flywheel, is 0·4. Calculate the force of friction tending to stop the wheel.

$$\frac{F}{P} = \mu$$

$$\therefore F = \mu P = 0\cdot4 \times 864$$
$$= 345\cdot6 \text{ lb.}$$

EXAMPLE. The brakes of a motor car are applied too fiercely so that the wheels become locked. The coefficient of friction between the tyres and the road is 0·2. If the weight of the car is $22\frac{1}{2}$ cwt., find the retarding force exerted by the road on the car.

$$\text{Weight of car} = 22\frac{1}{2} \text{ cwt.} = 2{,}520 \text{ lb.}$$
$$\text{Retarding force} = F = \mu P = 0\cdot2 \times 2{,}520$$
$$= 504 \text{ lb.}$$

66. Force and Reaction. When a weight simply rests on a horizontal plane as in fig. 66 (a), two forces and only two are acting. P is the downward pull of gravity and is equal, in this

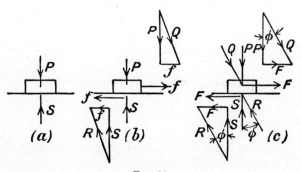

FIG. 66.

case, to the weight of the body. S is the upward reaction of
the plane, i.e. as P acts downwards, S *re*-acts upwards. Since
there is equilibrium P and S must be equal. Now apply a
horizontal force f acting to the right, not enough to cause sliding,
and the system of forces becomes as in fig. 66 (*b*). The application
of f at once brings into action an opposing force of friction at
the contact surface. This force is also f, but acts to the left ;
it is the reaction of the plane to the force f, applied to the right.
The diagram shows us at a glance that there are two pairs of
forces acting on the block. The first pair are the *applied forces*,
P and f (to the right). The second pair are the *reactions*, S and
f (to the left). By drawing the triangles of forces we find Q
the resultant of the applied forces P and f, and also R the resultant
reaction due to S and f. Q and R are obviously equal, but
opposite, as is essential for equilibrium.

Now let f be gradually increased until it reaches the value F,
just sufficient to maintain sliding at a steady speed. We see
in fig. 66 (*c*) that the directions of the forces and the relationships
between them are exactly as in (*b*) except that Q and R are more
inclined. Hence, when sliding occurs, the resultant Q of the
applied forces must be equal and opposite to R, the *resultant
reaction*.

From the above argument and the diagrams, it is apparent
that the following is true :

$$\frac{F}{P} = \frac{F}{S} = \mu = \tan \phi.$$

The angle ϕ is a very important quantity ; it is called the
angle of friction. When μ is given, the angle of friction, ϕ, is
known, or when ϕ is given, the coefficient of friction, μ, is
known, because

$$\mu = \tan \phi.$$

It should be noticed that there is some frictional resistance
before sliding occurs. In fact, it may have any value less than
F, which causes sliding, but it cannot be more than F. For this
reason, the force of friction, when sliding occurs, is called the
limiting friction.

When the limiting friction has been reached the angle between
R, the resultant reaction, and a perpendicular to the contact
surface, is always equal to ϕ.

EXAMPLE. An iron casting weighing 180 lb. lies on a concrete floor. The coefficient of friction between the two is 0·25. Find the force, inclined at 30° to the horizontal, which will drag the casting along.

$$\mu = \tan \phi = 0.25$$
$$\therefore \phi = 14° \text{ (from tables).}$$

The value of the resultant reaction is unknown, but we know it is inclined at 14° to the perpendicular to the contact surface.

The applied forces are W = 180 lb. = the pull of gravity and T, which we wish to find.

There are all the data to draw a triangle of forces as indicated. On drawing to scale starting with W, which is known, T is found to be 45·4 lb.

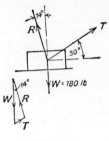

FIG. 67.

Alternative solution.

The following method is sometimes useful.
Resolve T vertically and horizontally.
Vertical component of T = T sin 30° = ½T.
This component has the effect of reducing the pressure on the floors.
∴ Total pressure between surfaces = P = W − ½T.
Horizontal component = T cos 30° = 0·866T.
This component produces the sliding motion and equals F.

$$\frac{F}{P} = \mu$$

$$\therefore \frac{0.866T}{W - \frac{1}{2}T} = 0.25.$$

$$0.866T = 0.25W - 0.125T.$$
$$0.991T = 0.25 \times 180 = 45.$$

$$T = \frac{45}{0.991} = 45.4 \text{ lb.}$$

EXAMPLE. A plane is inclined at 15° to the horizontal and on it rests a weight of 200 lb. The coefficient of friction is 0·3. Find (*a*) the force parallel to the plane which will pull the weight up, (*b*) the force parallel to

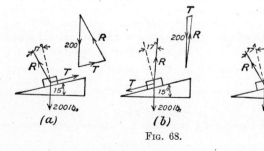

FIG. 68.

the plane which will pull it down, (c) the horizontal force which will pull it up.

$$\mu = \tan \phi = 0\cdot3$$
$$\therefore \quad \phi = 17° \text{ (from tables).}$$

In each case, a perpendicular to the plane is drawn. R is inclined to it at 17°.

As friction always opposes motion, the reaction is always drawn on that side of the perpendicular where it will oppose the motion.

Case (a). R opposes motion up the plane. The applied forces are W and T as shown.

The vector diagram is drawn starting with W = 200 lb. On measuring
$$T = 110 \text{ lb.}$$

Case (b). R opposes motion down the plane. It is inclined at 17° to the perpendicular on the side opposite to that in Case (a).

The vector diagram is drawn starting with W = 200 lb.. On measuring
$$T = 7\cdot22 \text{ lb.}$$

Case (c). This is similar to Case (a), but T is horizontal. The vector diagram is drawn starting with W = 200 lb.
$$T = 125 \text{ lb.}$$

67. Angle of Repose. When a body rests on a plane whose inclination to the horizontal is ϕ (the angle of friction), the force of gravity and the reaction are in line.

In this position, the component of W parallel to and down the

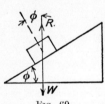

FIG. 69.

plane, is equal to the component of R parallel to the plane and up it. No sliding can, therefore, occur. If the plane is now given the slightest extra inclination W will have a greater component parallel to the plane than R will have. Hence the force down the plane exceeds the resistance to motion and sliding occurs.

The angle ϕ is thus the greatest inclination of the plane at which the body will rest. Hence, it is called the *angle of repose*.

This article suggests an experimental method of finding μ. If a plane be tilted until the body placed upon it just slides without accelerating, then the angle of tilt is ϕ and $\tan \phi = \mu$.

EXAMPLE. The brakes of a motor car are capable of locking the wheels. The coefficient of friction between the tyres and road is $0\cdot4$. Find the steepest gradient on which the car will stand without skidding down the incline
$$\mu = \tan \phi = 0\cdot4$$

The gradient is therefore $0\cdot4$ vertical to 1 horizontal or 1 vertical to $2\cdot5$ horizontal.

68. Journal and Bearing Friction. An important practical example of continuous rubbing, with its attendant friction, is the rotation of a journal or shaft in a bearing. The force of friction, occurring as a retarding force on the surface of the journal, has a moment which resists rotation. This force of friction will be equal to the product of the coefficient of friction and the total pressure exerted by the journal on the bearing. The exact distribution of the pressure on the bearing is very indefinite, as it depends upon circumstances difficult to estimate. We generally assume, however, that the total pressure is P, that is, the total load on the bearing.

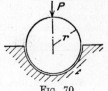

Fig. 70.

With this assumption, which gives satisfactory results, we have

Force of friction between journal and bearing

$$= \mu P.$$

Moment of force of friction about centre of shaft

$$= \mu P r$$

where r = radius of shaft.

69. Work of Friction. Work is done in overcoming resistance, hence, it is done in overcoming friction. The performance of this work results in the production of heat. This is a matter of common experience, and it admits of experimental proof.

For every 778 ft.-lb. of work done against friction 1 British Thermal Unit of heat is generated (see art. 149), and for every 1,400 ft.-lb. of work done against friction 1 Centigrade Heat Unit is generated.

EXAMPLE. A piece of timber weighing 240 lb. is dragged 40 yd. along a concrete floor. The value of μ is 0·28. Find the work done against friction.

Force of friction = 0·28 × 240 = 67·2 lb.
Work done = 67·2 × 40 × 3 = 8,064 ft.-lb.

EXAMPLE. A journal, 5 in. diameter, has a total load of 2,500 lb. upon it and makes 260 r.p.m. The coefficient of friction = 0·03. Find (a) the frictional torque, (b) the work done against friction per minute, (c) the horsepower wasted in friction, (d) the heat generated per minute.

(a) Frictional torque = $\mu P r$ = $0·03 \times 2,500 \times \dfrac{5}{2}$

                   = 187·5 lb.-in.
                   = 15·625 lb.-ft.

(b) Work done per minute   = torque × angle turned through
                        = 15·625 × (260 × 2π) radians
                        = 25,500 ft.-lb.

G

(c) Horse-power wasted $= \dfrac{25,500}{33,000} = 0.773.$

(d) Heat generated per minute $= \dfrac{25,500}{778} = 32.8$ B.Th.U.

EXAMPLE. The brake-shoe of an automobile brake operates on a drum 12 in. inside diameter. A force F = 250 lb. is applied to the free end of the shoe, which is pivoted at the other end. If $\mu = 0.4$ for the brake lining material, find the braking torque per shoe.—

Reaction of brake drum $\times a = $ F $\times 2a.$

$\therefore$ Reaction $= \dfrac{250 \times 2a}{a} = 500$ lb.

Force of friction at drum surface $= 500 \times 0.4 = 200$ lb.

Braking torque $= 200$ lb. $\times$ radius of drum

$= 200 \times 6$ lb.-in.

$= \dfrac{200 \times 6}{12}$ lb.-ft. $= 100$ lb.-ft.

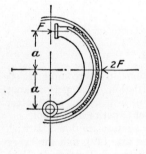

FIG. 71.

70. Lubrication. Friction is of very great use to the engineer in some circumstances, but in others he wants to reduce it to a minimum. When it causes waste of power or opposes the motion desired, he seeks to reduce it.

There are various means of doing this, but the two chief ways are (a) by lubrication, (b) by suitable design.

Lubrication consists in introducing between the rubbing surfaces some substance known as a lubricant. There are solid and liquid lubricants. By far the most important solid lubricant is graphite, a form of carbon with a metallic appearance. When placed between two solid surfaces it seems to fill the natural roughnesses, and form its own comparatively smooth surface. When used alone its uses are limited, and it is generally mixed with liquid lubricants. Other solid lubricants with their own special applications are French chalk and sulphur.

Liquid lubricants are more important, and of these, oils and greases are most used. Grease is not strictly a liquid, but it becomes one when heating results from the surface friction.

It has been proved by experiment that the action of oil is to form a thin film between the rubbing surfaces, thus separating them. Instead, then, of solid surfaces rubbing on each other the friction occurs in the liquid itself. As liquid friction is generally much less than solid friction the motion is eased. For proper lubrication two conditions must be fulfilled, first, the oil film must be formed, and secondly it must be maintained. A property of oils, not properly understood, called oiliness, is mainly responsible for setting up the film unless forced lubrication is adopted. The viscosity, or resistance to flow, of the oil resists the tendency of the pressure on the bearing to squeeze out the oil film. If the oil film is destroyed and solid contact results, ordinary bearings will " seize " in most cases.

Oil must be chosen for a particular service to withstand the pressure coming upon it. Account must also be taken of the working temperature since increase in temperature reduces viscosity. Hence, an oil with suitable viscosity at the known working temperature must be chosen.

71. Rolling Friction. By adopting rolling motion instead of sliding, frictional resistances are very greatly reduced. Although in rolling no rubbing is apparent, yet a small amount does occur due to the fact that no substance is perfectly rigid. This allows strain to occur due to a compression immediately in front of the rolling body, and a tension behind it. As the roller passes over the surface, rubbing takes place when the material of the surface changes its dimension locally, on account of this variation in stress and consequent strain.

During recent years ball and roller bearings have come extensively into use. The student should familiarize himself with typical examples of these, by reference to current works on such subjects as engineering drawing, and automobile engineering.

EXAMPLES VII

Section A

1. State clearly what you understand by the terms : Force of Friction and Coefficeint of Friction.

A steel block weighing 20 lb. is drawn slowly along a horizontal cast-iron plate by a force parallel to the plate. If the coefficient of friction between the two surfaces is 0·2, find the magnitude of the force.   U.E.I.

2. A plank of oak, with a rope tied to it, lies on the floor. When the rope is pulled horizontally with a force of 70 lb. it just moves. When pulled at an angle of 30° to the floor a force of 60 lb. just moves it. Find the weight of the plank and the coefficient of friction.   U.E.I.

3. The table of a small planing machine weighs 112 lb. and makes 6 single strokes of 4½ ft. each per minute. The coefficient of friction between the

surfaces is 0·07. Find how many foot-pounds of work per minute are expended in moving the table to and fro.   U.E.I.

4. In a certain electric motor with four sets of brushes, each set of brushes makes contact with the commutator over an area of 2·75 sq. in. The coefficient of friction between brushes and commutator is 0·3. The commutator is 12 in. diameter and runs at 800 r.p.m. and 0·5 H.P. is wasted by this friction. What was the bearing pressure per square inch on the brushes ?   U.E.I.

SECTION B

5. A gate of a canal lock is fitted with a sluice gate to permit the outflow of water to be controlled. This sluice gate is a flat rectangular door 2 ft. wide and 3 ft. deep sliding in guides vertically and being raised by a wire rope passing round a drum. The drum, of diameter 4 in., is turned by a handle of effective length 18 in. The average pressure over the surface of the sluice gate is 200 lb. per sq. ft. and the coefficient of friction between the sluice and the gate is 0·25. Find the force required to overcome this friction, also find the force exerted by the operator on the handle to raise the gate if the efficiency of the whole lifting apparatus is 0·35 and the dead weight of the parts lifted is 200 lb.   U.E.I.

6. A stone slab, weighing 50 lb., rests on a horizontal plane. Show in a diagram the forces, in magnitude and direction, acting on the body, describing the forces e.g. weight, etc. A horizontal force of 8 lb. is applied and the body remains at rest, show in a second diagram the forces, in magnitude and direction, acting on the body, describing the forces. If the coefficient of friction between the surfaces in contact is 0·23, find the horizontal force required to maintain steady motion. If the plane be gradually tilted, to what angle, to the nearest degree, can it be inclined to enable the slab to slide at uniform speed down the plane ?   U.E.I.

7. Describe any modern system of ball bearings designed to reduce friction in line shafting. The pressure on a shaft or journal bearing 8 in diameter is 5 tons and the speed of the shaft is 100 r.p.m. How many B.Th.U.s per second are generated by friction if $\mu = 0·02$ and 778 ft.-lb. = 1 B.Th.U. ?
                    U.E.I.

8. The total pressure on the bearings of a horizontal shaft is 5 tons. The shaft is 7 in. diameter and runs at a speed of 200 r.p.m. If the coefficient of friction is 0·02, find the number of foot-pounds of work absorbed by friction per minute and the heat equivalent of this work.   U.L.C.I.

9. What force would be necessary just to maintain motion in a body weighing 18 cwt., (a) along a horizontal plane, (b) up an incline of 1 in 10 ? The coefficient of friction in each case is 0·08.   U.L.C.I.

10. The pressure between the driving wheels of a locomotive and the rails is 60 tons. If the coefficient of friction is 0·15, calculate the maximum pull which the locomotive can exert in moving itself and train. Assuming a rolling resistance of 12 lb. per ton, determine the slope of the steepest gradient that could be climbed at uniform velocity if the weight of locomotive and train is 500 tons.   N.C.T.E.C.

11. A cylindrical bearing, 6 in. diameter, is subjected to a load of 6 tons. What power is absorbed in friction between the bearing and its journal ? The coefficient of friction is 0·06 and the shaft makes 60 r.p.m.
                    N.C.T.E.C.

12. A block of metal weighing 20 lb. is placed on an inclined plane the slope of which is 1 in 10. A force of 2 lb. parallel to the plane has to be applied to make the block move slowly down the plane. What is the coefficient of friction between the block and the plane ?   C.G.L.I.

CHAPTER VIII

MACHINES

72. Machine. The machine is a device for the transmission of force and motion. Generally both the force and motion are modified during transmission. In the first part of this chapter we deal with some cases where motion is transmitted without concerning ourselves with force. In the latter part forces will be important.

73. Belts. Belts and pulleys are one of the commonest arrangements for transmitting a pure rotary motion. In fig. 72, the upper diagram shows an open belt and the lower one a crossed belt. When the belt is open both shafts O_1 and O_2 rotate in the

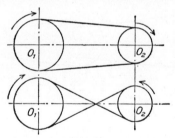

Fig. 72.

same direction, but when the belt is crossed they rotate in opposite directions.

If we assume that the belt does not slip, we may calculate the relation between the number of revolutions which the pulleys make in a given time.

Let d_1 = diameter of pulley on O_1

  ,, d_2 =   ,,   ,,   ,,   ,, O_2

  ,, N_1 = number of rev. per min. of pulley on O_1

  ,, N_2 =   ,,   ,,   ,,   ,,   ,,   ,,   ,, O_2

Now the speed of the belt is the same everywhere. As it

does not slip on the pulleys, the rims of the pulleys have the same speed as the belt.

$$\text{Circumference of pulley on } O_1 = \pi d_1$$
$$\text{Speed of rim of pulley on } O_1 = \pi d_1 N_1$$
$$\text{Circumference of pulley on } O_2 = \pi d_2$$
$$\text{Speed of rim of pulley on } O_2 = \pi d_2 N_2$$
$$\therefore \pi d_1 N_1 = \pi d_2 N_2$$
$$\therefore d_1 N_1 = d_2 N_2$$
$$\therefore \frac{N_1}{N_2} = \frac{d_2}{d_1}$$

Notice that the ratio of the pulley speeds is the *inverse* ratio of the pulley diameters. It is also useful to notice that $\pi d_1 N_1 = \pi d_2 N_2$ is the speed of the belt in feet per minute if d_1 and d_2 are in feet, or in inches per minute if d_1 and d_2 are in inches.

EXAMPLE. Three shafts A, B and C are connected with belts and pulleys as in fig. 73. The pulley on A is 22 in. diameter. The belt on pulley A drives a pulley on B which is 12 in. diameter. Another pulley keyed to B is 18 in. diameter and its belt drives a pulley on C of 15 in. diameter. If shaft A makes 80 r.p.m., find the speeds of B and C.

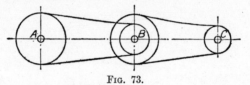

FIG. 73.

For shafts A and B we have :

$$\frac{\text{Speed of B}}{\text{Speed of A}} = \frac{\text{diameter of pulley on A}}{\text{diameter of pulley on B}}$$

$$\therefore \text{Speed of B} = \frac{\text{diameter of pulley on A} \times \text{speed of A}}{\text{diameter of pulley on B}}$$

$$= \frac{22 \times 80 \text{ r.p.m.}}{12}$$

$$= \frac{440}{3} = 146\tfrac{2}{3} \text{ r.p.m.}$$

For shafts B and C we have

$$\frac{\text{Speed of C}}{\text{Speed of B}} = \frac{\text{diameter of driving pulley on B}}{\text{diameter of pulley on C}}$$

$$\therefore \text{Speed of C} = \frac{18 \times 146\tfrac{2}{3}}{15}$$

$$= \frac{18 \times 440}{15 \times 3} = 176 \text{ r.p.m.}$$

In the above arrangement, the shaft B is called a countershaft.

Very often a shaft, driven at a constant speed, is required to drive another at different speeds. This is done by using speed cones or stepped pulleys. Each shaft carries two or more pulleys fastened together. They are arranged as in the sketch, fig. 74,

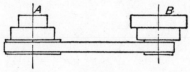

Fig. 74.

with the largest pulley on one shaft in line with the smallest on the other shaft. The sizes of the pulleys must be arranged so that the same length of belt will suit corresponding pairs.

EXAMPLE. Shafts A and B are fitted with speed cones. Shaft A is driven at a constant speed of 100 r.p.m. and the largest pulley is 10 in. dia. Find the size of the smallest pulley on the speed cone on shaft B, if B's highest speed is to be 250 r.p.m. If the smallest pulley on A is equal to the smallest pulley on B, find B's minimum speed.

Let diameter of smallest pulley on B = d_2 then

$$\frac{d_2}{10} = \frac{100}{250}.$$

$$\therefore d_2 = \frac{100 \times 10}{250} = 4 \text{ in.}$$

If the smallest pulley on A = 4 in. diameter, then largest on B = 10 in.

$$\frac{\text{Speed of B}}{\text{Speed of A}} = \frac{4}{10}$$

$$\therefore \text{ Speed of B} = \frac{4 \times 100}{10} = 40 \text{ r.p.m.}$$

74. Spur Wheels. Belts are never perfectly free from slipping and so the results of the last article are slightly inaccurate. When accurate speeds are to be transmitted it is necessary to use spur or cogged wheels. Suppose two discs A and B, fig. 75, on shafts O_1 and O_2 press on each other at P, then, owing to the friction, they will roll on each other.

Such an arrangement may be used to transmit motion, if the tangential force at P is not large enough to cause slipping. To ensure that there shall be no slip, teeth or cogs may be arranged to mesh with each other, as shown at C and D. It is clear that if the motion is to be smooth the teeth must be equally spaced along the circumferences of C and D. The distance from centre to centre of two adjacent teeth, measured along the circles C and D, is called the *pitch,* or *circular pitch* of the teeth. The circles

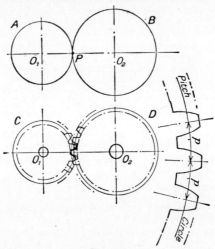

Fig. 75.

C and **D** are the *pitch circles* and the point where they touch is the *pitch point.* The motion of two spur wheels must always be the same as if the pitch circles rolled on each other without slipping.

Let $p =$ the pitch of the teeth.

,, $n_1 =$ number of teeth on one wheel.

,, $n_2 =$,,   ,,   ,,   ,, the other wheel.

,, $d_1 =$ diameter of pitch circle of wheel with n_1 teeth.

,, $d_2 =$,,   ,,   ,,   ,,   ,,   ,,   ,, n_2 ,,

Circumference of pitch circle $= n_1 p = \pi d_1$

$$\therefore \quad p = \frac{\pi d_1}{n_1}$$

$$\text{also } p = \frac{\pi d_2}{n_2}.$$

Let $N_1 =$ number of rev. per min. of wheel with n_1 teeth.

,, $N_2 =$,,   ,,   ,,   ,,   ,,   ,,   ,,   ,, n_2 ,,

As there is no slipping of the pitch circles, they must both have the same speed.

Speed of pitch circle = circumference × rev. per min.

$$= \pi d_1 N_1 = \pi d_2 N_2$$

$$\therefore \frac{N_1}{N_2} = \frac{\pi d_2}{\pi d_1} = \frac{n_2 p}{n_1 p} = \frac{n_2}{n_1}$$

Thus the number of revolutions are in the *inverse* ratio of the number of teeth on the wheels.

EXAMPLE. A wheel A has 25 teeth and makes 125 r.p.m. It gears with a wheel B, having 55 teeth. How many revolutions per minute will B make?

Let N_1 = number of revolutions per minute of B

then
$$\frac{N_1}{125} = \frac{25}{55}$$

$$\therefore N_1 = \frac{25 \times 125}{55} = 56\frac{9}{11}.$$

B will rotate in the opposite direction to A.

EXAMPLE. A wheel A has 20 teeth and makes 560 r.p.m. It gears with a wheel B of 48 teeth, whilst on the same shaft as B a wheel C of 22 teeth is keyed. C gears with a wheel D of 55 teeth. Find the rev. per min. of D.

Number of rev. per min. of B = $\frac{560 \times 20}{48} = 233\frac{1}{3}$.

Rev. per min. of B = rev. per min. of C = $233\frac{1}{3}$

Rev. per min. of D = $\frac{233\frac{1}{3} \times 22}{55} = \frac{700 \times 22}{3 \times 55}$

$$= 93\frac{1}{3}.$$

If the student will make a rough sketch, he will see that D rotates in the same direction as A. He is advised always to make sketches in solving such examples as the above.

75. The Screw. Long before the screw was used as a fastening like the bolt and nut, it was used for transmitting force and

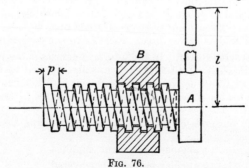

FIG. 76.

motion. It is still so used as in the screw jack, the leading screw of a lathe, the letter press, etc. The objects generally are (a) to change rotary motion into linear motion, (b) to increase the force. The threads of screws are made in many shapes for various purposes, but when used for transmitting motion the threads are generally square or some modification of that shape. Fig. 76 shows an approximate representation of a simple square thread.

The *pitch* of the thread is the distance from the face of one thread to the corresponding face of the next.

Suppose the nut B in the figure is fixed, and the head A of

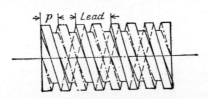

FIG. 77.

the screw is given one complete turn, then the screw as a whole will advance a distance equal to the pitch, p, along the direction of the axis of the screw. If the screw is turned by means of a spanner or a bar whose total length from the centre of the screw is l, then the end of the bar moves a distance $2\pi l$ while the screw moves a distance p.

Sometimes a screw has two entirely separate threads. They are called *double start* threads or simply *double threads*. The pitch of the screw is still the distance between the faces of two adjacent threads but a complete turn will now advance the screw a distance $2p$ along its axis. This is known as the " lead " of a screw. Even more than two threads may be used, but the number is seldom above three. Fig. 77 shows a two-start thread.

76. Velocity Ratio. In the foregoing articles it has been seen that the machines dealt with are generally supplied with motion at one speed and deliver it at a different speed. The ratio of these quantities is very important and is known as the *velocity ratio*.

For the purposes of this chapter we may define the velocity ratio as

$$\frac{\text{angular movement supplied}}{\text{angular movement delivered}}$$

in the case of rotary motion, both movements occupying the same period of time

or $\dfrac{\text{distance moved by force applied}}{\text{distance moved by resistance overcome}}$ in the

case of linear motion, both movements again being measured in the same time. Thus with belts and gear wheels, if N_1 is the number of revolutions supplied per minute and N_2 is the number of revolutions delivered per minute, then velocity ratio $= \dfrac{N_1}{N_2}$.

In the case of the screw we should have

velocity ratio $= \dfrac{\text{distance moved by force at end of lever}}{\text{distance advanced by screw}}$

$= \dfrac{2\pi l}{p}$ for a single thread.

77. Machines and Principle of Work. It has been seen that the work done at the point where the force is applied is equal to the work done in overcoming resistance. This principle applies to all machines.

Some of the resistance to the applied force is in the machine itself in the form of friction. The remainder of the resistance is generally that load or force which the machine is really intended to overcome. We take a few examples in which the friction is neglected.

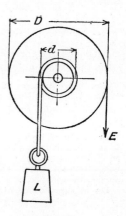

FIG. 78.

78. Wheel and Axle. A wheel of diameter D is fastened rigidly to an axle of diameter d. A rope is passed round the wheel and another round the axle. A load L is suspended by the rope which passes round the axle, and an effort, or pull, E is required on the other rope to lift L. By the principle of work, neglecting friction, we have

work done by effort = work done on load.

∴ assuming one complete turn is given to wheel and axle, we get
work done by effort = effort × distance moved
$$= E \times \pi D$$

work done on load = load × distance lifted

$$= L \times \pi d$$

$$\therefore L \times \pi d = E \times \pi D$$

$$\therefore L = \frac{E \times \pi D}{\pi d} = E \times \frac{D}{d}.$$

A load found in this way, neglecting friction, is called the *ideal load* and the corresponding effort is called the *ideal effort*.

Again, it should be noticed that

$$\frac{\pi D}{\pi d} = \frac{\text{distance moved by force applied}}{\text{distance moved by resistance overcome}}$$

$$= \text{velocity ratio.}$$

∴ ideal load = ideal effort × velocity ratio.

Whether the machine is an ideal one or not, the ratio

$$\frac{\text{load}}{\text{effort}} = \text{mechanical advantage.}$$

This is a very important quantity both for calculation purposes and in engineering practice.

In an ideal machine, where there is no friction, we have

ideal effort × velocity ratio = ideal load

$$\therefore \text{velocity ratio} = \frac{\text{ideal load}}{\text{ideal effort}} = \text{mechanical advantage.}$$

Although the foregoing results have been found in connection with the wheel and axle they are true in general.

EXAMPLE. A worm and worm-wheel mechanism has a velocity ratio of 32. What ideal load will be raised by an effort of 8 lb. ?

Ideal load = effort × velocity ratio
= 8 × 32 lb. = 256 lb.

EXAMPLE. A pulley, 12 in. diameter round which a rope passes, is keyed to the same shaft as a cogged wheel of 20 teeth. It gears with a wheel of 86 teeth on the same shaft as a drum 4-in. diameter. A load of 258 lb. hangs from the drum. Find the velocity ratio, and the ideal effort, which, applied to the rope, will raise the load.

Let us suppose one revolution to be given to the pulley, then

effort moves $\pi \times 12$ in. = 37·7 in.

For 1 turn of pulley, drum turns $\frac{20}{86}$ of a turn.

Distance weight is raised $= \frac{20}{86} \times \pi \times 4$ in.

$$= \frac{20 \times 22 \times 4}{86 \times 7} = 2\cdot93 \text{ in.}$$

$$\text{Velocity ratio} = \frac{37 \cdot 7}{2 \cdot 93} = 12 \cdot 84.$$

$$\text{Ideal effort} = \frac{\text{load}}{\text{vel. ratio}} = \frac{258}{12 \cdot 84} = 20 \cdot 1 \text{ lb.}$$

79. Mechanical Efficiency. A very few machines, such as weighing machines, are nearly ideal, but most are far from being so. Owing to the friction which resists the motion of the machine parts, a load, less than the ideal load, will be lifted. This means that some of the work done by the effort is spent in the machine itself and only a reduced amount of work is done on the load. This is true of every machine, whether it be a bicycle or a steam engine, a dynamo or a crane. In forming an opinion of a machine, we require to know what proportion of the work we supply to it will be delivered by it, and do useful work. This is the *mechanical efficiency* of the machine. Sometimes we merely call it the efficiency.

$$\text{Efficiency} = \frac{\text{useful work delivered}}{\text{work done by the effort}}.$$

The efficiency so calculated is always less than unity. If the student obtains a bigger value than unity, he will know there is an error in the calculation, or in the data.

The efficiency is commonly stated as a percentage; it is then always less than 100.

$$\text{Efficiency} = \left(\frac{\text{useful work delivered}}{\text{work done by the effort}} \times 100\right) \text{ per cent.}$$

In all cases the work done and the work delivered must be measured during the same period of time, and in the same units.

The ideal machines in the last article would have an efficiency of 1, or 100 per cent.

EXAMPLE. A lifting machine whose velocity ratio is 25 raises 800 lb. weight when an effort of 42 lb. is applied. Find the mechanical efficiency of the machine.

Suppose the load to be raised 1 ft., then
$$\text{work done on load} = 800 \times 1 = 800 \text{ ft.-lb.}$$
The effort moves 25 ft. in the same time,
$$\therefore \text{ work done by effort} = 25 \times 42 = 1,050 \text{ ft.-lb.}$$
$$\therefore \text{ efficiency} = \frac{\text{work delivered}}{\text{work supplied}} = \frac{800}{1,050} = 0 \cdot 762 \text{ or } 76 \cdot 2 \text{ per cent.}$$

EXAMPLE. A screw of ¾-in. pitch is operated by an arm (or lever) 20 in. long. The force applied at the end of the arm is 28 lb. and the force exerted by the screw is 2,200 lb. Find the efficiency of the screw.

For 1 complete turn of screw, end of arm moves
$$2\pi \times 20 \text{ in.} = 125{\cdot}7 \text{ in.}$$

For 1 complete turn, the screw advances $\frac{3}{4}$ in.

Work done by screw $= \frac{3}{4} \times 2{,}200 = 1{,}650$ in.-lb.
Work done on the arm $= 28 \times 125{\cdot}7 = 3{,}520$ in.-lb.

$$\therefore \text{ Mechanical Efficiency} = \frac{1{,}650}{3{,}520} = 0{\cdot}469 \text{ or } 46{\cdot}9 \text{ per cent.}$$

Another method of calculating the efficiency of a lifting machine may now be given.

Work done on load $=$ load $\times$ distance raised.
$\qquad\qquad\qquad = \text{L} \times$ distance raised.

Work done by effort $=$ effort $\times$ distance moved by effort.
$\qquad\qquad\qquad = \text{E} \times$ distance moved by effort.

$$\therefore \text{Efficiency} = \frac{\text{L} \times \text{distance raised}}{\text{E} \times \text{distance moved by effort}}$$

Now $\dfrac{\text{L}}{\text{E}} =$ mechanical advantage,

and $\dfrac{\text{distance raised}}{\text{distance moved by effort}} = \dfrac{1}{\text{velocity ratio}}$

$$\therefore \text{Efficiency} = \frac{\text{mechanical advantage}}{\text{velocity ratio}}.$$

80. The Testing of Machines. Mechanical efficiencies can generally only be determined as the result of experiment. We require to know the velocity ratio, the load and the effort in order to calculate efficiency.

The velocity ratio can be calculated if we have full knowledge of the dimensions of the machine, or, alternatively, it can be measured experimentally.

The mechanical advantage can only be found by experimentally finding corresponding values of load and effort.

The velocity ratio is a constant for any given machine and does not depend on the load.

The mechanical advantage will vary for different loads.

In the following articles, concrete examples are given of lifting machines.

81. Screw-jack. This machine is a practical application of the screw. It is suitable for lifting very heavy weights through small heights.

The effort E is applied at the end of the arm, which can be inserted in a series of holes in the head of the screw. The load L is lifted in the direction of the axis of the screw.

For experimental work, a drum or pulley generally replaces the arm, and the effort is measured as the pull on a rope passing round the drum. The pull may be applied by weights attached to the rope. It can also be applied by an actual pull, measured by a spring balance.

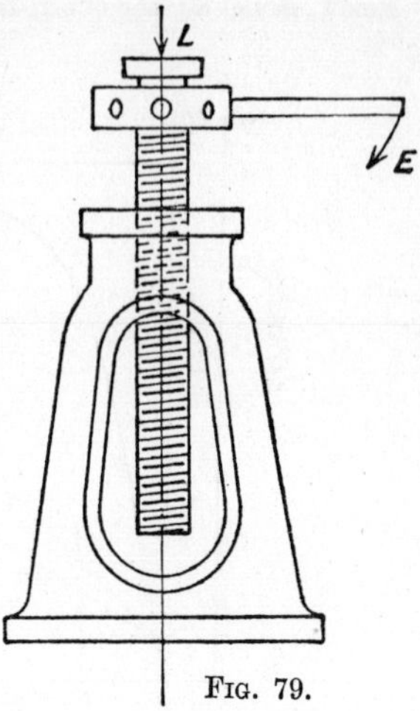

Fig. 79.

The following are the results of a test on a screw-jack.

Pitch of screw = 0·5 in. Diameter of drum = 7·5 in.

| Load (lb.) | . | . | . | . | 0 | 84 | 168 | 252 | 336 |
| Effort (lb.) | . | . | . | . | 1·5 | 5·5 | 10·5 | 16 | 21 |

To find velocity ratio.
For 1 turn of drum effort moves $7·5 \times \pi = 23·5$ in.
During the same time the load is raised 0·5 in.

$$\therefore \text{ velocity ratio} = \frac{23·5}{0·5} = 47.$$

Consider the load of 168 lb. and the corresponding effort 10·5 lb.

Ideal effort for load of 168 lb. $= \dfrac{\text{load}}{\text{vel. ratio}} = \dfrac{168}{47} = 3·58$ lb.

This would be the effort if there were no friction.
Hence, effort spent on friction $= 10·5 - 3·58 = 6·92$ lb.
This is called the *friction effort* or simply the *friction*.

$$\text{Mechanical advantage} = \frac{\text{load}}{\text{effort}} = \frac{168}{10·5} = 16$$

$$\text{Efficiency} = \frac{\text{mechanical advantage}}{\text{vel. ratio}} = \frac{16}{47} = 0·341$$
$$= 34·1 \text{ per cent.}$$

or $\quad$ efficiency $= \dfrac{\text{load} \times \text{height raised}}{\text{effort} \times \text{distance moved}} = \dfrac{168 \times 1 \text{ ft.}}{10·5 \times 47}$
$$= 0·341.$$

The results worked out as above for each load are tabulated below.

Load (lb.)	.	.	0	84	168	252	336
Effort (lb.)	.	.	1·5	5·5	10·5	16	21
Ideal effort	.	.	0	1·78	3·58	5·37	7·15
Friction	.	.	1·5	3·72	6·92	10·63	13·85
Efficiency (per cent.)	.	0	32·4	34·1	33·6	34·1

Below, in fig. 80, the effort, friction and efficiency are plotted on a load base.

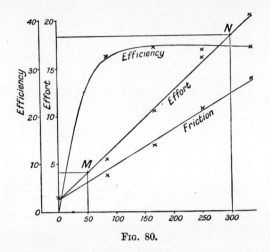

Fig. 80.

In mathematics we find that when two quantities, such as E and L, give a straight line on being plotted, there is a simple formula which connects them. It is of the form

$$E = aL + b$$

where a and b are constants which we must find. In the case of a machine, this formula, when a and b have been found, is called the *law of the machine*.

To find the formula, take two points *on the line* of effort. M and N have been taken and it is best to choose them near the ends of the straight line.

M corresponds to a load of 50 lb., i.e. L = 50.
The curve shows that the effort is 4·1 lb., i.e. E = 4·1.
At N it is found that L = 300 and E = 18·3.

Putting these values in the equation

$$E = aL + b$$

we have $18 \cdot 3 = 300a + b$
and $4 \cdot 1 = 50a + b$
on subtracting $14 \cdot 2 = 250a$
∴ $a = 0 \cdot 0568$.

Putting this value in the second equation to find b we have

$$4 \cdot 1 = 0 \cdot 0568 \times 50 + b$$
$$\therefore \ b = 4 \cdot 1 - 0 \cdot 0568 \times 50$$
$$= 4 \cdot 1 - 2 \cdot 84$$
$$= 1 \cdot 26.$$

These are the values of a and b in the formula. Hence the law of the machine is

$$E = 0 \cdot 0568L + 1 \cdot 26.$$

82. Pulley Blocks. Arrangements of pulleys in sets with a continuous rope passing around them have long been used, especially for marine work, as a lifting machine. Fig. 81 gives a general idea of pulley blocks with rope. The number of pulleys can be varied, but it is not often that more than four in a set are used. The number of pulleys in the upper and lower sets may be the same, or one block may have one more pulley than the other.

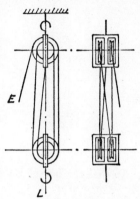

To find the velocity ratio, imagine the load lifted 1 ft. Then each rope supporting the lower block will shorten 1 ft. In the figure, there are four such ropes. Hence, 4 ft. of rope must be taken up by the effort.

$$\therefore \ \text{velocity ratio} = 4.$$

FIG. 81.

A test on a pulley block tackle, made by the authors, gave the following results :

Velocity ratio = 5.

Load (lb.)	.	.	0	14	28	42	56	70
Effort (lb.)	.	.	3·5	7	11	15	19	24
Ideal Effort	.	.	0	2·8	5·6	8·4	11·2	14
Friction.	.	.	3·5	4·2	5·4	6·6	7·8	10
Efficiency (per cent.)	.	0	40	50·9	56	59	58·4

As an example we may take the load of 42 lb.

$$\text{Ideal effort} = \frac{\text{load}}{\text{vel. ratio}} = \frac{42}{5} = 8 \cdot 4 \text{ lb.}$$

$$\text{Effort spent on friction} = 15 - 8 \cdot 4 = 6 \cdot 6 \text{ lb.}$$

$$\text{Mechanical advantage} = \frac{42}{15} = 2 \cdot 8$$

H

$$\text{Efficiency} = \frac{\text{work done on load}}{\text{work done by effort}} = \frac{42 \times 1}{15 \times 5} = 0.56 \text{ or } 56 \text{ per cent.}$$

In fig. 82, the above results are plotted on a load base.

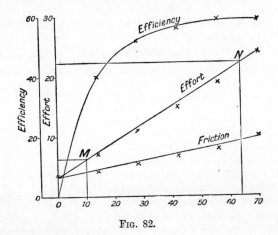

F𝗜𝗀. 82.

To find the law of the machine two points have been taken *on the line* of effort.

For a load of 10 lb. the effort from the curve is 6·2 lb.

For a load of 64 lb. the effort from the curve is 22 lb.

Thus E = 6·2 lb. when L = 10 lb.

and E = 22 lb. when L = 64 lb.

Substituting in the equation

$$\text{E} = a\text{L} + b$$

we have $22 = 64a + b$

and $6\cdot2 = 10a + b$

subtracting $15\cdot8 = 54a$

∴ $a = 0\cdot293$

∴ $22 = 64 \times 0\cdot293 + b$

∴ $b = 22 - 64 \times 0\cdot293$

$= 22 - 18\cdot75$

$= 3\cdot25.$

Hence, the law of the machine is

$$\text{E} = 0\cdot293\text{L} + 3\cdot25.$$

EXAMPLE. Using the law formula just found, calculate the effort required to lift 55 lb. by means of the pulley blocks.

$$E = 0.293L + 3.25$$
$$= 0.293 \times 55 + 3.25$$
$$= 16.1 + 3.25$$
$$= 19.35 \text{ lb.}$$

The student may check this result against that given by the effort line.

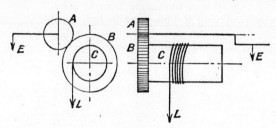

FIG. 83.

83. Other Machines. It is not necessary to deal in detail with every type of lifting machine, since the mechanical principles involved are the same in all of them. The student should learn carefully to observe which is effort and which is load in any machine.

Fig. 83 shows the essentials of a single purchase crab winch. It is the machine used in many hand-operated cranes. A shaft on which is keyed a wheel A is rotated by a handle. A gears with a larger wheel B which is keyed to the same shaft as a drum C on which the rope is wound that lifts the load.

If a greater mechanical advantage is needed a double purchase winch can be used. That means that the shaft of A, instead of being turned by hand, is operated by means of another pair of gear wheels.

Fig. 84 shows in diagrammatic form a differential pulley block. Two pulleys C and D are fastened together and rotate on the same axis. An endless chain passes round C and D, and also the pulley F, which carries the load. The pulley D is

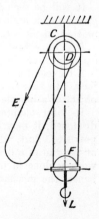

FIG. 84.

made slightly smaller than C, and the grooves are so shaped that the chain cannot slip in them.

Suppose C has a diameter d_1, and D a diameter d_2. Let the effort move so that C receives one complete turn ; D will also make one turn.

$$\therefore \text{ chain winding on C} = \pi d_1$$
$$\text{and chain unwinding from D} = \pi d_2.$$

The chain carrying F thus shortens $(\pi d_1 - \pi d_2)$.

The lift of F is only half of this $= \dfrac{\pi d_1 - \pi d_2}{2}$

$$\therefore \text{ Velocity ratio} = \frac{\text{distance moved by E}}{\text{distance moved by L}}$$

$$= \frac{\pi d_1}{\dfrac{\pi d_1 - \pi d_2}{2}} = \frac{2 d_1}{d_1 - d_2}$$

This lifting tackle is sometimes called the Weston differential pulley block.

EXAMPLE. In a differential pulley block the diameter of the larger pulley is 8 in. and of the smaller one $7\frac{3}{4}$ in. Calculate the velocity ratio.

$$\text{Velocity ratio} = \frac{2 \times 8}{8 - 7\frac{3}{4}} = \frac{16}{\frac{1}{4}} = 64.$$

It will be seen that a Weston pulley block can be made to give a much higher velocity ratio than a rope pulley block such as that in fig. 81.

It is important to realize that all machines are subject to the same laws as those which have been illustrated here.

A bicycle, for example, is just as truly a machine as is a screw-jack. In this case, the velocity ratio is less than one since the object of a bicycle is to develop speed and not to increase force.

In later chapters when steam, gas and petrol engines are discussed, it may be noted that the force on the piston corresponds to effort, whilst the torque on the crankshaft or the force at the rim of a driving pulley constitutes the load. In all cases work is done in overcoming friction in the machine or engine, hence, the mechanical efficiency is less than 100 per cent.

EXAMPLES VIII

Section A

1. The following figures were taken from a student's laboratory notebook:

RESULT OF TEST ON A SCREW JACK

Effort applied.	Load lifted.	Mechanical Efficiency.
lb.	lb.	
0·74	15	0·405
2·5	60	—

Deduce the velocity ratio of the machine and fill in the omitted mechanical efficiency.   U.E.I.

2. A worm and worm wheel used for experimental purposes consists of a single-threaded worm A, on the shaft of which is keyed a wheel B of effective circumference 14 in. The worm gears with a worm wheel C having 80 teeth. On the worm wheel shaft is keyed a wheel D of effective circumference 16 inches. Around the wheel B is coiled a cord to which the effort is applied and around the wheel D a cord is coiled to which is attached the weight to be lifted. Make a line diagram of the machine and determine its velocity ratio.

In an experiment with the above machine it was found that when the load lifted was 60 lb. the mechanical efficiency was 0·28. What was the magnitude of the applied effort?   U.E.I.

3. Describe how you would experimentally determine the velocity ratio of any lifting machine with which you are familiar.

In an experiment with a lifting machine whose velocity ratio is 30, the following results were obtained:

Load lifted (lb.)	.	50	100	150	200	250
Effort required (lb.)	.	6·5	9·9	13·2	16·6	20·0

Determine the efficiency for each load and plot a curve, on a load base, to show the efficiency of the machine for all loads lifted from 0 to 250 lb.
                                                                      U.E.I.

4. The following results were obtained in a test of a wheel and axle in which the velocity ratio is 25 to 1.

Load raised (lb.)	.	0	50	100	150	200	250	300
Force used (lb.)	.	5	10	15	21	28	36	45

Calculate the mechanical advantage and the efficiency of each load.

Plot on squared paper provided the graphs of (1) effort, (2) mechanical advantage, (3) efficiency, each as ordinate against load lifted as base.   U.E.I.

5. The largest and smallest diameters of the pulleys of a speed cone fitted to a machine mandrel are 14 in, and 5 in. respectively. This speed cone is driven by a belt from a similar speed cone keyed to a countershaft which makes 220 r.p.m. Find the greatest and least speeds, in revolutions per minute, at which the machine mandrel may be driven.   U.L.C.I.

6. Show that if two toothed wheels are in gear their speeds are inversely proportional to their diameters or to their numbers of teeth.

Three spur wheels, B, and C, on parallel shafts are in gear. A has 12 teeth, B 40 teeth and C 48 teeth. Find the speed of C when A makes 80 r.p.m. What is the purpose of the wheel B?   U.L.C.I.

7. Explain the meaning of the term " velocity ratio " of a lifting machine.

In a wheel and axle having a diameter of wheel equal to 5 times the diameter of the axle, it is found that an effort of 66 lb. raises a load of $2\frac{1}{2}$ cwt. Assuming ideal conditions, what load ought the effort of 66 lb. to raise ? Account for the difference between the actual and ideal loads.
U.L.C.I.

8. Sketch a simple screw-jack. If the screw has pitch $\frac{3}{8}$ in. and length of lever 10 in., calculate the ideal load which can be raised when the effort is 42 lb.   N.C.T.E.C.

9. By means of a belt gearing, a shaft A drives a shaft B and the latter drives shaft C. The speed of shaft A is 600 r.p.m. and shafts B and C are required to run at 200 and 100 r.p.m. respectively. If the belt pulley on shaft A is 6 in. diameter and that on shaft C 12 in., find the diameters of the pulleys on shaft B.   N.C.T.E.C.

10. A simple wheel and axle, having wheel diameter 36 in. and axle diameter 8 in., is used to raise a load of 2,000 lb. Calculate the ideal effort required.   N.C.T.E.C.

11. A screw-jack has a single thread of $\frac{1}{4}$-in. pitch. What effort applied at the end of a handle 1 ft. long will be required to lift a load of $1\frac{1}{2}$ tons ? Neglect friction.   N.C.T.E.C.

12. A shaft, A, rotating at 500 r.p.m., drives a shaft, B, at a speed of 40 r.p.m., by means of wheel gearing. Keyed to shaft A is a pinion having 20 teeth which gears with a wheel of 75 teeth. The latter is keyed to a spindle together with a pinion of 30 teeth gearing with a wheel keyed to shaft B. Find the required number of teeth in the latter wheel.   N.C.T.E.C.

SECTION B

13. Experiments with a hauling gear having a velocity ratio of 34 gave the following results :

| Effort (E) (lb.) | . | 0·7 | 1·15 | 1·6 | 2·1 | 2·53 | 3 |
| Load (L) (lb.) | . | 10 | 20 | 30 | 40 | 50 | 60 |

Determine the " law " of the machine, i.e. an expression connecting E and L.
What is the efficiency of the gear for the 60-lb. load ?   U.L.C.I.

14. Describe, with the aid of a sketch, a simple lifting machine. How would you proceed to obtain a load-efficiency curve for such a machine ?
N.C.T.E.C.

15. The following results were obtained in a laboratory test of a lifting tackle, the velocity ratio of which was 25 to 1 :

| Load raised (lb.) | . | . | . | 0 | 50 | 100 | 150 | 200 |
| Effort applied (lb.) | . | . | 5 | 10 | 15 | 21 | 28 |

Calculate the mechanical efficiency for each load. Plot, on the load as base, the effort applied and the mechanical efficiency.   N.C.T.E.C.

16. A crane is used to lift a load of 3 cwt. The effort required is 23 lb, and the velocity ratio of the crane is 25 to 1. The same crane requires an effort of 9 lb. to lift 1 cwt. What effort would be required to lift a load of 2·5 cwt. and what would be the efficiency of the crane at that load?
C.G.L.I.

17. The gear-box of a motor car has a reduction ratio in one of its gears of 8 to 1. When the driving torque from the engine is 50 lb.-ft. the torque delivered by the gear-box is 384 lb.-ft. Calculate the efficiency of the gear-box.   C.G.L.I.

CHAPTER IX

MOTION

84. Kinematics. Although motion is an effect of force, it is the object of this chapter to discuss it without reference to force. The study of pure motion is known as kinematics.

85. Displacement. When a body moves from one position to another it has been displaced. Its *displacement* is the distance, measured in a straight line, between the initial and final positions. It does not matter in what path the body moved.

Displacements are generally measured in feet for engineering calculations, though large displacements may be stated in miles and small ones in inches.

One *foot* is $\frac{1}{3}$ of a yard.

The *yard* is the British legal standard of measurement and is the distance between two marks on a bronze bar, at 62° F., carefully kept as a standard of reference. Thus, the fundamental British unit is the yard and all other units are fractions or multiples of it.

In working problems on motion, it is generally best to work in feet and so avoid confusion. Displacement is a vector quantity, like force, because it is not completely known until we state its direction and sense. Thus we may say that a body has been given a displacement of 10 ft., but if we say that it was in a westerly direction it is completely known.

If a body is displaced, first, from A to B in an easterly direction, and then, from B to C in a northerly direction, the resultant displacement is AC. For example, if A to B is 8 ft. and B to C is 6 ft., then the resultant displacement is 10 ft. in the direction A to C.

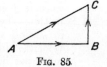

When there are several displacements a polygon may be drawn to find the resultant displacement as in the following example.

Fig. 85.

EXAMPLE. A surveyor in laying out his lines walks 700 ft. due north, then 600 ft. north-west and finally 800 ft. 30° south of west. How far must he walk in a straight line to reach his starting-point ?

This is equal to finding his final displacement.

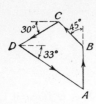

Suppose A is the starting-point. Set off AB representing 700 ft. to any suitable scale. Draw BC 45° west of north, making it 600 ft. to the same scale as AB. From C, set off CD, 30° south of west, making it 800 ft. to scale   AD is the resultant displacement. DA gives the direction in which the man must walk.

On measuring we find:

Displacement = 1,332 ft.

The man must walk in a direction 33° south of east.

86. Velocity. For practical purposes we cannot ignore the speed with which any desired object is attained. Rate at which displacement occurs is, therefore, important.

Velocity is rate of change of displacement.

This brief statement requires some explanation. A rate involves time and in mechanics we use the second as our unit of time. Hence, velocity is change of displacement per second. This does *not* mean that we can measure the displacement which takes place in 1 sec. and call that the velocity, because the velocity can change in value during a single second. If, however, at any instant, we could make the body continue without change of its velocity for 1 second after that instant, then the displacement during that second would be the velocity.

Again, since velocity is rate of change of displacement it must have direction. Hence, a complete statement of velocity requires its magnitude, direction and sense to be given. Velocity is thus a vector quantity.

There are two points the student may note here.

(*a*) Although a velocity involves direction, there are many problems where the direction of the velocity is not changing. In that case, the direction is often not stated, since it does not affect the result.

(*b*) Sometimes the minute or hour is used as the unit of time in stating velocities. Thus, while it is usual to state velocities in feet per second, we sometimes speak of miles per hour, or feet per minute.

87. Speed. It is convenient to have a term to express rate of movement without paying any heed to direction. Such a term is *speed*. Speed and velocity are numerically the same, but a change of direction changes the velocity but not necessarily the speed. For example, a train may run round a circular track at uniform speed, but its velocity constantly changes because of change of direction.

EXAMPLE. A ball rolls in a straight path with a uniform velocity of 8 ft. per sec. How far will it travel in 5 sec. ?

Distance moved in 1 sec. = 8 ft.
„   „   „ 5 sec. = 8 × 5 = 40 ft.

EXAMPLE. A train is moving with a velocity of 1 mile per min. What is its velocity in feet per second ?

No. of feet in 1 mile = 5,280.

∴ Distance moved in 60 sec. = 5,280 ft.

∴ Distance moved in 1 sec. $= \dfrac{5,280}{60} = 88$ ft.

∴ A velocity of 1 mile per min. = 88 ft. per sec.
The student will find this a useful number to remember.

EXAMPLE. Express a velocity of 66 ft. per sec. in miles per hour.

Distance moved in 1 sec. = 66 ft.
Distance moved in 1 hr. = 66 × 60 × 60 ft.

Distance moved in 1 hr. in miles $= \dfrac{66 \times 60 \times 60}{5,280}$

$= 45$ miles.

∴ The required velocity is 45 m.p.h.

88. Average Velocity. If a body moves in a straight line from A to B, then the distance from A to B divided by the time taken is the *average velocity* of the body. The average velocity is that velocity which, if it remained uniform, would cause a given distance to be covered in the same time as that which is taken under the actual conditions.

EXAMPLE. An aeroplane flies a distance of 32 miles in 20 min. Find its average velocity in feet per second.

Distance covered = 32 × 5,280 ft.
Time taken = 20 min. = 20 × 60 sec. = 1,200 sec.

Average velocity $= \dfrac{32 \times 5,280}{1200} = 140 \cdot 8$ ft. per sec.

In general :

let $s =$ displacement
„ $t =$ time taken
„ $v =$ average velocity

then $v = \dfrac{s}{t}$.

If the velocity is uniform the *average* and *actual* velocities are the same.

EXAMPLE. A racer covers 100 yd. of track at a uniform speed of 27 ft. per sec. What is the time taken ?

100 yd. = 300 ft.

time taken $= \dfrac{300}{27} = 11\tfrac{1}{9}$ sec.

In symbols, this is $t = \dfrac{s}{v}$; in words, time = $\dfrac{\text{space}}{\text{velocity}}$.

89. Acceleration. Velocities and speeds are very seldom uniform. There are cases, where, for some considerable period, they are nearly uniform, and for practical purposes we treat them as such. When a velocity is increasing the body is said to have an *acceleration*, and when the velocity is decreasing the body has a *retardation*. Another term for retardation is *deceleration*. A retardation is a *negative* acceleration. In this book, so far as calculation is concerned, we shall only deal with cases where the acceleration is uniform.

Suppose, at a given instant of time, a body is moving with a velocity of 8 ft. per sec., and one second later it is found to have a velocity of 10 ft. per sec. Its velocity has increased by 2 ft. per sec. during the one second. The body, therefore, has an acceleration. Suppose after another second the velocity has increased to 12 ft. per sec. ; again, there is an increase in velocity of 2 ft. per sec. in one second.

If the body goes on in this way, second after second, we see that its velocity increases 2 ft. per sec. each second, hence we say that it has an *acceleration of 2 feet per second per second*. For brevity we often write this as : 2 ft. per sec.^{2} or 2 f.p.s.^{2} In this case the small figure 2 is not an algebraic index.

EXAMPLE. A body is moving at a given instant with a velocity of 12 ft. per sec. It has an acceleration of 3 ft. per sec.^{2} Find its velocity after 5 sec.

Each second 3 ft. per sec. is added to the velocity.

Thus after 1 sec. velocity = $(12 + 3)$ ft. per sec.

　　,,　 2　,,　　　,,　　= $(12 + 3 + 3)$ ft. per sec.

　　,,　 3　,,　　　,,　　= $(12 + 3 + 3 + 3)$ ft. per sec.

　　,,　 4　,,　　　,,　　= $(12 + 3 + 3 + 3 + 3)$ ft. per sec.

　　,,　 5　,,　　　,,　　= $(12 + 3 + 3 + 3 + 3 + 3)$ ft. per sec.

　　　　　　　　　　　　= $12 + (5 \times 3)$

　　　　　　　　　　　　= $12 + 15 = 27$ ft. per sec.

The calculation may, of course, be written more briefly :

Final velocity = $12 + 5 \times 3 = 27$ ft. per sec.

EXAMPLE. A train starts from rest and in 2 min. is travelling at 45 m.p.h. Calculate the acceleration in feet per second per second, assuming it to be uniform.

$$45 \text{ m.p.h.} = \frac{45}{60 \times 60} \text{ miles per sec.}$$

$$= \frac{45 \times 5,280}{60 \times 60} \text{ ft. per sec.}$$

$$= 66 \text{ ft. per sec.}$$

Time taken to reach this speed = 2 min. = 120 sec.

Increase in velocity per second = $\frac{66}{120}$ = 0·55 ft. per sec.

∴ Acceleration = 0·55 ft. per sec.²

The work of the foregoing examples may be put in a general form.

Let u = the *initial* velocity in feet per second.

,, f = the acceleration in feet per second per second.

,, t = the time in seconds.

,, v = the *final* velocity in feet per second after t seconds.

Then velocity after 1 sec. = $u + f$

,,   ,,   ,,   2 sec. = $u + 2f$

,,   ,,   ,, t sec. = $u + ft$

∴ $v = u + ft$.

If there is a retardation instead of an acceleration, then f is negative and the formula becomes :

$$v = u - ft.$$

90. Velocity Graphs. If we know the velocity of a body at a number of successive times, we can plot a graph of the velocity. It is usual to plot times horizontally and velocities vertically. This is plotting the velocity on a *time base*.

In fig. 87 is shown the graph for a body with no acceleration,

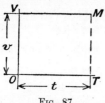

Fig. 87.

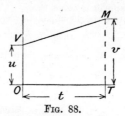

Fig. 88.

that is, a uniform velocity. The height of the diagram is OV, which represents v to some scale. The length is OT, which represents t to some scale.

The product $v \times t$ = the distance moved.

Let the vertical scale be v_s ft. per sec. to 1 in.

,,   ,,   horizontal ,,   ,, t_s sec. to 1 in.

Then 1 sq. in. of the diagram = $v_s \times t_s$ ft.

Let s = the distance moved in t sec.; then the distance moved = area OVMT $\times v_s t_s = s$.

Another simple case, fig. 88, is that of a uniformly increasing velocity, that is, the case of uniform acceleration. The graph is VM, a straight line, inclined to the horizontal.

The distance moved by the body = area OVMT $\times v_s t_s = s$.

The area OVMT $= \dfrac{OV + TM}{2} \times OT$.

Let OV = the initial velocity = u
,, TM = ,, final ,, = v

Then $s = \dfrac{u + v}{2} \times t$.

That is, s = average velocity $\times$ time.

EXAMPLE. At a given instant the speedometer of a motor car indicates 10 m.p.h., and 12 sec. later it shows 38 m.p.h. How far has it travelled during the 12 sec., assuming uniform acceleration ?

$$\text{Average speed} = \frac{10 + 38}{2} = \frac{48}{2} = 24 \text{ m.p.h.}$$

$$24 \text{ miles per hr.} = \frac{24 \times 5{,}280}{60 \times 60} \text{ ft. per sec.}$$

$$= 35\cdot2 \text{ ft. per sec.}$$

$$\text{Distance travelled} = 35\cdot2 \times 12$$
$$= 422\cdot4 \text{ ft.}$$

EXAMPLE. A train is running up an incline at 40 m.p.h. when the steam is shut off. The effect of friction and the incline is to produce a retardation of $1\cdot2$ ft. per sec.[2] How long will the train continue before stopping, and how far will it travel ?

Convert the 40 m.p.h. to feet per second (f.p.s.).

$$\text{then } 40 \text{ m.p.h.} = \frac{40}{60} \times 88 = 58\cdot7 \text{ f.p.s.}$$

Note. We are making use of the fact that 60 m.p.h. = 88 f.p.s. (art. 87).

$$\text{Time taken for velocity to fall to zero} = \frac{58\cdot7}{1\cdot2} \text{ sec.}$$

$$= 48\cdot9 \text{ sec.}$$

$$\text{Average speed} = \frac{58\cdot7 + 0}{2} = 29\cdot35 \text{ f.p.s.}$$

$$\therefore \text{ Distance travelled} = 29\cdot35 \times 48\cdot9 = 1{,}435 \text{ ft.}$$

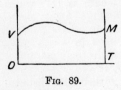

FIG. 89.

The plotting of a graph may be used as the method of finding the distance travelled when the velocity does not vary according to any simple rule. If corresponding values of time and velocity are known and the curve is plotted, the area may be found by the mid-ordinate rule. Then we have

distance travelled = area OVMT $\times v_s t_s$.

91. Algebraic Statement. It has been shown (art. 89) that,
when initial velocity $= u$, time $= t$, and acceleration $= f$,

then final velocity $v = u + ft$ . . (I)

Let a body start with a velocity u having acceleration f;
let it move for t sec.,

then average velocity during t sec.

$$= \frac{\text{initial velocity} + \text{final velocity}}{2}$$

$$= \frac{u + v}{2} \text{ (but } v = u + ft) \text{ and substituting}$$

average velocity $= \dfrac{u + (u + ft)}{2} = \dfrac{2u + ft}{2}$

$$= u + \tfrac{1}{2}ft.$$

Distance travelled $=$ average velocity $\times$ time

$\therefore \; s = (u + \tfrac{1}{2}ft) \times t$

$s = ut + \tfrac{1}{2}ft^2$ . . . . . (II)

Another useful formula may be obtained as follows:

$v = u + ft$

$\therefore \; v^2 = u^2 + 2uft + f^2t^2$

$= u^2 + 2f(ut + \tfrac{1}{2}ft^2)$ substituting II

$= u^2 + 2fs$ . . . . . (III)

The three formulæ given above are known as the *equations
of uniformly accelerated motion*.

92. Falling Bodies. It is common experience that, when
a body is dropped, it falls to the ground, being acted upon by
the force of gravity. It has also been shown experimentally,
that if two very dissimilar bodies, such as a feather and a metal
coin, are dropped at the same instant from the same height
in a vacuum, they will strike the ground after the same interval
of time. The conclusion is that all bodies fall with the same
acceleration no matter what their weight may be. Moreover,
for moderate heights, this acceleration is uniform, and is always
signified by the letter " g." Air resistance can affect the above
statements very materially, but for a great range of engineering
calculations they are substantially true. If, in the equations of
motion, g is substituted for f, they become the equations of the
motion of falling bodies. For Britain, a fair average value of
g is 32·2 ft. per sec.^{2} The value varies, increasing progressively
from the equator as the poles are approached.

EXAMPLE. A stone is dropped from the top of a tower 200 ft. high. Find its velocity on reaching the ground, taking $g = 32 \cdot 2$.

Let v = final velocity, initial velocity = 0.

$$\therefore \text{ average velocity} = \frac{v + 0}{2} = \frac{v}{2}.$$

$$\text{Time taken } (t) = \frac{200}{\text{average vel.}} = \frac{200}{\dfrac{v}{2}} = \frac{400}{v}$$

Also $v = 32 \cdot 2t$ or $t = \dfrac{v}{32 \cdot 2}$.

$$\therefore \frac{v}{32 \cdot 2} = \frac{400}{v}$$

$$v^2 = 400 \times 32 \cdot 2$$
$$v = 113 \cdot 5 \text{ ft. per sec.}$$

The problem may be solved directly by applying formula (III):

$$v^2 = u^2 + 2gs$$
$$v^2 = 0 + 2 \times 32 \cdot 2 \times 200$$
$$= 32 \cdot 2 \times 400$$
$$v = 113 \cdot 5 \text{ ft. per sec.}$$

93. C.G.S. Units. When using metric measurements the centimetre (cm.) is the unit of length and the second the unit of time.

Velocities then are stated in centimetres per second (cm. per sec.) and accelerations in centimetres per second per second (cm. per sec.²).

All reasoning and formulæ hold exactly as for the British system.

94. Angular Motion. Rotating bodies play such an important part in engineering that angular velocity and acceleration need to be understood.

The student is probably familiar with the term "revolutions per minute" which is really a statement of angular velocity. In connection with mechanical calculations it is not a convenient method of statement.

The unit of angle used is the *radian* and the unit of time, the *second*. An angular velocity is therefore stated in radians per second (rad. per sec.).

Let a rotating body, such as a flywheel, turn through an angle of θ radians in t seconds.

then average angular velocity $= \dfrac{\theta}{t} = \omega$ (Greek letter omega)

EXAMPLE. A flywheel turns through 18 revolutions in 12·56 sec. Find the average angular velocity in radians per second.

$$1 \text{ revolution} = 2\pi \text{ radians.}$$
$$\therefore 18 \text{ revolutions} = 2\pi \times 18 \text{ radians} = \theta.$$

Average angular velocity $\omega = \dfrac{2\pi \times 18}{12 \cdot 56} = 9$ rad. per sec.

Angular acceleration is rate of change of angular velocity, or change of angular velocity per second. It is generally denoted by α (Greek letter alpha).

Let ω_2 = final angular velocity

,, ω_1 = initial ,, ,,

Then after time t sec.

$$\omega_2 = \omega_1 + \alpha t.$$

EXAMPLE. An electric motor starts from rest, and after 5 sec. it rotates at 1,800 r.p.m. Find the angular acceleration. How many radians will it turn through during acceleration?

$$1,800 \text{ r.p.m.} = \frac{1,800}{60} = 30 \text{ rev. per sec.}$$

Angular velocity in rad. per sec. $= 30 \times 2\pi = 60\pi$

Angular acceleration $= \dfrac{60\pi}{5} = 12\pi = 37 \cdot 7$ rad. per sec.[2]

Average angular velocity $= \dfrac{\text{initial vel.} \times \text{final vel.}}{2}$

$$= \frac{0 + 60\pi}{2} = 30\pi \text{ rad. per sec.}$$

Angle turned through $= \theta = 30\pi \times 5 = 150\pi = 471 \cdot 4$ radians.

The student may use the same reasoning in relation to angular as to linear motion, and the equations of motion correspond.

$$v = u + ft \qquad\qquad \omega_2 = \omega_1 + \alpha t$$
$$s = ut + \tfrac{1}{2}ft^2 \qquad\qquad \theta = \omega_1 t + \tfrac{1}{2}\alpha t^2$$
$$v^2 = u^2 + 2fs \qquad\qquad \omega_2{}^2 = \omega_1{}^2 + 2\alpha\theta.$$

95. Angular and Linear Motion.

Let a disc, with centre O, fig. 90, rotate about its centre at a uniform velocity through the angle AOB, so that a point, originally at A, traverses the arc between A and B. The length of this arc, if the angle AOB is in radians,

$$= \text{AOB} \times \text{OA}$$

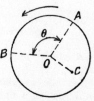

FIG. 90.

If the time taken is t sec., then the speed of the point

$$= \frac{AOB \times OA}{t}$$

Let $AOB = \theta$ radians, and $OA =$ radius of path $= r$,

$$\text{then, speed of point} = \frac{\theta \times r}{t} = \frac{\theta}{t} \times r$$

$$= \omega r.$$

Or writing v for speed, $v = \omega r$.

This result is of the greatest importance.

Linear speed at radius r always equals angular speed times radius.

Also it should be noted that

$$\omega = \frac{v}{r}$$

If we take another point, C, on the disc at a radius OC. Then the speed of C

$$= \omega \times OC.$$

The speed of points such as A and C, calculated in this way, is called their *linear velocity*.

Hence, v is the linear velocity of the point and ω is its angular velocity.

EXAMPLE. The flywheel of a gas engine is 5 ft. in diameter and makes 210 r.p.m. Find the linear velocity of a point on the rim.

Angular velocity = 210 r.p.m.

$$= 2\pi \times 210 \text{ rad. per min.}$$

$$= \frac{2\pi \times 210}{60} \text{ rad. per sec.}$$

$$= 21 \cdot 99 \text{ rad. per sec.}$$

Linear velocity $v = \omega r = (21 \cdot 99 \times 2 \cdot 5)$ ft. per sec.

$$= 54 \cdot 9 \text{ ft. per sec.}$$

EXAMPLE. A locomotive travels at 50 m.p.h. and its driving wheels are 6 ft. 9 in. diameter. Find the angular velocity of the wheels

$$50 \text{ m.p.h.} = \frac{50 \times 5,280}{60 \times 60} = 73 \cdot 3 \text{ ft. per sec.}$$

Angular velocity $= \omega = \dfrac{v}{r} = \dfrac{73 \cdot 3}{3\frac{3}{8} \text{ (ft.)}} = 19 \cdot 55$ rad. per sec.

A similar relation holds between linear and angular acceleration.

Let the angular velocity of a body increase from ω_1 to ω_2 in 1 sec. at a uniform rate, then

$$\omega_2 - \omega_1 = \text{the angular acceleration} = \alpha.$$

If there is a point at radius r on the rotating body, its linear velocity changes from

$$\omega_1 r \text{ to } \omega_2 r.$$

Hence, the linear acceleration $f = \omega_2 r - \omega_1 r$

$$= (\omega_2 \times \omega_1)r$$

$$= \alpha r.$$

Also $\alpha = \dfrac{f}{r}$.

EXAMPLE. A motor-car with wheels 28 in. diameter is travelling at 30 m.p.h. and is pulled up by its brakes in 36 ft. Find (a) the angular velocity of the wheels before braking, (b) the retardation of the car, (c) the angular retardation of the wheels.

Linear velocity of car = 30 m.p.h. = 44 ft. per sec.

Angular velocity of wheels $= \dfrac{v}{r} = \dfrac{44 \times 12}{14} = 37 \cdot 7$ rad. per sec.

To find retardation of car,

$$v^2 = u^2 - 2fs$$
$$0 = 44^2 - 2f \times 36$$
$$\therefore 72f = 44^2$$

$$f = \frac{44 \times 44}{72} = 26 \cdot 9 \text{ ft. per sec.}^2$$

Angular retardation $= \alpha = \dfrac{f}{r}$

$$= \frac{26 \cdot 9 \times 12}{14} = 23 \cdot 1 \text{ rad. per sec.}^2$$

since $r = \dfrac{14}{12}$ ft.

96. Velocity Vectors. Suppose a boat sets out from a point X on one bank of a river at a velocity of 4 ft. per sec. to reach a point Y immediately opposite. In one second it would travel 4 ft. towards Y. Now suppose the stream flows with a velocity of 3 ft. per sec., the boat, instead of being found at M, will have been carried 3 ft. down the stream to N. Hence its displacement is XN at the end of 1 sec. Thus XN is its velocity, i.e. its displacement per second. At the end of the next second the boat will have been carried a further 3 ft. down-stream but will also have progressed 4 ft. nearer the opposite bank. The boat will actually have continued in its path along XN to R. We

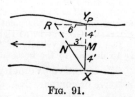

FIG. 91.

I

see that by setting out a vector XM = 4 and another MN = 3 we obtain XN = 5 and the actual velocity of the boat is 5 ft. per sec. in the direction of XN.

EXAMPLE. A ship sails in a westerly direction whilst a man on deck walks across it with his face set south-west. Velocity of ship = 8 m.p.h. and velocity of man on deck = 4 m.p.h. Find the resultant velocity of the man.

Set off a vector AB due west and 8 units in length. Then, from B, set off BC, 4 units in length and in a direction south-west. Notice how the vectors point A to B and B to C. Then the resultant velocity is A to C, and will be found on measurement to be 11·2 m.p.h.

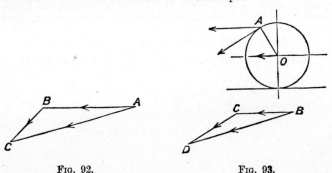

<table>
<tr><td>FIG. 92.</td><td>FIG. 93.</td></tr>
</table>

EXAMPLE. A locomotive is moving at 24 m.p.h. and one of the wheels is 6 ft. diameter. Find the velocity of a point A on the rim of the wheel. A is the end of a radius inclined at 30° to the vertical.

A has two velocities :

(1) That due to the forward motion of the engine.
(2) That due to the rotation of the wheel, at right angles to the radius OA.

The value of (1) = $\frac{24}{60} \times 88 = 35\cdot2$ ft. per sec.

The value of (2) = 35·2 ft. per sec. also.

Set off BC = 35·2 units, then set off CD = 35·2 units. Note that the arrows on BC and CD point circuitally, i.e. in the same way round the diagram. CD will be at right angles to OA.

The resultant velocity of A = BD = 67·6 ft. per sec. and its direction is 15 degrees to the horizontal.

97. Relative Velocity. All our knowledge of motion is relative or comparative. Most often we speak of velocity relative to the earth's surface as if the earth were fixed. We know, however, that the earth is moving but it is not observed because everything moves together. It is relative motion or difference of motion which we observe.

In order completely to describe velocity we should state to what it is relative.

As a simple illustration of relative velocity, consider two railway trains on parallel tracks running in the same direction. Suppose one to travel at 50 m.p.h. and the other at 30 m.p.h. To a person on the slower train the faster one appears to be going at (50 — 30) = 20 m.p.h. To a person on the faster train the slower one appears to be going at 20 m.p.h. in the opposite direction. Note that the relative velocity of 20 m.p.h. is found by subtracting.

Next, let us examine more closely the example in the last article of the man on the ship. The ship has a velocity of 8 m.p.h. *relative to the earth.* The man's velocity of 4 m.p.h. is *relative to the ship.* The resultant is the man's velocity *relative to the earth.* The resultant is the *vector sum* of the other two velocities, and it may be written :

$$\text{vector AB} + \text{vector BC} = \text{vector AC.}$$

By transposing it is seen that

$$\text{vector BC} = \text{vector AC} - \text{vector AB.}$$

In words this means that the man's velocity relative to the ship is given by subtracting the velocity of the ship relative to the earth from the man's velocity relative to the earth. It should be noted that the two velocities being subtracted are relative to the same body, i.e. the earth in this instance. This is always the case. When velocities are added together vectorially the velocity of the second moving body is relative to the first moving body.

Stating these facts geometrically it means that to add vectors they must be drawn so that the arrows are circuital. Thus in fig. 92 the arrows on AB and BC point the same way round the triangle. When two vectors are to be subtracted they must be set off from the same point (or towards the same point) and the closing line of the triangle gives the vector difference. Thus again in fig. 92, vectors AB and AC are set off from A to scale, the arrows both pointing away from A and being non-circuital.

Again, the locomotive in the above example has a velocity *relative to the earth,* and the point A, fig. 93, has a velocity *relative to the locomotive.* The resultant (the sum of these vectors) is the velocity of point A *relative to the earth.* Again, we see that the velocity *relative to the moving body, the locomotive, is a difference.*

In fig. 93, CD is the *difference* of BC and BD, which are set off from the same point.

EXAMPLE. A ship sails due north at 25 m.p.h. and a wind blowing from the south-west at 16 m.p.h. carries the smoke from the funnel with it.

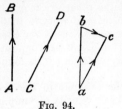

FIG. 94.

Find in what direction the smoke appears to a person on deck to be going.

The ship travels at 25 m.p.h. *relative to the earth* as shown by AB. The smoke travels at 16 m.p.h. *relative to the earth* as shown by CD. To find the velocity of smoke *relative to the ship* we must set off vectors from the same point.

ab is parallel to AB and 25 units in length; *ac* is parallel CD and 16 units in length.

bc gives the velocity of the smoke in magnitude and direction *relative to the ship*.

98. Centripetal Acceleration. A very important application of vector subtraction is here given. Let a point A move at *uniform speed* on the circumference of a circle of radius *r* and with centre O. Let the speed of A be *v* and its angular velocity *ω*.

When a point moves in a circle its velocity is in the direction of the tangent; thus it is always changing direction. Hence, in the case under consideration, the magnitude of the velocity does not change, but its direction does change. To find a change in any value we subtract the first value from the final value.

lm is the vector for velocity of the point at A

ln is the vector for velocity of the point at A'

∴ *mn* is the change which has taken place.

In other words, a velocity *mn* has been added to *lm* to produce the final value *ln*.

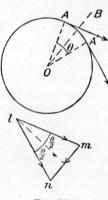

The change in velocity is due to a change in direction and causes the acceleration.

We wish to find the value of the acceleration.

Let AOA' = θ radians.

Then angle *mln* = θ radians.

By trigonometry $\sin \frac{\theta}{2} = \frac{\frac{1}{2}mn}{lm}$

FIG. 95.

$$\therefore mn = 2lm \sin \frac{\theta}{2}$$

$$= 2v \sin \frac{\theta}{2}.$$

When an angle is very small its sine = the angle in radians (very nearly) (see tables).

$$\therefore \ mn = 2v\frac{\theta}{2} = v\theta.$$

Let t = time taken for A to move to A'.

Then $\dfrac{\text{change of velocity}}{\text{time}}$ = acceleration.

$$\therefore \text{A has an acceleration} \ \frac{v\theta}{t} = v\omega.$$

But $\omega = \dfrac{v}{r}$, see art. 95.

$$\therefore \text{acceleration of A} = v\frac{v}{r} = \frac{v^2}{r} \quad . \quad . \quad . \quad \text{(I)}$$

Also $v = \omega r$.

$$\therefore \text{acceleration of A} = \omega r \times \omega = \omega^2 r. \quad . \quad \text{(II)}$$

The values in (I) and (II) are very important and will be used in the next chapter.

Notice, too, that mn is parallel to OB, the bisector of AOA'. Hence mn, and therefore the acceleration, is *towards the centre* of the circle. The following conclusion should be remembered :

When a point moves with uniform speed in a circular path, it has an acceleration towards the centre of the circle. The value of that acceleration is $\dfrac{v^2}{r}$ or $\omega^2 r$.

EXAMPLES IX

Section A

1. A train travels a distance of 196 miles in 3 hr. 40 min. Find its average speed in feet per second.

2. The minute hand of a public clock is 5 ft. long. Find the average speed of the end of this hand in inches per minute.

3. A cage is hauled up a pit shaft at an average speed of 40 ft. per sec. The shaft is 2,500 ft. deep. How long will a winding take ?

4. Change the following velocities into feet per second : (a) 70 m.p.h., (b) 25 in. per min., (c) 5,000 yd. per hr.

5. Change the following velocities into centimetres per second : (a) 5 metres per min., (b) 80 kilometres per hr., (c) 5 ft. per sec. 1 ft. = 30·5 cm.

6. A ball rolls down an incline with uniform acceleration. Starting from rest, its final velocity is 12 ft. per sec. Find its average velocity.

7. In the last example the time occupied was 5 sec. Find the acceleration.

8. A body starts with a velocity of 40 ft. per sec. If it comes to rest in 8 sec., what is its retardation ?

9. A body starts with a velocity of 18 ft. per sec. and moves with an acceleration of 2 ft. per sec.^{2} for 8 sec. What is the velocity at the end of the period ? Find the average velocity and the distance travelled.

10. The angular velocity of a crank is 17·5 rad. per sec. and the crank pin is 2·5 ft. from the centre of the crank-shaft. Find the linear velocity of the crank-pin.

11. A jib crane is raising a block of stone vertically with a velocity of 6 ft. per sec. At the same time the jib is swinging round, thus giving the stone a horizontal velocity of 4 ft. per sec. What is the resultant velocity of the stone relative to the ground and in what direction is it moving.

C.G.L.I.

SECTION B

12. In a laboratory experiment a trolley running down an inclined plane covered a distance of 67·35 in. in the first 2 sec. of its motion from rest. Determine the acceleration of the trolley's motion in feet per second per second and the distance covered by the trolley in the next $\frac{1}{10}$ sec.   U.L.C.I.

13. A steamship is going due north at 12 m.p.h. and the wind is blowing from the north-east at 8 m.p.h. Determine, either graphically or by calculation, the direction of the trail of smoke as observed from the steamer.

U.L.C.I.

14. A car with wheels 30 in. diameter moving at 15 m.p.h. is brought to rest under a uniform retardation in a distance of 200 ft. Find :

(a) The retardation of the car.

(b) The initial angular velocity and the angular retardation of the wheels. State clearly the units in which each answer is expressed.   U.E.I.

15. A tram car, moving at 15 m.p.h., is brought to rest by the application of the brakes in a distance of 20 yd. on a level track. The diameter of the wheels is 2 ft. Find :

(a) The average retardation of the car in feet and second units ;

(b) the time taken to come to rest from time of application of brakes ;

(c) the angular retardation of the wheels in radians per second per second.

U.E.I.

16. Define " linear acceleration." A train, starting from a station, is uniformly accelerated for 1 minute, travels with uniform speed for 2 min., and is uniformly retarded for 1 min., coming to rest at a second station. The distance travelled during the period of uniform acceleration is 1,800 ft. Draw to scale, on a time base, curves showing the speed and the displacement for the time $t = 0$ to $t = 4$ min.   U.E.I.

17. A flywheel is speeded up from rest with uniform angular acceleration. After the wheel has turned through 40 revolutions the angular velocity is 18 rad. per sec. Find the angular acceleration and the time taken.

18. Two ships start from the same point. One goes due N.E. at 10 miles per hr., the other due S.E. at 15 m.p.h. The water drifts due N. at 2 m.p.h. What is the distance between the two ships 2 hr. after the start and what are their respective distances from the starting point ?   C.G.L.I.

19. A motor car starts from rest and its speed increases uniformly from nil to 30 miles per hr. in 1 min., after which it travels at that speed for 30 sec. and is then brought to rest with uniform loss of speed in another 30 sec. How far did the motor car travel in the 2 min. ? Give the answer in yards.   C.G.L.I.

20. A vehicle starts from rest and moves with uniform acceleration. It passes a point 100 yd. from the starting-point in 30 sec. In how many seconds will it traverse the next 150 yd. ? C.G.L.I.

21. A weight is raised up a mine shaft 1,200 ft. deep. The weight is accelerated at 3 ft. per sec.^{2} for the first 480 ft. and then is retarded uniformly for the rest of the journey so that it just stops at the top of the shaft. Find the rate of retardation and the total time taken for the journey. C.G.L.I.

CHAPTER X

FORCE AND MOMENTUM

99. Force and Motion. Hitherto motion has been treated without considering the force producing it. It is now necessary to deal with this important matter.

100. Inertia. Motion, in relation to the force producing it is governed by three *Laws of Motion* commonly called Newton's Laws of Motion, because they were first propounded by Sir Isaac Newton.

1*st Law. A body continues in its state of rest, or of uniform motion in a straight line, unless compelled to change that state by the action of an externally applied force.*

This means that all material substances resist change of motion; if they are at rest, force must be applied to move them ; if they are moving, it requires an opposing force to stop them. If a body is moving, and no force acts upon it, it will continue to move in a straight line indefinitely.

This law cannot be proved experimentally because we cannot get rid of all disturbing forces on the earth's surface, but we feel sure of its truth because it leads to consistent results.

The tendency of a body to maintain a state of rest or motion depends upon a property possessed by all matter, called *inertia*.

All bodies have not the same amount of inertia. Consider a cricket ball and a ball of lead exactly the same size. It would be impossible for a person to throw the lead ball as far as he could throw the cricket ball. Or, if the lead ball were thrown high into the air like a cricket ball, it would be impossible for an ordinary person to catch it. The lead ball is more difficult to throw because, owing to its high inertia, it cannot be started into motion easily. Moreover, once in motion, it is more difficult to stop. Similar experiences occur in swinging a light hammer and a heavy hammer, or, in swinging a small pendulum as against a very large one.

The property of inertia is measured in terms of what is called *mass*. The lead ball has a much greater mass than the cricket ball. It will be noticed that the lead ball is also much heavier or has a greater weight than the cricket ball. Mass and weight are not the same thing, but they are proportional to each other. In fact, the amount of attraction which the earth exerts upon a body (i.e. its weight) depends upon the same property as the inertia, that is, upon the mass.

Let W = the weight of a body.

Then the *mass of the body* = $W \times$ a constant, since weight and mass are proportional.

If we put $\dfrac{1}{g}$ for the constant, we have

$$\text{Mass} = \frac{W}{g}.$$

This is the engineer's unit of mass when W is in lb. This unit is called the *slug*.

101. Momentum. Momentum is a combined effect of inertia and velocity, or mass and velocity. The lead ball moving with the same velocity has more momentum than the cricket ball. Obviously, too, the momentum of a body is greater when its velocity is greater.

Algebraically expressed,

$$\text{momentum} = \frac{W}{g}v.$$

This expression is also called the *quantity of motion* in the body. Momentum is quantity of motion.

102. Newton's Second Law. This law enables us to establish a connection between force and the motion it produces.

The law states : *Rate of change of momentum is proportional to the force producing the change, and the change takes place in the direction of the force.*

Now, the momentum of a body can only be changed by changing its velocity, because the mass is a constant. Rate of change of momentum is change of momentum per second.

$\therefore$ Rate of change of momentum = rate of change of $\dfrac{W}{g}v.$

which can be written

$$\frac{W}{g} \times \text{(rate of change of } v\text{)}.$$

But rate of change of velocity is acceleration

$$\therefore \text{ Rate of change of momentum} = \frac{W}{g}f.$$

where f is the acceleration.

Newton's second law tells us that the force producing the acceleration is proportional to the above, that is,

$$\text{Force is proportional to } \frac{W}{g}f.$$

Let $F =$ the force applied to a body of mass $\frac{W}{g}$, and let it produce an acceleration f.

Then $F \propto \frac{W}{g}f$.

We can make this an equation by finding a suitable value for g.

Let us take a well-known case. Suppose a body of weight W is allowed to fall freely under the action of gravity, it will have an acceleration of 32·2 ft. per sec.[2] This can be proved by direct experiment. The force acting on the body is W. We want the above variation to become an equation, i.e.

$$F = \frac{W}{g}f$$

substituting

$$W = \frac{W}{g} \times 32 \cdot 2$$

$$\therefore Wg = W \times 32 \cdot 2$$

$$\therefore g = 32 \cdot 2.$$

Hence, if g is given the value 32·2, in this country, we can write

$$F = \frac{W}{g}f.$$

The value of g varies at different points on the earth's surface, but W also varies in the same proportion. Hence, for a given piece of matter, $\frac{W}{g}$ always has the same value, i.e. it is constant.

For this purpose the weight of the piece of matter should be determined by some apparatus which actually measures the force of gravity, such as a spring balance. This is the true weight. An ordinary balance does not determine weights, it only compares masses.

We have now two important conclusions which should be carefully remembered.

(1) Force = change of momentum per second.

(2) Force = mass × acceleration

$$\text{or } F = \frac{W}{g}f.$$

EXAMPLE. A weight of 500 lb. moves with a velocity of 24 ft. per sec. What is its momentum ?

$$\text{Momentum} = \frac{W}{g}v = \frac{500 \times 24}{32 \cdot 2} = 373 \text{ units.}$$

There is no special name for units of momentum. This result is simply in engineer's units. These units are used throughout the book.

EXAMPLE. A force of 18 lb. acts steadily on a weight of 56 lb. There is no friction. Find the acceleration.

$$\text{Force} = \text{mass} \times \text{acceleration}$$

$$18 = \frac{56}{32 \cdot 2} \times \text{acceleration}$$

$$\therefore \text{ acceleration} = \frac{18 \times 32 \cdot 2}{56} = 10 \cdot 34 \text{ ft. per sec.}^2$$

EXAMPLE. A locomotive exerts a pull of 25,000 lb. on its train, which weighs 300 tons. The track is level but there is frictional resistance of 12 lb. per ton. Find the acceleration of the train.

$$\text{Total frictional resistance} = 300 \times 12 = 3,600 \text{ lb.}$$

This must be overcome before any force is available to produce acceleration. Hence

$$\text{available accelerating force} = 25,000 - 3,600 = 21,400 \text{ lb.}$$

$$\text{Applying the formula } F = \frac{W}{g}f$$

$$21,400 = \frac{300 \times 2,240}{32 \cdot 2}f$$

$$\therefore f = \frac{21,400 \times 32 \cdot 2}{300 \times 2,240} = 1 \cdot 025 \text{ ft. per sec.}^2$$

EXAMPLE. A railway truck weighing 15 tons runs down an incline of 1 in 90. The friction is 15 lb. per ton. Find the acceleration of the truck. If it starts from rest and the length of the incline is ¼ mile, what is the velocity on reaching the bottom of the incline ?

Resolving force of gravity to find its component down the plane and parallel to it, by art. 28, we have

$$\text{Force tending to move truck} = (15 \times 2,240 \times \tfrac{1}{60}) \text{ lb.}$$
$$= 373 \cdot 3 \text{ lb.}$$
$$\text{Frictional resistance} = 15 \times 15 = 225 \text{ lb.}$$
$$\text{Force available for acceleration} = 373 \cdot 3 - 225$$
$$= 148 \cdot 3 \text{ lb.}$$

$$F = \frac{Wf}{g} \quad \therefore f = \frac{Fg}{W}$$

$$f = \frac{148 \cdot 3 \times 32 \cdot 2}{15 \times 2,240} = 0 \cdot 142 \text{ ft. per sec.}^2$$

$$v^2 = u^2 + 2fs$$
$$v^2 = 0 + 2 \times 0 \cdot 142 \times \tfrac{1}{4} \times 5,280 = 375$$
$$\therefore v = 19 \cdot 36 \text{ ft. per sec.} = \text{velocity at bottom of incline.}$$

EXAMPLE. A motor-car engine can develop a maximum of 36 H.P. The weight of the car is 22 cwt. and it starts from rest at the bottom of an incline of 1 in 12. The friction is equal to 14 lb. per ton. Find (a) the acceleration of the car when moving at 10 m.p.h., (b) the maximum speed it can attain.

$$\text{Work available per second} = 36 \times 550 = 19,800 \text{ ft.-lb.}$$

$$10 \text{ m.p.h.} = \frac{10}{60} \times 88 \text{ ft. per sec.} = 14 \cdot 7 \text{ ft. per sec.}$$

$$\text{Work done per second against friction} = \frac{22}{20} \times 14 \times 14 \cdot 7$$
$$= 226 \text{ ft.-lb.}$$

$$\text{Work done against gravity per second} = \frac{22 \times 112}{12} \times 14 \cdot 7$$
$$= 3,080 \text{ ft.-lb.}$$

$$\text{Work done per second in acceleration} = 19,800 - 226 - 3,080$$
$$= 16,494 \text{ ft.-lb.}$$

$$\text{Accelerating force} = \frac{W}{g}f$$

$$\text{Work done per second in acceleration} = \frac{W}{g}f \times \text{distance moved per second}$$

$$\therefore \frac{22 \times 112}{32 \cdot 2} \times f \times 14 \cdot 7 = 16,494 \text{ ft.-lb.}$$

$$\therefore f = \frac{16,494 \times 32 \cdot 2}{14 \cdot 7 \times 22 \times 112} = 14 \cdot 63 \text{ ft. per sec.}^2$$

This is the acceleration required in (a).

The maximum speed is attained when all the available power is spent against friction and gravity.

Let $v = $ maximum velocity in feet per second.

Then car rises vertically through $\dfrac{v}{12}$ ft. per sec.

$$\therefore \text{Work done per second against gravity} = 22 \times 112 \times \frac{v}{12} = 205 \cdot 3\,v \text{ ft.-lb.}$$

also work done per second against friction $= \dfrac{22}{20} \times 14 \times v = 15\cdot 4\,v$ ft.-lb.

Total work done per second $= 205\cdot 3\,v\ +15\cdot 4\,v\ = 19,800$ ft.-lb

$$\therefore\ 220\cdot 7\,v = 19,800$$
$$v = 89\cdot 7 \text{ ft. per sec.}$$
$$\text{or } 61\cdot 1 \text{ m.p.h.}$$

EXAMPLE. Brakes are applied to a car when travelling at 30 m.p.h. so as to lock the wheels. Taking the weight of the car as 25 cwt. and the coefficient of friction between the tyres and the road as 0·4, find (a) the retarding force, (b) the retardation produced, (c) distance traversed during stopping.

(a) Retarding force in lb. $= 25 \times 112 \times 0\cdot 4 = 1,120$ lb.

(b) Using $F = \dfrac{W}{g} f$, f will be the retardation.

$$\therefore\ f = \frac{Fg}{W} = \frac{1,120 \times 32\cdot 2}{25 \times 112} = 12\cdot 88 \text{ ft. per sec.}^2$$

(c) 30 m.p.h. $= 44$ ft. per sec.

$$\therefore\ \text{time required to stop car} = \frac{44}{12\cdot 88} \text{ sec.}$$
$$= 3\cdot 41 \quad \text{,,}$$

Average velocity during retardation $= \dfrac{44}{2} = 22$ ft. per sec.

$$\therefore\ \text{distance travelled} = 22 \times 3\cdot 41 = 75 \text{ ft.}$$

103. Other Units. In the previous article the engineer's units have been used, where force is in pounds, acceleration in feet per second per second and mass the quotient of W and g.

There are, however, other systems in common use. The *foot-pound-second* system uses the pound as the unit of mass. The acceleration is in feet per second per second as before.

Let $m = $ mass of a body in pounds.

Then $P = mf$ where P is the accelerating force, *but not in pounds.*

Let $m = 1$ and $f = 1$, then $P = 1$.

Thus P will be unity when a mass of 1 lb. is given an acceleration of 1 foot per second per second.

The unit of force thus obtained is called the *poundal*.

One pound $= g$ poundals, thus the force of 1 poundal is a little less than the weight of half an ounce.

The C.G.S. system, already referred to, uses the mass of one gram as the unit of mass. Acceleration is in centimetres per second per second.

Again, $P = mf$.

Now, however, the unit of force is the *dyne* (see art. 55).

The *dyne* may be defined as the force which will give a mass of 1 gram an acceleration of 1 centimetre per second per second.

EXAMPLE. A uniform force of 48 dynes acts upon a mass of 18 grams for 10 sec. Find the velocity of the mass, starting from rest, at the end of this period, and the distance it has moved. Neglect friction.

$$P = mf$$
$$\therefore 48 = 18f$$
$$f = \frac{48}{18} = 2\frac{2}{3} \text{ cm. per sec. per sec.}$$

Velocity at end of 10 sec. $= 2\frac{2}{3} \times 10$
$$= 26\cdot7 \text{ cm. per sec.}$$

Average velocity $= \dfrac{26\cdot7}{2} = 13\cdot35$ cm. per sec.

$\therefore$ Distance moved $= 13\cdot35 \times 10 = 133\cdot5$ cm.

It has been mentioned that a falling body has an acceleration towards the earth which we call g. Suppose a mass of m grams is falling freely, it has an acceleration g.

$$\therefore P = mf = mg \text{ dynes.}$$

This means, for example, that the earth's pull on a mass of 10 grams is $10g$ dynes.

In centimetre-second units $g = 981\cdot17$ cm. per sec.^{2} at London, say 981 for practical purposes.

Hence, gravity acts upon a mass of 1 gram with a force of 981 dynes.

EXAMPLE. A mass of 50 grams hangs by a string; what is the force on the string ?

Force on string $= 50 \times 981$ dynes $= 49,050$ dynes.

EXAMPLE. A mass of 50 grams hanging by a string is lowered with an acceleration of 250 cm. per sec.^{2} Find the pull on the string.

Force required to accelerate mass $= 50 \times 250$ dynes $= 12,500$ dynes.
Pull on string $= 49,050 - 12,500 = 36,550$ dynes.

104. Fletcher's Trolley. The principle of the Fletcher's trolley is illustrated in fig. 86. A trolley mounted on wheels with friction as small as possible, is hauled by a string passing over a pulley. A weight w supplies the force to haul the trolley along. Some device, usually a vibrating arm, is used to time the movement of the trolley.

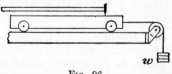

FIG. 96.

The following examples will illustrate some of the principles involved.

EXAMPLE. It was found that a small trolley travelled 3 in. in $\frac{1}{10}$ of a second and 3·25 in. in the next $\frac{1}{10}$ of a second. The weight of the trolley was 6·4 lb. Find the acceleration in feet per second per second and the force in the string.

$$3 \text{ in.} = 0\cdot25 \text{ ft.} \qquad 3\cdot25 \text{ in.} = 0\cdot2708 \text{ ft.}$$

Average velocity during first $\frac{1}{10}$ sec. $= \dfrac{0\cdot25}{\frac{1}{10}} = 2\cdot5$ ft. per sec.

Average „ „ second $\frac{1}{10}$ sec. $= \dfrac{0\cdot2708}{\frac{1}{10}} = 2\cdot708$ ft. per sec.

Assuming uniform acceleration these are the actual velocities at the middle of each interval of $\frac{1}{10}$ sec.

∴ Increase in velocity in $\frac{1}{10}$ sec. $= 2\cdot708 - 2\cdot5 = 0\cdot208$ ft. per sec.

∴ „ „ „ „ 1 sec. $= 0\cdot208 \times 10 = 2\cdot08$ ft. per sec.

This is the acceleration $= 2\cdot08$ ft. per sec.^{2}

$$\text{Force in string} = \frac{W}{g}f = \frac{6\cdot4 \times 2\cdot08}{32\cdot2} = 0\cdot414 \text{ lb.}$$

EXAMPLE. If in the last example the weight suspended by the string is 0·45 lb., find the value of g.

Let T = tension in string in lb.

$$\text{Then } T = \frac{\text{wt. of trolley}}{g} \times \text{accel.} = \frac{6\cdot4 \times 2\cdot08}{g} = \frac{13\cdot32}{g} \text{ lb.}$$

$$\text{Force required to accelerate weight} = \frac{0\cdot45 \times 2\cdot08}{g} = \frac{0\cdot936}{g} \text{ lb.}$$

$$\therefore T = \left(0\cdot45 - \frac{0\cdot936}{g} \right) \text{ lb.}$$

$$\text{Hence, } 0\cdot45 - \frac{0\cdot936}{g} = \frac{13\cdot32}{g}$$

$$\therefore 0\cdot45 = \frac{14\cdot256}{g}$$

$$\therefore g = \frac{14\cdot256}{0\cdot45} = 31\cdot68 \text{ ft. per sec.}^2$$

105. Impulse. When a force acts upon a body for a very short time it is called an impulsive force. The result produced is known as the *impulse* of the force. Such forces occur when two moving bodies collide or when a blow is struck. We are now to show that the result of impulsive forces acting on a body which is free to move is stated in terms of momentum.

Let a force F act on a weight W for t sec., then

$$F = \frac{W}{g}f$$

$$\therefore \ Ft = \frac{W}{g}ft$$

But $\quad ft = v$ (i.e. velocity if starting from rest)

$$\therefore \ Ft = \frac{W}{g}v = \text{momentum.}$$

EXAMPLE. A force of 25,000 lb. acts on a weight of 240 lb. for $\frac{1}{100}$ sec. What velocity will be given to the weight?

$$\frac{W}{g}v = Ft$$

$$\frac{240}{32 \cdot 2}\,v = 25,000 \times \tfrac{1}{100}$$

$$v = \frac{25,000 \times 32 \cdot 2}{240 \times 100} = 33 \cdot 5 \text{ ft. per sec.}$$

If force be plotted on a time base the area under the curve thus obtained is the impulse of the force, or the momentum given to the body on which the force acts. The average force on a time base could be found from such a diagram.

It will be seen that

Average force $\times$ time = impulse = momentum.

It will be remembered (art. 60) that the space average of a force multiplied by the distance moved gives the work done. It is very important that the distinction between these two cases should be understood.

106. Conservation of Momentum. When two moving bodies come into contact and then move together, the momentum of the combined bodies is equal to the sum of the momenta of the separate bodies.

In finding this sum account must be taken of direction of motion. In fact, momentum is a vector quantity.

If two bodies move along the same line, but with opposite sense, one momentum must be taken as positive and the other as negative.

EXAMPLE. Two wagons weighing 14 tons and 16 tons respectively have velocities of 12 and 18 ft. per sec. respectively. The faster one overtakes the other and they become locked by an automatic coupling. Find the velocity of the linked wagons.

$$\text{Momentum of first wagon} = \frac{14 \times 2,240}{32 \cdot 2} \times 12 = 11,700 \text{ units.}$$

$$\text{Momentum of second wagon} = \frac{16 \times 2,240}{32 \cdot 2} \times 18 = 20,020 \text{ units.}$$

Total momentum $= 11,700 + 20,020 = 31,720.$

$$\text{Combined mass} = \frac{(14 + 16)\, 2,240}{32 \cdot 2} = 2,085 \text{ engineer's units.}$$

$$\therefore\ 2,085 \times v = 31,720$$

$$v = \frac{31,720}{2,085} = 15 \cdot 2 \text{ ft. per sec.}$$

EXAMPLE. Two balls of 5 lb. and 8 lb. weight roll towards each other from opposite directions. Their velocities are 18 and 7 ft. per sec. respectively. After colliding they roll together. Find their common velocity. We will take the momentum of the first body as being positive.

$$\text{Positive momentum} = \frac{5 \times 18}{32 \cdot 2} = 2 \cdot 79$$

$$\text{Negative momentum} = \frac{8 \times 7}{32 \cdot 2} = 1 \cdot 74$$

Combined momentum $= 2 \cdot 79 - 1 \cdot 74 = 1 \cdot 05$

$$\text{Combined masses} = \frac{5 + 8}{32 \cdot 2} = \frac{13}{32 \cdot 2}$$

$$\therefore\ \text{Common velocity} = \frac{1 \cdot 05 \times 32 \cdot 2}{13} = 2 \cdot 602 \text{ ft. per sec.}$$

107. Newton's Third Law. *To every force there is an equal and opposite force reacting.*

There are many illustrations of this. A weight exerts a downward force on a table ; there is an equal and upward force reacting. A cage hangs by a rope and the cage exerts a downward force ; the rope exerts an equal upward force on the cage. A ladder presses against a wall and the wall presses against the ladder with an equal force. These are all cases of static forces. but it is equally true when there is relative motion between the two bodies.

Two boats on a lake are pushed apart by a pole held by a man in one of the boats. The force on one boat is equal to the reaction on the other. Since the two forces act during the same time, the impulse of both forces will be the same ; hence, neglecting friction, both boats will have the same momentum, because the product Ft is the same for both.

EXAMPLE. A bullet weighing 1 oz. is fired from a rifle weighing 12 lb. with a velocity of 1,200 ft. per sec. Find the velocity of the recoil of the rifle.

$$\text{Momentum of bullet} = \frac{\frac{1}{16}}{32 \cdot 2} \times 1,200 = \frac{1,200}{32 \cdot 2 \times 16} = 2 \cdot 33.$$

Momentum of rifle is the same.

$$\therefore \text{ Momentum of rifle} = \frac{W}{g}v = 2 \cdot 33$$

$$\frac{12}{32 \cdot 2}v = 2 \cdot 33$$

$$\therefore v = \frac{2 \cdot 33 \times 32 \cdot 2}{12} = 6 \cdot 25 \text{ ft. per sec.}$$

108. Change of Momentum. The definite cases of change of momentum, so far considered, have been dealing with changes taking place in the same direction as that of the motion. Newton's second law, however, states that the change of momentum takes place in the direction of the applied force. In art. 97 it has been shown how a change in velocity may be found where change of direction of motion has occurred. This change of velocity involves change of momentum. Suppose a body is moving due north with a velocity represented by the vector ab, and that t seconds later it moves north-west with a velocity represented by the vector ac, then bc is the change in velocity. If we multiply it by the mass, it gives the change of momentum. That is,

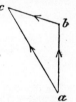

FIG. 97.

$$\text{change of momentum} = \frac{W}{g} \times \text{velocity } bc.$$

This change took place in t sec.

$$\therefore \text{ change of momentum per second} = \frac{W}{g} \times \frac{\text{velocity } bc}{t}.$$

If the force acting to produce the change is uniform,

$$\text{then, force acting} = \frac{W}{g} \times \frac{\text{velocity } bc}{t}.$$

If the force is not uniform then the average force is given by the expression.

K

FIG. 98.

Moreover, the force which has produced the change acts, according to the second law of motion, in the direction *bc*.

EXAMPLE. A ball weighing 10 oz. is thrown in a certain direction with a velocity of 40 ft. per sec. Due to a side wind its course is deflected in 3 sec. through 30°. Find the force exerted by the wind and its direction, if the velocity is still 40 ft. per sec. in the new direction.

Original direction is *ab* and final direction is shown by *ac*.

$$ab = 40 \text{ ft. per sec.} \qquad ac = 40 \text{ ft. per sec.}$$

$$bc = 2 \times 40 \times \sin\frac{30°}{2} \text{ (see art. 98)}$$

$$= 2 \times 40 \times \sin 15°$$
$$= 2 \times 40 \times 0\cdot259$$
$$= 20\cdot72 \text{ ft. per sec.}$$

∴ Change of momentum $= \dfrac{10}{16 \times 32\cdot2} \times 20\cdot72 = 0\cdot4025.$

The time taken was 3 sec.

∴ Force of side wind = change of momentum per second.

$$= \frac{0\cdot4025}{3} = 0\cdot1342 \text{ lb.}$$

The direction of the wind makes an angle of 75° with *ab*. Another method would be as follows :

change of velocity $= 20\cdot72$ ft. per sec.
change of velocity per second = acceleration

$$= \frac{20\cdot72}{3} = 6\cdot91 \text{ ft. per sec.}^2$$

$$= f$$

$$\text{Force} = \frac{W}{g}f = \frac{10}{16 \times 32\cdot2} \times 6\cdot91 = 0\cdot1342 \text{ lb.}$$

109. Centrifugal Force. An important application of the principle of the previous article occurs in centrifugal force. In art. 98 it was shown that when a point moves in a circular path with uniform speed, v ft. per sec., there is an acceleration towards the centre of $\dfrac{v^2}{r}$.

If the point is replaced by a body with mass $\dfrac{W}{g}$, a force is required,

acting towards the centre of the circle, to compel the body to move in a circle instead of moving on in a straight line.

The magnitude of this force

= mass × acceleration towards centre of circle

$$= \frac{W}{g} \times \frac{v^2}{r} = \frac{Wv^2}{gr}$$

But $\dfrac{v^2}{r} = \omega^2 r$.

∴ force acting towards the centre of the circle $= \dfrac{W}{g}\omega^2 r$

The force acting towards the centre is called the *centripetal force* and its reaction, acting outwards, from the centre is called the *centrifugal force*.

Hence, centrifugal force $= \dfrac{Wv^2}{gr}$

$$= \frac{W}{g}\omega^2 r.$$

This force is commonly experienced, as when a stone attached to a string is caused to rotate. The string pulls with centripetal force on the stone, whilst the stone exerts centrifugal force on the string.

EXAMPLE. A flywheel 8 ft. diameter has a block of metal weighing 160 lb. attached to its rim by bolts. The centre of gravity of the weight is 4 ft. 3 in. from the centre of the wheel and the wheel makes 120 r.p.m. Find the pull in the bolts and their total area of section if the stress allowed in them is 5,000 lb. per sq. in.

$$\text{Speed of block} = \frac{120}{60} \times 2\pi \times 4\tfrac{1}{4} \text{ ft. per sec.}$$

$$= 53 \cdot 4 \text{ ft. per sec.}$$

$$\text{Centrifugal force} = \frac{Wv^2}{gr} = \frac{160 \times 53 \cdot 4 \times 53 \cdot 4}{32 \cdot 2 \times 4 \cdot 25}$$

$$= 3{,}340 \text{ lb.}$$

$$\text{Area of section of bolts} = \frac{3{,}340}{5{,}000} = 0 \cdot 668 \text{ sq. in.}$$

110. Balancing. Suppose a disc rotates on a shaft at O, whilst at A a weight is attached to the disc. A centrifugal force will act away from the centre. This force will set up a pressure in the bearing thus increasing friction and wear. Moreover, as the force will pull in different directions at different times, vibrations are set up which may be dangerous, or at least objectionable. To obviate these things we

FIG. 99.

arrange to place weights so that all the centrifugal forces will balance. This is called *balancing the rotating masses*.

The following will illustrate the methods in simple cases.

EXAMPLE. A block of metal, of weight 22 lb., is being machined in a lathe and is bolted to a face-plate, as in fig. 99, so that its centre of gravity is $r = 8$ in. from the mandrel centre. Find where a block, 18 lb. weight, must be placed to balance the centrifugal force.

$$\frac{W}{g}\omega^2 r \text{ is the most convenient form here.}$$

Now if the centrifugal forces are balanced at any one speed, they are balanced at all speeds. We can, therefore, assume any angular velocity.

Let us assume an angular velocity $= \sqrt{g}$, i.e. $\omega = \sqrt{g}$

$$\text{C.F. on block of 22 lb.} = \frac{W}{g}\omega^2 r = \frac{22}{32\cdot2} \times (\sqrt{g})^2 \times \frac{8}{12}$$

$$= 22 \times \frac{8}{12} = 14\tfrac{2}{3} \text{ lb.}$$

This force pulls from O to A. To balance, we want a diametrically opposite pull of $14\tfrac{2}{3}$ lb.

$$\therefore 14\tfrac{2}{3} = \frac{18}{g} \times (\sqrt{g})^2 \times r = 18r$$

$$\therefore r = \frac{14\tfrac{2}{3}}{18} \text{ ft.} = 0\cdot815 \text{ ft.} = 9\cdot78 \text{ in.}$$

Hence a weight at B, fig. 99, such that OB = 9·78 in. produces balance.

Note that when $\omega = \sqrt{g}$ our formula reduces to Wr.

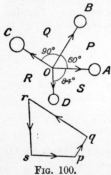

FIG. 100.

EXAMPLE. Weights A, B and C, arranged as shown and rotating about O, have weights 18, 12, 24 lb. respectively. OA = 15 in. OB = 12 in. OC = 18 in. Find what weight, placed at a radius of 16 inches, will establish balance, and the direction in which it must lie:

C.F. of A acting from O to A $= Wr = 18 \times \frac{15}{12}$ $= 22\cdot5$.

C.F. of B acting from O to B $= 12 \times \frac{12}{12} = 12$.

C.F. of C acting from O to C $= 24 \times \frac{18}{12} = 36$.

Now draw a polygon of forces to find the equilibrant of the centrifugal forces (fig. 100). This is given by rs which, on measurement, $= 28\cdot6$. The direction is 84° clockwise from OA.

To find the weight at D.

$$W \times OD = W \times \frac{16}{12} = 28\cdot6$$

$$\therefore W = \frac{28\cdot6 \times 12}{16} = 21\cdot4 \text{ lb.}$$

Thus, the balance weight is 21·4 lb. at a radius of 16 in. in a direction making an angle of 84° with OA. In calculating the above centrifugal forces the angular velocity has been taken as $\sqrt{g}$.

EXAMPLES X

Section A

1. A bullet weighing 1 oz. has a velocity of 1,200 ft. per sec. Calculate its momentum.

2. A motor weighs $18\frac{1}{2}$ cwt. What force, in pounds, will give it an acceleration of 4 ft. per sec.² ?

3. A stone, 0·25 lb. weight, is dropped from a tower 96 ft. high. What is its momentum on reaching the ground ?

4. A mass of 500 grams is given an acceleration of 8·5 cm. per sec.² What is the magnitude of the accelerating force ? State the units.

5. A force of 10,000 lb. acts on a weight for $\frac{1}{70}$ sec. What is the momentum of the weight ?

6. What tensile stress will be induced in each of two bolts in the following circumstances ? The least cross-sectional area of each bolt is 1·1 sq. in. and they are used radially to attach a pole piece complete, on to the rotor of an alternator whose speed is 480 r.p.m. The pole piece weighs 64 lb. and its centre of gravity describes a circle of 3 ft. diameter. U.E.I.

7. A pole piece weighing 48 lb. is attached to the rotor of an alternator and has its centre of gravity 16 in. from the axis of the shaft. Calculate the pull in the attachment to the rotor when the speed of the alternator is 420 r.p.m. U.E.I.

Section B

8. A motor car, weighing 20 cwt., is fitted with four-wheel brakes. When travelling at 25 m.p.h. on a level road the brakes are suddenly applied, locking the wheels. The coefficient of sliding friction between the wheels and the road is 0·60. Find the time taken for the car to be brought to rest. What distance will the car travel before coming to rest after the application of the brakes ? U.E.I.

9. A car starting from rest has velocities v ft. per sec. after t sec. from starting as given in the following table :

| t . | . | 0 | 4 | 9 | 17 | 24 | 30 | 32 | 40 | 53 | 58 | 62 |
| v . | . | 0 | 11 | 22·6 | 33·6 | 44·5 | 49·0 | 48·9 | 40·6 | 26·8 | 24·3 | 24·0 |

Plot velocity v in feet per second vertically and t horizontally. From your diagram find the distance covered from the starting-point by the car after 20, 40 and 60 sec. N.C.T.E.C.

10. Two masses, A and B, are attached to a disc, centre O, which revolves at a speed of 120 r.p.m., the plane of the disc being at right angles to the axis of motion, which passes through O. The mass A weighs 8 lb. and is 10 in. from O, and B weighs 10 lb. and is 8 in. from O. The angle AOB is 120°. Determine the resultant effect of the centrifugal forces of A and B. U.L.C.I.

11. What do you understand by acceleration ? A car weighing 1 ton is impelled along a horizontal road by force of 100 lb. If the resistance to motion is 32 lb., find the car's acceleration. How far would the car move in 10 sec. from rest ? U.L.C.I.

12. A motor-car weighing 25 cwt. and carrying 4 passengers of total weight 600 lb. is travelling at 30 m.p.h. What is its momentum ? If the motive power be suddenly shut off, what average force would bring the car to rest in 6 sec. ? U.L.C.I.

13. A wheel of a railway van is 4 ft. diameter, weighs 750 lb., and has its centre of gravity $\frac{1}{10}$ in. from its geometrical axis. Find the unbalanced force due to centrifugal action when the van is travelling at 40 m.p.h. If the vertical load on the wheel is 3 tons, find the greatest and least pressures on the rail at the above speed.   U.L.C.I.

14. A train starts from a station. In the third second after starting it is observed to travel 7 ft. and in the fourth second 8·2 ft. Find the velocity at the end of the third second and the acceleration, assuming it to be uniform.

15. A train of 320 tons is hauled up an incline of 1 in 120 and the frictional resistance is 12 lb. per ton. What pull must the engine exert on the train to give it an acceleration of 0·5 ft. per sec.² ?

16. A block whose weight is 20 lb. is placed on a horizontal rail. The coefficient of friction between the block and the rail is 0·1. If the block is given an initial velocity of 8 ft. per sec. by means of a push, how far would it travel before coming to rest ?   C.G.L.I.

CHAPTER XI

ENERGY

111. Energy. When a body is capable of doing work it is said to possess energy. Thus energy is a store which may be drawn upon to do work. It has many forms, amongst which are mechanical, heat, electrical and chemical energy. Under suitable conditions one form of energy may be changed into another form, and there are definite relationships between them.

There are several forms of mechanical energy, but only two are treated of in this chapter, viz. *potential* and *kinetic*. The units of mechanical energy are the same as those of work.

112. Conservation of Energy. All experiment and experience have led to the conclusion that energy cannot be destroyed. It may change in form, but when energy of one kind ceases to exist, an equal amount of some other kind is formed.

113. Potential Energy. The force of gravity, acting on all bodies, enables them, when they descend from a higher to a lower level, to do work in overcoming some form of resistance. On the contrary, when a body is raised from a lower to a higher level work is done upon it. In the first case the body is giving up potential energy ; in the second case potential energy is being given to it.

The *potential energy* of a body is the work it can do, due to the force of gravity, in descending from a higher to a lower level, which is referred to as a datum level.

Let W = weight of a body in lb.

,, h = height through which it descends in feet.

Then decrease in potential energy = Wh ft.-lb.

Generally speaking, especially in elementary mechanics, we are only concerned with increases and decreases in potential energy and not with the total potential energy.

EXAMPLE. A reservoir contains 30,000,000 gall. of water at an average vertical height of 340 ft. above a power station. What is the potential energy available ? 1 gall. weighs 10 lb.

$$\text{Wt. of water in reservoir} = 30 \times 10^6 \times 10 \text{ lb.}$$
$$= 30 \times 10^7 \text{ lb.}$$
$$\therefore \text{ Potential energy} = 30 \times 10^7 \times 340 \text{ ft.-lb.}$$
$$= 102 \times 10^9 \text{ ft.-lb.}$$

A larger unit of energy, which enables us to avoid such large numbers as the above, is the *horse-power-hour*. This is the amount of energy which will do work at the rate of 1 H.P. for 1 hr.

$$1 \text{ H.P.} = 33,000 \text{ ft.-lb. per min.}$$
$$\therefore 1 \text{ H.P.-hr.} = 33,000 \times 60 = 1,980,000 \text{ ft.-lb.}$$

EXAMPLE. How many horse-power-hours of energy are represented by the result of the last example ?

$$102 \times 10^9 \text{ ft.-lb.} = \frac{102 \times 10^9}{1,980,000} \text{ H.P.-hours.}$$
$$= 51,600 \text{ H.P.-hours.}$$

114. Kinetic Energy. A moving body, in being brought to rest, can overcome resistance and therefore do work. The work is drawn from the supply of energy due to the motion of the body. Energy of motion is called *kinetic energy*. Let a force F act on a body of weight W. Let there be no resistance, such as gravity or friction, so that F is expended in overcoming the inertia, that is, in giving motion

$$\text{Then, } F = \frac{W}{g}f. \quad \text{(art 102).}$$

Let the body move from rest through a distance s. Then the work done

$$= Fs = \frac{W}{g}fs.$$

Let v = final velocity attained

Then the average velocity = $\frac{v}{2}$ since the acceleration is uniform, if F is constant.

Hence $s = \dfrac{v}{2}t$ where $t = $ time force acts.

$$\therefore \ Fs = \dfrac{W}{g}fs = \dfrac{W}{g}ft\dfrac{v}{2}.$$

but $ft = v$

$$\therefore \ Fs = \dfrac{W}{g}v\dfrac{v}{2} = \dfrac{Wv^2}{2g}.$$

The work done on the body has produced and is equal to the kinetic energy.

Therefore, Kinetic Energy $= \dfrac{Wv^2}{2g}.$

In the case of both potential and kinetic energy it should be noted that the units used are the units of work.

EXAMPLE.   A motor-car weighs 24 cwt. and is travelling at 45 m.p.h. Find its kinetic energy in foot-pounds.

$$45 \text{ m.p.h.} = \dfrac{45}{60} \times 88 \text{ ft. per sec.} = 66 \text{ ft. per sec.}$$

$$\therefore \ \text{K.E.} = \dfrac{Wv^2}{2g} = \dfrac{24 \times 112 \times 66 \times 66}{2 \times 32 \cdot 2} = 181,300 \text{ ft.-lb.}$$

In the formula $\dfrac{Wv^2}{2g}$ the mass is $\dfrac{W}{g}$. If using other than engineers' units we need only substitute the unit of mass, whatever it may be, and we can write the formula.

K.E. $= \frac{1}{2}mv^2$ where $m = $ mass in any units.

EXAMPLE.   A mass of 20 grams moves with a velocity of 24 cm. per sec. Calculate the kinetic energy.

K.E. $= \frac{1}{2}mv^2 = \frac{1}{2} \times 20 \times 24^2 = 5,760$ ergs.

In the C.G.S. system the *erg* is the *unit of energy*.

EXAMPLE.   A weight of 16 lb. moves with a velocity of 12 ft. per sec. The velocity is reduced to 8 ft. per sec.   Find the loss of kinetic energy.

$$\text{K.E. at 12 ft. per sec.} = \dfrac{16 \times 12^2}{2 \times 32 \cdot 2} = 35 \cdot 8 \text{ ft.-lb.}$$

$$\text{K.E. at 8 ft. per sec.} = \dfrac{16 \times 8^2}{2 \times 32 \cdot 2} = 15 \cdot 9 \text{ ft.-lb.}$$

$$\text{Loss of K.E.} = 35 \cdot 8 - 15 \cdot 9 = 19 \cdot 9 \text{ ft.-lb.}$$

115. Interchange of Energy.   Suppose a body of weight W lb. is h ft. above the ground, it contains Wh ft.-lb. of potential energy. Let it be dropped. Then, on reaching the ground all its available potential energy has been given up. If we neglect all friction loss, then, by the principle of the conservation of energy, the body has gained kinetic energy equal to the original potential energy.

∴ K.E. on reaching the ground = Wh.

But the K.E. also $= \dfrac{Wv^2}{2g}$

$$\therefore \frac{Wv^2}{2g} = Wh$$
$$\therefore v^2 = 2gh$$
$$v = \sqrt{2gh}.$$

This is a useful result.

When the body has fallen a portion of the height h, say x ft., then part of the energy is potential and part kinetic.

Potential energy lost = Wx
= kinetic energy gained.

Potential energy still remaining = W$(h - x)$.

EXAMPLE. A body, weight 72 lb., falls from a height of 60 ft. Find the kinetic energy.

The K.E. = potential energy before falling = Wh
= 72 × 60 = 4,320 ft.-lb.

EXAMPLE. A body, weighing 5 lb., slides down an inclined plane without friction. The plane is 8 ft. long and is raised 2 ft. at the higher end. Find the velocity of the body on reaching the bottom of the plane.

Potential energy of weight at top = 5 × 2 = 10 ft.-lb. At the bottom this is all transformed to K.E.

$$\therefore \text{K.E.} = \frac{Wv^2}{2g} = 10 \text{ ft.-lb.}$$
$$\therefore \frac{5 \times v^2}{2 \times 32 \cdot 2} = 10$$
$$v^2 = \frac{10 \times 2 \times 32 \cdot 2}{5} = 128 \cdot 8$$
$$\therefore v = 11 \cdot 32 \text{ ft. per sec.}$$

Notice that the length of plane can be ignored by this method.

EXAMPLE. A railway truck weighing 15 tons runs down an incline of 1 in 90. The friction is 15 lb. per ton. If it starts from rest and runs down ¼ mile of the incline, what will be its velocity?

Vertical height corresponding to ¼ mile of the incline

$$= \frac{\frac{1}{4} \times 5,280}{90} = 14 \cdot 66 \text{ ft.}$$

Potential energy of truck = $15 \times 2{,}240 \times 14\cdot66$ ft.-lb.
$$= 492{,}500 \text{ ft.-lb.}$$
Energy used against friction = frictional force parallel to plane $\times$ distance moved
$$= 15 \times 15 \times 5{,}280 \times 0\cdot25$$
$$= 297{,}000 \text{ ft.-lb.}$$

Kinetic energy = $492{,}500 - 297{,}000 = 195{,}500$ ft.-lb.

$$\therefore \frac{Wv^2}{2g} = 195{,}500$$

$$\therefore v^2 = \frac{195{,}500 \times 2 \times 32\cdot2}{15 \times 2{,}240} = 374\cdot5$$

$$\therefore v = \sqrt{374\cdot5} = 19\cdot4 \text{ ft. per sec.}$$

(Compare fourth example, art. 102.)

EXAMPLE. Brakes are applied to a car when travelling at 30 m.p.h. so as to lock the wheels. The weight of the car is 25 cwt. and the coefficient of friction of tyres on the road = $0\cdot4$. Find the retarding force and the distance moved during stopping.

Retarding force = $0\cdot4 \times 25 \times 112 = 1{,}120$ lb.

30 m.p.h. = 44 ft. per sec.

K.E. of car initially = $\dfrac{Wv^2}{2g} = \dfrac{25 \times 112 \times 44 \times 44}{2 \times 32\cdot2} = 84{,}100$ ft.-lb.

This energy is all spent against friction.
Work done against friction = $1{,}120 \times$ distance moved = $84{,}100$ ft.-lb.

$$\therefore \text{ distance moved} = \frac{84{,}100}{1{,}120} = 75 \text{ ft.}$$

(Compare sixth example, art. 102.)

116. Energy of Rotation. Suppose a very small body of weight W lb. rotates about centre O in a circular path with a speed v feet per second. Then its kinetic energy $= \dfrac{Wv^2}{2g}$ ft.-lb.

Let the radius of the circular path $= r$ ft. and the angular

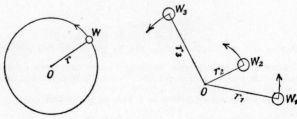

FIG. 101.   FIG. 102.

velocity of the body $= \omega$ rad. per sec.; then, since $v = \omega r$, we have

$$\text{kinetic energy} = \frac{Wv^2}{2g} = \frac{W}{2g}(\omega r)^2 \text{ ft.-lb.}$$
$$= \frac{W}{g}r^2 \times \frac{\omega^2}{2}.$$

Now for any particular weight at a fixed radius the quantity $\frac{W}{g}r^2$ is a constant, and it has an important place in energy calculations for rotating bodies.

Next consider any number of weights W_1, W_2, W_3, etc., arranged as in fig. 102, at radii r_1, r_2, r_3, etc., respectively.

Let all rotate together at an angular velocity ω rad. per sec.

$$\text{Then kinetic energy of } W_1 = \frac{W_1}{g}r_1{}^2 \times \frac{\omega^2}{2}$$

$$\text{,,} \qquad \text{,,} \qquad \text{,,} \qquad \text{,, } W_2 = \frac{W_2}{g}r_2{}^2 \times \frac{\omega^2}{2}$$

$$\text{,,} \qquad \text{,,} \qquad \text{,,} \qquad \text{,, } W_3 = \frac{W_3}{g}r_3{}^2 \times \frac{\omega^2}{2}\text{, and so on.}$$

$\therefore$ total kinetic energy of the system

$$= \frac{\omega^2}{2}\left(\frac{W_1}{g}r_1{}^2 + \frac{W_2}{g}r_2{}^2 + \frac{W_3}{g}r_3{}^2 \ldots\right)$$

The quantity in the bracket is a constant for the given system, and does not depend upon the speed of rotation.

Let the total weight $= W$

$$\text{then } W = W_1 + W_2 + W_3 \ldots$$

It is possible to find a value k such that

$$\frac{W}{g}k^2 = \frac{W_1}{g}r_1{}^2 + \frac{W_2}{g}r_2{}^2 + \frac{W_3}{g}r_3{}^2 \ldots$$

k is called the " radius of gyration " of the collection of weights which all rotate together.

We may define the *radius of gyration* as that radius at which all the mass may be regarded as being concentrated for equal kinetic energy of rotation at any given speed.

The quantity, $\frac{W}{g}k^2$, is known as the *moment of inertia* of the total mass in engineer's units. No special name is given to these units.

EXAMPLE. A weight of 2 lb. rotates at the end of a thin rod 2 ft. long whose weight may be neglected, at an angular velocity of 16 radians per sec. Find its kinetic energy of rotation.

$$\text{Kinetic energy of rotation} = \tfrac{1}{2}\omega^2 \times \frac{W}{g}r^2$$

$$= \tfrac{1}{2} \times 16 \times 16 \times \frac{2}{32\cdot2} \times 2 \times 2$$

$$= 31\cdot9 \text{ ft.-lb.}$$

EXAMPLE. On a rotating disc the following weights are secured : 3 lb. at 1·5 ft. radius, 7 lb. at 2 ft. radius, 5 lb. at 2·5 ft. radius, 8 lb. at 1 ft. radius. Find the radius of gyration of the system of weights, neglecting the disc ; also find the kinetic energy when making 270 r.p.m.

$$\frac{W}{g}k^2 = \frac{W_1}{g}r_1{}^2 + \frac{W_2}{g}r_2{}^2 + \frac{W_3}{g}r_3{}^2 + \frac{W_4}{g}r_4{}^2$$

$$\frac{3+7+5+8}{g}k^2 = \frac{3}{g} \times 1\cdot5^2 + \frac{7}{g} \times 2^2 + \frac{5}{g} \times 2\cdot5^2 + \frac{8}{g} \times 1^2$$

g cancels out.

$$\therefore \ 23k^2 = 6\cdot75 + 28 + 31\cdot25 + 8 = 74$$

$$\therefore \ k^2 = \frac{74}{23} = 3\cdot22$$

$$\therefore \ k = 1\cdot8 \text{ ft.}$$

$$270 \text{ r.p.m.} = \frac{270 \times 2\pi}{60} \text{ radians per second.}$$

$$= 28\cdot3 \text{ rad. per sec.} = \omega$$

$$\text{K.E.} = \frac{\omega^2}{2} \times \frac{W}{g}k^2$$

$$= \frac{28\cdot3^2}{2} \times \frac{23 \times 1\cdot8^2}{32\cdot2} = 920 \text{ ft.-lb.}$$

The rotating bodies met with in engineering practice, such as flywheels, dynamo armatures and turbine rotors, have their radii of gyration. Sometimes they may be found by calculation methods which are beyond our scope ; sometimes they are found by experiment. In any case, the kinetic energy, when they rotate, is calculated as in the last example and is equal to

$$\frac{W}{g}k^2 \times \frac{\omega^2}{2}.$$

117. Heat Energy. In this country heat is generally obtained as the result of combustion. As combustion is a chemical process, chemical energy is the original form of our heat energy. In turn, heat energy supplies us with the bulk of our mechanical and electrical energy. The means whereby mechanical energy is obtained from heat are treated at length in the chapters on Applied Heat.

Heat is obtained from mechanical energy when the latter is spent in overcoming friction and when it is used to compress a gas.

There are two units of heat in common use ; (art. 149)

(1) the British Thermal Unit, B.Th.U.

(2) the gram-calorie.

The pound-centigrade heat unit (C.H.U.) is also used in some branches of engineering.

Each of these is equal to a definite amount of mechanical energy. This equivalent amount is called the *mechanical equivalent of heat.*

$$1 \text{ B.Th.U.} = 778 \text{ ft.-lb.}$$
$$1 \text{ C.H.U.} = 1400 \text{ ft.-lb.}$$
$$1 \text{ gram-calorie} = 4 \cdot 2 \times 10^7 \text{ ergs}$$
$$= 4 \cdot 2 \text{ joules.}$$

To connect gram-calories and foot-pounds we know that

$$1 \text{ ft.-lb.} = 1 \cdot 356 \text{ joules (art. 61).}$$

$$\therefore 1 \text{ gram-calorie} = \frac{4 \cdot 2}{1 \cdot 356} \text{ ft.-lb.} = 3 \cdot 1 \text{ ft.-lb.}$$

EXAMPLE. A tram-car weighing 12 tons and travelling at 10 m.p.h. is brought to rest by braking. How much heat is generated by the friction (a) in B.Th.U., (b) in C.H.U., (c) in gram-calories ?

$$\text{Kinetic energy of car} = \frac{Wv^2}{2g} = \frac{12 \times 2{,}240 \times 14 \cdot 6 \times 14 \cdot 6}{2 \times 32}$$
$$= 89{,}100 \text{ ft.-lb.}$$

(a) Heat generated in B.Th.U. $= \dfrac{89{,}100}{778} = 114 \cdot 3$

(b) „   „   „ C.H.U. $= \dfrac{89{,}100}{1{,}400} = 63 \cdot 6$

(c) „   „   „ gram-calories $= \dfrac{89{,}100}{3 \cdot 1} = 28{,}720.$

118. Electrical Energy. When an electric current of *one ampere* flows with a potential difference of *one volt*, work is done at the rate of *one watt*. When this operates for one second the work done or energy expended is *one-watt-second* or *one joule.*

When the current is I amperes and the potential difference E volts, then

$$\text{Watts} = EI.$$

$$\therefore \text{ Energy expended per second} = EI \text{ joules.}$$

The watt and joule are small units of power and energy respectively. Hence we have for practical use.

1 kilowatt = 1,000 watts, for the unit of power
1 kilowatt-hour = 1 Board of Trade Unit of Energy, as the unit of energy.

EXAMPLE. An electric motor uses 18 amperes at 230 volts. Find the energy consumed in $8\frac{1}{2}$ hr. in B.O.T. Units.

$$\text{The power} = (18 \times 230) \text{ watts} = \frac{18 \times 230}{1,000} \text{ kilowatts.}$$

$$= 4\cdot14 \text{ kilowatts.}$$

Energy per hour = 4·14 kilowatt-hours or B.O.T. Units.
Energy used in $8\frac{1}{2}$ hr. = 4·14 × 8·5 B.O.T. Units
$$= 35\cdot19 \text{ B.O.T. Units.}$$

EXAMPLE. A lift with total weight of 3 tons has to ascend at a speed of 6 ft. per sec. The electric motor driving the lift has an efficiency of 85 per cent. Adding 20 per cent. to the work done on the lift for friction and other losses, find the electrical power in kilowatts, and the energy consumed in B.O.T. Units, in $4\frac{1}{2}$ hr. of actual working.

Work done per minute on lift = 3 × 2,240 × 6 × 60 ft.-lb.
$$= 2,419,200 \text{ ft.-lb.}$$
Add 20 per cent. = 483,840

Total = 2,903,040 ft.-lb.

$$\therefore \text{ Horse-power of motor} = \frac{2,903,040}{33,000} \times \frac{100}{85} = 103\cdot5$$

$$\therefore \text{ Kilowatts of motor} = \frac{103\cdot5 \times 746}{1,000} \text{ (see art. 61)}$$

$$= 77\cdot2 \text{ kilowatts.}$$
$$\therefore \text{ Number of kilowatt-hours} = 77\cdot2 \times 4\frac{1}{2}$$
$$= 347\cdot4 \text{ B.O.T. units.}$$

Note that, in practice, balance weights are used so that the energy consumed is less than the above.

EXAMPLES XI

SECTION A

1. A tank 30 ft. by 20 ft. contains water to a depth of 8 ft. The bottom of the tank is 80 ft. above the ground. Find the potential energy of the water in the tank. If it gives up this energy at a uniform rate in 5 min. what horse-power will be developed ?

2. A truck, weighing 4 tons, is moving at 20 ft. per sec. Find its kinetic energy. If it begins to run up an incline of 1 in 40, how far will it travel before coming to rest ?

3. 800 ft. of rope weighing 1·5 lb. per ft. is partly wound on a drum 4 ft radius. What is the kinetic energy of the rope when the drum makes 80 r.p.m. ?

4. A string is coiled on the rim of a flywheel, and to the end of the string a weight of 4 lb. is attached. What is the kinetic energy of weight and flywheel when the weight has descended 3·5 ft. ?

5. If all the energy of question 1 were converted into heat, how much would be produced (*a*) in B.Th.U., (*b*) in C.H.U. ?

6. A bullet weighing 20 grams has a velocity of 36,000 cm. per sec. Find its K.E. in (*a*) ergs, (*b*) joules.

7. A motor of 8 B.H.P. has an efficiency of 80 per cent. How many B.O.T. units will it consume in 8 hr. ?

SECTION B

8. At a certain instant a truck weighing 5 tons is moving along a leve road at a speed of 6 m.p.h. Find the number of foot-pounds of kinetic energy stored in the truck. Assuming all power shut off, how far would the truck move before coming to rest if the resistances were 12 lb per ton ?

U.L.C.I.

9. A body weighing 20 lb. is constrained to move in a vertical circular path. It falls from rest through a vertical height of 30 in. before it reaches the bottom of the circle. What is the velocity of the body when in its lowest position ? If, in this position, 20 ft.-lb. of energy are withdrawn from the body, through what vertical height would the body rise on the other side ? Neglect all frictional resistances.

U.L.C.I.

10. A car weighing 1,200 lb. is moving at 15 m.p.h. What is its kinetic energy and what is its momentum ?

If the speed of the car is reduced to 2 m.p.h. in 5 sec., what is the average force acting on the car during these 5 sec. ?

U.E.I.

11. Define " kinetic energy " and " radius of gyration." A flywheel, weighing 2,240 lb., gives out 2,300 ft.-lb. of energy when its speed changes from 120 to 118 r.p.m. How much energy is stored in the flywheel when rotating at 120 r.p.m. ? What is the radius of gyration ?

U.E.I.

12. What do you understand by the term " Radius of Gyration " ? A cast-iron flywheel has a rim 20 in. wide and 9 in. thick. Its radius of gyration is 5·75 ft. Find its kinetic energy at 160 r.p.m. Take 1 cu. in. of cast iron = 0·26 lb.

U.E.I.

13. A rigid framework consisting of bars OA, OB and OC rotates about a vertical axis through O at 120 r.p.m. OA, OB and OC are 2, 1½, and 3 ft. long respectively and are at right angles to the axis of the shaft. Masses of 4, 6, and 2 lb. are attached to the bars at A, B, and C respectively. Neglecting the weight of the bars, determine the kinetic energy of the system. If the three masses be concentrated at a radius R ft., find the value of R if it be so chosen that the kinetic energy at the same speed as before remains unchanged. What name is given to this radius R ? U.E.I.

14. A hammer weighing 5 tons and moving at a speed of 16 ft. per sec. strikes a stationary body of weight 15 tons. Find the resulting velocity after the blow when the two bodies move together. Also find the amount of kinetic energy lost by the impact. Assume perfect freedom of motion, and resistances negligible.

U.L.C.I.

15. A pendulum is seen to be swinging and the total arc covered is 60°. If the length of the pendulum is 4 ft., what is the maximum velocity of the pendulum bob ?

C.G.L.I.

16. The rim of a flywheel weighs 500 lb. and its mean effective diameter is 3 ft. At what speed must it run if the energy to be stored in it is to be 10ft.-tons ?

C.G.L.I.

17. A wagon starts from rest and runs down an incline of 1 in 60 for a distance of 600 ft. If 20 per cent. of its potential energy at the top of the incline is lost in friction, find the velocity of the wagon at the end of the 600 ft.   C.G.L.I.

18. A rotating wheel is 5 ft. diameter and contains 4,000 ft.-lb. of kinetic energy. A brake block is pressed against the rim of the wheel with a force of 20 lb. and the coefficient of friction is 0·33. Calculate the number of revolutions the wheel will make in coming to rest.   C.G.L.I.

CHAPTER XII

HYDRAULICS—WATER AT REST

119. Liquids. Hydraulics may be described as the mechanics of liquids. It deals with force and motion as related to liquids.

All substances fall into three classes, viz. : solids, liquids and gases. Solids are rigid, resisting change of shape. The various parts of a solid body do not move freely relative to each other. Liquids and gases readily take the shape of the boundaries of any vessel containing them and they permit of internal movement comparatively freely. There is, in fact, some resistance to internal motion, which is of the nature of friction between adjacent particles. This internal friction is known as *viscosity*. When the motion falls to nothing the friction also becomes zero. The forces required to overcome internal friction are equivalent to shearing force, so that a liquid which is at rest has no shearing force or shear stress in it.

Because there is no shear stress in a liquid at rest all forces on surfaces within the liquid are perpendicular to the surfaces. This is a very important property of liquids.

120. Pressure. It is not usual to speak of stress in relation to liquids. The forces concerned are referred to as pressure (see chap. I). In a fluid (liquid or gas), the pressure is always normal to any surface exposed to it if the fluid is at rest.

Intensity of pressure is the pressure per unit area of surface.

Intensity of pressure may vary from point to point so that it would be impossible, except in special cases, to expose a unit area (i.e. one square foot or one square inch) to a pressure of the same intensity at all points. If, however, the pressure intensity at any point we are considering be imagined to remain uniform over the whole of a unit area containing that point, then, the force or pressure on that unit area would be the *intensity of pressure*.

Another property of pressure intensity in a liquid is that it is the same in all directions at any one point.

The student, then, should be careful to remember the following facts :

    (1) Pressure of a fluid is always normal (perpendicular) to any surface which is exposed to it.

    (2) The pressure intensity is the pressure per unit area.

    (3) The pressure intensity at any point in a fluid is the same in all directions.

121. Density. The *density* of any substance is the *weight of unit volume*.

This is true of all substances, solids, liquids and gases. (See also arts. 169, 178, 228.)

Generally densities are stated per cubic foot or per cubic inch.

Water has a density of 62·4 lb. per cu. ft., or 0·0361 lb. per cu. in.

Air has a density of 0·0807 lb. per cu. ft. at 32° F. and 14·7 lb. per sq. in. (art. 171).

Copper has a density of 546 lb. per cu. ft.

The ratio of the density of a substance to that of water is called the *relative density*.

$$\text{The relative density of copper} = \frac{546}{62\cdot4} = 8\cdot75.$$

Another name for relative density is *specific gravity*.

EXAMPLE. A cylinder of brass is 2 in. long and 0·8 in. diameter. It is found to weigh 0·33 lb. Find its density per cubic inch.

$$\text{Volume of brass} = 0\cdot7854 \times 0\cdot8 \times 0\cdot8 \times 2$$
$$= 1\cdot005 \text{ cu. in.}$$
$$\text{Density} = \frac{\text{weight}}{\text{volume}} = \frac{0\cdot33}{1\cdot005} = 0\cdot328 \text{ lb. per cu. in.}$$

122. Pressure at a Given Depth. It is required to find the pressure intensity at a point M, whose depth below the surface of a liquid is h.

Let w = the density of the liquid.

Take a cylinder of the liquid with imaginary boundaries, its base containing the point M and its axis vertical. The upper end is in the surface of the liquid.

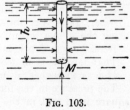

FIG. 103.

L

Let A = area of section of the cylinder

,, h = the length of the axis

,, p = intensity of pressure at M.

The forces acting on this cylinder of liquid are :

(1) The pressure on its sides. Since the cylinder is vertical, all this pressure acts horizontally.

(2) Force of gravity downwards ; this is the weight of the cylinder of liquid.

(3) The total pressure of the liquid on the base of the cylinder acting vertically upwards.

(1) The side pressure has no resultant effect, otherwise the cylinder of liquid would move in the direction of the resultant, since there is nothing to stop it doing so.

(2) The force of gravity downwards = wt. of cylinder

= volume × density of liquid

= Ah × w.

(3) The upward total pressure = pA.

Forces (2) and (3) have to balance if the liquid is at rest.

$$\therefore pA = Ahw$$
$$\therefore p = wh \qquad . \qquad . \qquad . \qquad . \qquad \text{(I)}$$

Hence, the intensity of pressure is the density of liquid multiplied by the depth.

If there is a pressure on the surface of the liquid, e.g. the pressure of the atmosphere, then it must be added to that already found.

Let the pressure intensity on the surface = p_a

Then the above equation of the vertical forces will be

Total downward force = weight of cylinder + pressure on surface

= Ahw + p_aA

Total upward pressure = pA

$$\therefore pA = Ahw + p_aA$$
$$\therefore p = wh + p_a \qquad . \qquad . \qquad . \qquad \text{(II)}$$

Both the above formulæ (I) and (II) are very useful.

Note. It is very important to pay attention to the units in using the above formulæ.

Density and depth must use the same unit of length.

That is, if h is in feet, w must be weight per cubic foot.

If h is in inches, w must be weight per cubic inch.

The pressure in the former case, if w is in lb., will be in lb. per square foot, and in the latter case in lb. per square inch.

Other units than the lb. may be used, but it is not often that we meet with them.

Pressures in lb. per square foot and lb. per square inch are easily converted from one to the other.

Let P = pressure in lb. per square foot.

„ p =   „   „ „ „ square inch.

Then $P = 144p$ or $p = \dfrac{P}{144}$.

123. Absolute Pressure. As the pressure of the atmosphere is ordinarily everywhere around us, we are apt to ignore it. It is, however, 14·7 lb. per sq. in. on the average.

Most pressure gauges, used for steam, water and compressed air, are constructed to indicate the intensity of pressure in excess of that of the atmosphere. When such a gauge reads zero, there is, in fact, a pressure of 14·7 lb. per sq. in. We must therefore either state which pressure is referred to, or there must be some clear understanding which of the two is meant. Pressure as indicated by the ordinary gauge is called *gauge pressure*.

The pressure above that of a vacuum, that is, above the true zero, is called *absolute pressure*.

In lb. per square inch units we have

pressure (absolute) = gauge pressure + 14·7

In lb. per square foot units we have

pressure (absolute) = gauge pressure + (14·7 × 144)
= gauge pressure + 2,116.

EXAMPLE. The density of sea water is 64 lb. per cu. ft. Find the pressure intensity at a depth of 80 fathoms.

1 fathom = 6 ft.
$p = wh = 64 \times 80 \times 6 = 30{,}720$ lb. per sq. ft.

$$p \text{ (lb. per sq. in.)} = \frac{30{,}720}{144} = 213 \text{ lb. per sq. in.}$$

Note. This is *not* absolute pressure.

EXAMPLE. A layer of oil 2·5 ft. thick rests on water. Find the intensity of pressure at a depth of 6 ft. below the upper surface of the oil. Density of oil = 56·1 lb. per cu. ft. Density of water = 62·3 lb. per cu. ft.

Pressure due to 2·5 ft. of oil   = 2·5 × 56·1 = 140·25 lb. per sq. ft.
„   „   „ 3·5 ft. of water = 3·5 × 62·3 = 218·05 „   „   „
Total pressure = 140·25 + 218·05 = 358·3 lb. per sq. ft.

$$= \frac{358\cdot3}{144} = 2\cdot49 \text{ lb. per sq. in.}$$

EXAMPLE. The horizontal plate which forms the bottom of a water

tank is 7·25 ft. × 6·75 ft. Find the pressure intensity and the total **pressure**
on the plate when the water is 9·5 ft. deep in the tank.

Intensity of pressure = wh
$$= 62·3 × 9·5 = 592 \text{ lb. per sq. ft.}$$
$$= 4·11 \text{ lb. per sq. in.}$$
Total pressure = $7·25 × 6·75 × 592 = 28{,}970$ lb.

Note. The absolute pressure would not be needed here because the
atmospheric pressure acts underneath the tank and so neutralizes the effect
of the atmospheric pressure on the surface of the water.

Also notice that the shape of the tank, i.e. whether it has vertical side
or sloping ones does not enter into the calculation.

The Manometer. When it is desired to measure a small difference of pressure, a manometer gauge
is used. It consists of a U-tube
filled with water or other liquid.
The difference of level of the liquid in
the two arms indicates the difference
of pressure between the gas or vapour
in the vessel and the outside atmosphere. It may be higher or lower.
The arrangement is shown in fig. 104,
and the following example makes the
method of calculation clear.

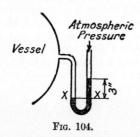

FIG. 104.

EXAMPLE. A U-tube pressure gauge gives a reading of 3 in. difference
in level when denoting the pressure of air in a vessel. What is the pressure
difference ?

The pressure at level XX, fig. 104, is the same in both limbs. On the left
it is the pressure in the vessel, and on the right it is the pressure at a depth
of 3 in. in water plus the pressure of the atmosphere.

Pressure at a depth of 3 in. = $wh = 62·3 × \frac{3}{12}$
$$= 15·6 \text{ lb. per sq. ft.}$$
$$= 0·1082 \text{ lb. per sq. in.}$$

Total pressure on right = $14·7 + 0·1082 = 14·808$ lb. per sq. in.
This pressure is absolute and is the pressure also in the vessel.

Difference in pressure between
vessel and atmosphere $\Big\} = 0·1082$ lb. per sq. in.

If the pressure difference is greater the manometer is sometimes
filled with mercury. The relative density of mercury is 13·6,
i.e. it is 13·6 times heavier than water.

The difference in pressure is thus 13·6 times greater than in
the above example,

i.e. difference in pressure for 3 in. of mercury
$$= 0·1082 × 13·6 = 1·472 \text{ lb. per sq. in.}$$

124. Pressure on a Submerged Surface. In an example
in art. 123, the pressure on the bottom of a tank was found.

The problem was simple because the pressure intensity was the same at all points. When, however, the surface on which the total pressure is required is vertical or inclined, the pressure intensity will vary, being greater at points of greater depth. In such cases, we must find the *average pressure intensity and multiply by the area.*

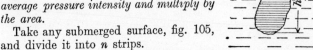

Fig. 105.

Take any submerged surface, fig. 105, and divide it into n strips.

Let the first one be at depth h_1 and have area a_1.

Let the second be at depth h_2 and have area a_2, and so on.

Let the last one be at depth h_n and have area a_n.

Now total pressure on the first strip $= wa_1h_1$

Because the strip is narrow, the pressure may be taken as uniform.

Pressure on second strip $= wa_2h_2$

    ,,   ,, n^{th} ,, $= wa_nh_n$

Let $p =$ average pressure

  ,, A $=$ total area $= a_1 + a_2 + a_3 \ldots a_n$

Total pressure on the surface

$$= pA = wa_1h_1 + wa_2h_2 + wa_3h_3 \ldots wa_nh_n$$
$$= w(a_1h_1 + a_2h_2 + a_3h_3 \ldots a_nh_n)$$
$$\therefore\ p = w \times \frac{a_1h_1 + a_2h_2 + a_3h_3 \ldots a_nh_n}{A}$$
$$= w \times \frac{a_1h_1 + a_2h_2 + a_3h_3 \ldots a_nh_n}{a_1 + a_2 + a_3 \ldots a_n}.$$

But the above fraction is the moment of area (see art. 42) of the surface divided by the area.

This is the distance of the centre of area (or centroid) from the line XX in the surface.

Hence, average pressure on a submerged area.

$= p = w \times$ depth of centre of area below the surface.

This result is very important and should be carefully remembered.

EXAMPLE. A rectangular plate 4 ft. by 3 ft. is submerged in water with its upper 3 ft. edge parallel to the surface and 5 ft. below it. The 4 ft. edges are vertical. Find the total pressure on the surface.

The centroid, i.e. centre of area, of the rectangle is midway between the top and bottom edges, i.e. 2 ft. below the top edge of the plate.

∴ Depth of centroid $= 5 + 2 = 7$ ft.

Average pressure $= 62\cdot3 \times 7 = 436\cdot1$ lb. per sq. ft.

Area of plate $= 4 \times 3 = 12$ sq. ft.

Total pressure on plate $= 436\cdot1 \times 12 = 5,233$ lb.

EXAMPLE. A pipe $1\frac{1}{2}$ ft. diameter leading from a reservoir is stopped by a circular plate whose centre is 28 ft. below the surface of the reservoir. Find the total pressure on the plate.

Average pressure = pressure at centre of plate

$= 62\cdot3 \times 28 = 1,744$ lb. per sq. ft.

Area of circle $= 0\cdot7854 \times 1\cdot5 \times 1\cdot5 = 1\cdot767$ sq. ft.

Total pressure $= 1,744 \times 1\cdot767 = 3,080$ lb.

Note, that in the last two examples, we have found the pressure on one side of the surfaces only, and also that atmospheric pressure has been neglected.

EXAMPLE. Find the magnitude of the resultant pressure on a lock gate 18 ft. wide when the water on one side is at a depth of 16 ft. and on the other at a depth of 5 ft.

Average pressure intensity on deep side $= 62\cdot3 \times \frac{16}{2}$

$= 498\cdot4$ lb. per sq. ft.

Wetted area on deep side $= 18 \times 16 = 288$ sq. ft.

Total pressure on deep side $= 288 \times 498\cdot4$

$= 143,400$ lb.

Average pressure intensity on shallow side $= 62\cdot3 \times \frac{5}{2}$

$= 155\cdot7$ lb. per sq. ft.

Wetted area on shallow side $= 18 \times 5 = 90$ sq. ft.

Total pressure ,,   ,,   ,, $= 155\cdot7 \times 90 = 14,013$ lb.

Resultant pressure $= 143,400 - 14,013 = 129,387$ lb.

125. Pumps. A pump is a machine for raising water from a lower to a higher level or for forcing water against a resisting pressure. Amongst the many types of pump which are in use we shall deal only with reciprocating pumps, so called because the piston, ram or plunger works with a backward and forward motion.

Such pumps consist essentially of a barrel or cylinder, a piston, ram, or plunger, together with suitable valves.

126. Suction Pump. This pump is popularly regarded as "sucking" the water up the suction pipe. In reality, the pressure of the atmosphere *forces* the water up. The barrel B is fitted with a piston P, through which one or more holes penetrate. The barrel opens at the upper end of the delivery pipe D, and at its lower end to the suction pipe S. The holes in the piston are fitted with valves which are normally closed, but which will lift when pressure is applied below them. The upper end of the suction pipe has a similar valve.

On moving the piston upwards a partial vacuum is produced beneath it, so reducing the pressure in the cylinder. The greater

pressure of the atmosphere on the water in the sump forces it
up the suction pipe, and lifts the valve at its upper end.

The cylinder thus fills with water. When
the piston is forced down, the valve on the
suction pipe closes and those in the piston lift.
This causes the water under the piston to
flow through the holes in it to the upper side
of the piston. On the next upward movement of the piston its valves close, and the
water above it flows through the delivery
pipe, whilst the space below it is filled with
another supply of water.

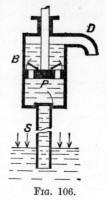

These pumps can only lift water a limited
height, because the atmosphere has only a
limited pressure.

Suppose a perfect vacuum, i.e. a space
of zero pressure, could be produced under
the piston, then the whole pressure of the

Fig. 106.

atmosphere, 14·7 lb. per sq. in., would be available for forcing
water up the pipe. It would thus lift the water to a height, h,
such that the pressure due to a column of water h ft. in height
would produce a pressure at its base = (14·7 × 144) lb. per sq. ft.

Hence, since

$$p = wh$$
$$14·7 \times 144 = 62·3h$$
$$\therefore \ h = \frac{14·7 \times 144}{62·3} = 34 \text{ ft.}$$

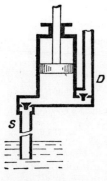

This is the ideal height of suction lift,
but in practice, due to leakage at piston
and valves, as well as other causes, about
26 ft. is a fair working limit. The variations in the pressure of the atmosphere, as
indicated by the barometer, will affect the
lift of a suction pump.

127. Force Pump. In this pump
there are no valves as a rule in the
piston. There is a valve at the top of
the suction pipe and one at the foot of the
delivery pipe. On the suction (upward in
this case) stroke, water enters the cylinder

Fig. 107.

through the valve at the top of the

suction pipe S. On the delivery stroke the suction valve closes and the delivery valve D opens, whilst water is forced through it up the delivery pipe. There is no theoretical limit to the height to which a force pump may raise water. It is usual to place a force pump as near the sump level as practicable, and thus reduce the lift on the suction side to a minimum.

Let A = area of a pump piston
 ,, l = length of piston stroke
 ,, n = number of delivery strokes per minute.
  Then volume swept by piston per stroke = A × l
   volume of water lifted per minute = nAl.

This value is not usually attained because of leakage and slip. Slip refers to the water which " slips " back through the valves, when they are in the act of closing.

EXAMPLE. The diameter of a pump piston is 5 in, and the stroke is 10 in. The number of strokes per minute is 48. Find the volume, in cubic feet and gallons, delivered per minute if 12 per cent. slips back.

$$\text{Ideal volume per stroke} = \frac{0\cdot7854 \times 5 \times 5 \times 10}{1,728} \text{ cu. ft.}$$

$$= 0\cdot1135 \text{ cu. ft.}$$

Ideal volume per minute = $0\cdot1135 \times 48 = 5\cdot46$ cu. ft.
Actual volume ,, ,, = $5\cdot46 \times 0\cdot88 = 4\cdot80$ cu. ft.
1 cu. ft. = 6·23 gall.
∴ Number of gallons per minute = $4\cdot80 \times 6\cdot23 = 29\cdot9$.

EXAMPLE. The pump of the last example lifts the water 300 ft. above the level of the cylinder. Find the total force on the piston during delivery.

Intensity of pressure due to a column of water of 300 ft.
$$= 62\cdot3 \times 300 = 18,690 \text{ lb. per sq. ft.}$$

$$\text{Area of piston in square feet} = \frac{0\cdot7854 \times 5 \times 5}{144} = 0\cdot1362$$

$$\text{Total pressure on piston} = 0\cdot1362 \times 18,690 = 2,545 \text{ lb.}$$

EXAMPLE. The difference in level between the sump and delivery point in a certain pump is 240 ft. The quantity of water lifted is 100,000 gall. per hr. If the efficiency of the pump and delivery pipe is 66 per cent., find the horse-power required to drive the pump. 1 gallon of water = 10 lb.

$$\text{Weight of water lifted per minute} = \frac{100,000 \times 10}{60} = 16,667 \text{ lb.}$$

$$\text{Work done per minute} = 16,667 \times 240 = 4,000,000 \text{ ft.-lb.}$$

$$\text{Horse-power} = \frac{4,000,000 \times 100}{33,000 \times 66} = 183\cdot6$$

128. Pressure Transmission. When a closed vessel is completely filled with fluid and any increase in intensity of pressure occurs at one point, it is transmitted equally to all points in the vessel. In fig. 108, if a force is applied to a piston A increasing the pressure intensity beneath it, then the pressure intensity under B is increased by the same amount. This arrangement is used for obtaining very great forces in the many forms of hydraulic press met with in engineering practice. It is also the principle of the hydraulic jack, in which a pump ram of small diameter is operated through a lever. This pump is in communication by a pipe with a cylinder of much larger diameter. The piston of this cylinder is operated upon by the same pressure intensity as the small piston, and so the total pressure is much greater.

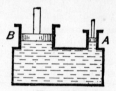

Fig. 108.

EXAMPLE. A hydraulic jack has a pump ram $\frac{3}{8}$-in. diameter which is worked by a lever. The distance from handle to fulcrum is 24 in., and from ram to fulcrum 1·5 in. The lifting piston is 2 in. diameter. When a force of 20 lb. is applied to the handle, find the lifting force of the jack.

$$\text{Force on pump ram} = \frac{24}{1 \cdot 5} \times 20 = 320 \text{ lb.}$$

$$\text{Pressure increase in liquid} = \frac{320}{0 \cdot 7854 \times \frac{3}{8} \times \frac{3}{8}} = \frac{320 \times 8 \times 8}{0 \cdot 7854 \times 3 \times 3}$$
$$= 2{,}895 \text{ lb. per sq. in.}$$

$$\text{Total pressure increase on large piston} = 0 \cdot 7854 \times 2 \times 2 \times 2{,}895$$
$$= 9{,}100 \text{ lb.}$$

Note that this is the lifting force of the jack.

EXAMPLES XII

SECTION A

1. If 1 cu. ft. of water weighs 1,000 oz., find its density in lb. per cubic inch.

2. One gallon of oil weighs 9 lb. and there are 6·25 gallons in 1 cu. ft. Find the density of the oil in lb. per cubic foot and lb. per cubic inch.

3. Find the pressure in lb. per square foot and lb. per square inch at a depth of 500 ft. in the sea if 1 cu. ft. of sea water weighs 64 lb.

4. A manometer containing water reads 5 in. difference of level. What is the difference of pressure indicated in lb. per square inch ?

5. A square of 4 ft. side is immersed horizontally in water 2 ft. below the surface. Find the total pressure on the upper side of the square.

6. If the square of question 5 is immersed vertically with one edge in the surface, find the average pressure intensity and the total pressure on one side of the square.

7. A cylinder of 3-in. bore is connected by a pipe to another cylinder 14-in. bore also fitted with a piston. The cylinders and pipe are full of water. If a force of 80 lb. is applied to the small piston, determine the force on the large one.

8. A manometer is filled with a liquid of relative density 2·3. What difference of pressure is indicated when the reading is 4 in. ?

9. The gate of a dry dock, which is 40 ft. wide, has water outside it to a depth of 26 ft. What is the total water pressure on the gate, and what is the intensity of the water pressure at the bottom of the gate ?
(1 cu. ft. of salt water weighs 64 lb.) U.L.C.I.

10. The centre of a circular door 3 ft. diameter in the side of a tank is 40 ft. below the surface of the sea. Determine the intensity of pressure at this depth in lb. per square inch and the total pressure on the door. (1 cu. ft. of sea-water weighs 64 lb.) U.L.C.I.

11. The diameter of the barrel of a reciprocating water pump is 12 in., the stroke of the plunger is 3 ft., and the number of working strokes per minute is 20. The lift is 60 ft. If the efficiency of the pump is 55 per cent., determine the horse-power of the motor which drives the pump. (1 cu. ft. of water weighs 62·5 lb.) N.C.T.E.C.

CHAPTER XIII

HYDRAULICS—WATER IN MOTION

129. Water in Motion. In the foregoing problems on liquids it has always been assumed that the liquid was at rest. Although in pumps we knew the water to be moving, the effects of the motion were neglected because they were small in comparison with the effects of the static forces. The laws governing the motion of water are based chiefly on energy and momentum.

130. Small Orifice. Let us consider a tank of water with a small sharp-edged orifice near the base of the tank. It is made sharp-edged to reduce the friction to a minimum.

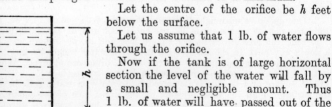

FIG. 109.

Let the centre of the orifice be h feet below the surface.

Let us assume that 1 lb. of water flows through the orifice.

Now if the tank is of large horizontal section the level of the water will fall by a small and negligible amount. Thus 1 lb. of water will have passed out of the tank and will have taken its energy with it. The water which has been extracted from the tank has left the top layer.

If we take the centre of the orifice as the datum from which we reckon, then the 1 lb. of water which has left the tank had in it h ft.-lb. of potential energy.

As the water left the tank it contained kinetic energy due to its motion. Let the velocity of the water leaving the orifice be v ft. per sec. Then

$$\text{kinetic energy of the 1 lb. of water} = \frac{v^2}{2g}.$$

This is equal to the potential energy lost if we neglect friction.

$$\therefore \ \frac{v^2}{2g} = h$$

$$\therefore \ v^2 = 2gh$$

$$\therefore \ v = \sqrt{2gh} \text{ (see art. 115).}$$

If the water is constantly replenished by a supply pipe, and the level kept constant with a *head* above the orifice of h ft., the velocity will remain constant at $\sqrt{2gh}$.

There is, in an actual case, a slight amount of friction so that the velocity is a little less than the above value, being about $0.98\sqrt{2gh}$. This quantity by which we multiply $\sqrt{2gh}$ is called the *coefficient of velocity*, say C_v.

$$\therefore \ v = C_v\sqrt{2gh}$$

Now let A = the area of the orifice in square feet. It is found that the jet is not equal in cross-sectional area to the orifice, but is somewhat less. The actual area is C_cA where C_c is a quantity less than 1 and is called the *coefficient of contraction*.

The volume of water flowing per second

$$= \text{area of jet} \times \text{velocity of jet}$$
$$= C_cA \times C_v\sqrt{2gh}$$
$$= C_cC_vA\sqrt{2gh}.$$

We combine C_cC_v as one constant, C, which is known as the *coefficient of discharge*.

Hence, $Q = CA\sqrt{2gh}$ where Q = the volume of water flowing per second in cubic feet.

EXAMPLE. An orifice 2-in. diameter discharges with a head of 10 ft. Find the quantity of water discharged in gallons per minute. C = 0·62.

Volume per second $= Q = CA\sqrt{2gh}$

$$= 0.62 \times 0.7854 \times \tfrac{1}{6} \times \tfrac{1}{6}\sqrt{64.4 \times 10}$$
$$= 0.343 \text{ cu. ft. per sec.}$$

Quantity in gallons per minute $= 0.343 \times 60 \times 6.23 = 124.5$.

131. Energy of Water. In the last article we have seen two things incidentally.

(1) Water may have potential energy which amounts to h ft.-lb. per lb., h being in feet.

(2) Water may have kinetic energy which amounts to $\dfrac{v^2}{2g}$ ft.-lb. per lb.

Water may also have energy due to being under pressure.

FIG. 110.

Suppose water is available in a pipe P with a pressure of p lb. per sq. ft.

Let the pipe be attached to a cylinder fitted with a piston of area A square feet. Let 1 cu. ft. of the water be admitted to the cylinder and act upon the piston, doing work upon it.

$$\text{The weight of the 1 cu. ft.} = w \text{ lb.}$$
$$\text{Then total force on piston} = p\text{A lb.}$$
$$\text{Distance moved by piston} = \frac{1}{\text{A}} \text{ ft.}$$

$$\therefore \text{Work done by 1 cu. ft. of water} = p\text{A} \times \frac{1}{\text{A}}$$
$$= p \text{ ft.-lb.}$$

But this work is done by w lb. of water.

$$\therefore \text{Work done by 1 lb. of water} = \frac{p}{w} \text{ ft.-lb.}$$

Therefore, under pressure p lb. per sq. ft., 1 lb. of water contains $\dfrac{p}{w}$ ft.-lb. of energy.

132. Velocity due to Pressure. If water under pressure issues from an orifice or nozzle, the whole of the pressure energy is converted into kinetic energy, provided we neglect friction, which is usually small. This fact enables the velocity of such jets to be calculated.

Kinetic energy of jet per lb. = pressure energy of water per lb.

$$\frac{v^2}{2g} = \frac{p}{w}$$
$$\therefore v^2 = 2g\frac{p}{w}$$
$$\therefore v = \sqrt{2g\frac{p}{w}} = \sqrt{64 \cdot 4 \frac{p}{w}}.$$

EXAMPLE. A machine, known as a Pelton Wheel, has its main nozzle connected to a water-pipe where the pressure is 180 lb. per sq. in. above the atmosphere. The nozzle is 2 in. diameter. Assuming a $1\frac{1}{2}$ per cent. loss of energy, find (a) the velocity of the jet, (b) the quantity of water delivered per second, (c) the kinetic energy delivered per second, (d) the horse-power supplied to the wheel.

Kinetic energy = $98\frac{1}{2}$ per cent. of pressure energy ($1\frac{1}{2}$ per cent. loss).

$$\therefore \frac{v^2}{2g} = 0.985 \frac{p}{w} = \frac{0.985 \times 180 \times 144}{62.3}$$

$$\therefore v^2 = \frac{0.985 \times 180 \times 144 \times 64.4}{62.3} = 26,350$$

$$\therefore v = 162.4 \text{ ft. per sec.}$$

$$\text{Area of jet} = \frac{0.7854 \times 2 \times 2}{144} = 0.02183 \text{ sq. ft.}$$

Volume of water delivered per second = 0.02183×162.4
$$= 3.55 \text{ cu. ft.}$$

Weight of water delivered per second = 3.55×62.3
$$= 221 \text{ lb.}$$

Kinetic energy per second = $\dfrac{Wv^2}{2g} = \dfrac{221 \times 162.4 \times 162.4}{64.4}$ ft.-lb.

$$= 90,800 \text{ ft.-lb.}$$

$$\text{Horse-power} = \frac{90,800}{550} = 165.$$

133. Momentum of a Jet.
We have seen that a mass $\frac{W}{g}$ moving with a velocity v ft. per sec. possesses momentum

$$= \frac{W}{g} v.$$

Water is no different from any other substance in this respect.

Let a jet of water flowing with velocity v ft. per sec. have an area of A sq. ft.

Then volume of water flowing per second = Av. cu. ft.

If w = density of water, we have

Weight of water flowing per second = wAv lb.

$$\therefore \text{ momentum of the water per second} = \frac{wAv}{g} \times v$$

$$= \frac{wAv^2}{g}.$$

134. Force of a Jet.
When a jet of water strikes an object which changes its flow a force is exerted by the jet. If we know how the flow is affected it is possible to calculate the force exerted.

When water strikes a flat plate, fig. 111, placed at right angles
to its path, it glances off in radial directions. The momentum
in the direction of flow becomes zero.

Force in any direction, exerted by a jet, is change of momentum
per second in that direction.

FIG. 111.   FIG. 112.

Hence, original momentum in direction of flow of jet per
second $= \dfrac{wAv^2}{g}$.

Final momentum in direction of jet $= 0$.

$\therefore$ Change of momentum per second $= \dfrac{wAv^2}{g}$

$\qquad\qquad\qquad\qquad = $ force on plate in lb.

Another interesting case is that in which the jet strikes a
semicircular vane. It enters the vane, gliding on to one edge.
The vane deflects it until the jet leaves in the opposite direction
with the same magnitude of velocity.

Hence, original momentum per second $= \dfrac{wAv^2}{g}$.

Final momentum per second $= -\dfrac{wAv^2}{g}$.

The sign is negative because the momentum is now reversed.
Hence, change of momentum per second.

$$= \frac{wAv^2}{g} - \left(-\frac{wAv^2}{g}\right)$$

$$= \frac{2wAv^2}{g} = \text{force on vane in lb.}$$

Note that this force is twice that on the flat plate.

EXAMPLE. A jet of water 3 in. diameter and having a velocity of 80 ft.

per sec. strikes (a) a flat plate, (b) a semicircular vane. Calculate the force exerted in each case.

$$\text{Weight of water delivered per second} = \frac{0 \cdot 7854 \times 3^2 \times 80 \times 62 \cdot 3}{144}$$

$$= 244 \cdot 2 \text{ lb.}$$

$$\text{Momentum of jet per second} = \frac{244 \cdot 2 \times 80}{32 \cdot 2} = 607 \text{ units.}$$

(a) On striking the flat plate all this momentum is deflected at right angles.

∴ Change of momentum per second in direction of jet = 607
= force on plate in lb.

(b) In this case the momentum is reversed

∴ Force = change of momentum per second
= 607 − (− 607) = 607 + 607
= 1,214 lb.

EXAMPLES XIII

Section A

1. A tank has a small orifice 10 ft. below the surface of the water. Find the velocity of discharge assuming no losses.

2. What is the pressure energy per lb. of water 12 ft. below the surface ?

3. An orifice is 2 in. diameter and is 14 ft. below the surface of the water in a tank. How many cubic feet of water are discharged per second ? C = 0·62.

4. A jet of water is 4 in. diameter and has a velocity of 64 ft. per sec. Find the weight of water conveyed by the jet per second.

5. An orifice is $1\frac{1}{2}$ in. square and the head of water above the orifice is 15 ft. Find the discharge in gallons per second if C = 0·64. 1 cu. ft. = 6·24 gall.

Section B

6. It is desired to make a circular sharp-edged orifice which will discharge 96 lb. of water per minute under a head of 16 in. What must be its diameter ? C = 0·62.

7. Water in a main is under a pressure of 54 lb. per sq. in. Find the velocity with which it will flow from a nozzle, 2 in. diameter, if the coefficient of velocity is 0·96. What is the kinetic energy of the jet per second ? Hence find the horse-power of the jet.

8. A jet of water conveys 5,000 lb. per min. with a velocity of 66 ft. per sec. The jet glides on to one edge of a semi-circular vane ; find the force exerted on the vane.

9. A jet of water $\frac{1}{4}$ in. in diameter issuing from a nozzle under a head of 20 ft. impinges normally on a flat stationary disc. Find (a) the weight of water issuing from the nozzle per second, (b) the momentum of the water issuing from the nozzle per second, and (c) the pressure exerted by the water on the disc.   U.L.C.I.

10. A bowl was suspended from a spring balance. Water is falling from a tap in a steady stream straight into the bowl. The sectional area of the stream is 1 sq. in. and the maximum velocity attained by it is 10 ft. per sec.

Find the weight of water reaching the bowl per second and its momentum, given 1 cu. ft. of water, weighs 62·3 lb. Does the spring balance record the correct weight of water in the bowl at any instant ? If not, what is the amount of the error in pounds weight ? U.E.I.

CHAPTER XIV

HEAT AND THERMOMETRY

135. Heat Energy. Heat is a form of energy, which, under certain conditions, can be used for the purpose of doing work. Heat is a quantity which is not directly measurable, and in this respect it differs from force, weight, pressure, etc. Other quantities have to be measured, from which the heat can be determined by calculation. The engineer, in his capacity of engine builder, bridge builder, and general constructor, frequently needs to measure heat quantities and he must know what will be the effect of heat on his materials of construction. His knowledge of the effect of heat on metals is needed when hardening and tempering steels, when making castings and forgings, and when arranging for shrinkage fits in the construction of various details. The observant person will be acquainted with the effects of heat on the more common substances, but it is necessary for the student of engineering to make a more thorough examination of these effects, and to be able to make calculations involving quantities of heat and temperatures.

136. Effects of Heat. The application of heat to substances produces definite effects as follows

The substance (i) alters its dimensions,
  (ii) becomes hotter,
  (iii) may change its state of existence, that is, from solid to liquid or liquid to vapour.
All or any of these events may happen if heat is applied to the substance. This is also true if heat is removed from the substance but in this case the substance becomes colder. These effects are more fully discussed in later articles. Before heat calculations can be attempted it is necessary to consider that state of a substance called temperature.

137. Thermometry. This is the science of temperature measurement, and it must be studied as the first step in the science of heat measurement. The science of heat measurement is called *Calorimetry*.

Temperature is a quantity used by scientists to indicate the relative degree of hotness of a body. This degree of hotness must not be confused with amount of heat. The amount of heat depends on other data as well as on the temperature, as will be shown in art. 147. Temperature is a number on a scale. The scale is called the scale of temperatures. There are various scales of temperature in use including the Centigrade, the Fahrenheit, and the corresponding Absolute scales. The numbers on the first two scales are usually fixed by reference to the " temperature " of water in definite states and under well-defined conditions. The numbers on the last two scales are chosen so as to fit in with the laws of gases (art. 224). If the number which represents the temperature of a body A, on a given scale, is greater than that which represents the temperature of a body B, on the same scale, then the body A is said to be at a higher temperature than that of B. Another way of stating the same thing is to say that the degree of hotness of the body A, is greater than that of B ; or that the intensity of the heat of A is greater than the intensity of the heat of B. We regard heat as flowing from the hotter to the colder body since all experience leads to the conclusion that this is the natural direction of heat flow.

138. Thermometers. A thermometer is an instrument constructed to indicate temperature. A glance at a thermometer conveys to the mind information regarding the intensity of the heat in the body to which the thermometer is applied. A simple mercury-in-glass thermometer is illustrated in fig. 113. Its action depends on the fact that mercury, in common with other substances, increases in volume when heated. The mercury can readily be seen through the glass stem and to render the reading easier a strip of white glass is introduced into the tube during manufacture. The thermometer consists of a glass tube, S, with a small bore, B, of thread-like dimensions. Such a tube is called a capillary tube. The end of the bore is enlarged to form a bulb R, the walls of which are reduced in thickness to enable the heat to reach the contained mercury quickly, and thus make the thermometer more sensitive, or responsive, to changes of temperature. The mercury is introduced into the bulb and the fine bore tube is sealed off. The sealing process is carried out with the bore full of mercury and with the whole thermometer at a temperature slightly above the maximum temperature for which it is to be used. Thus there is no air or gas on the top of the mercury in the ordinary thermometer. The small enlargement of the bore

M

at the top of the thermometer is to receive mercury if the temperature should rise to a higher value than that for which the thermometer is intended. There is danger of the thermometer bursting if the mercury rises to fill the bore completely. If the mercury-in-glass thermometer is to be used for temperatures over about 550° F. it is necessary to fill the bore with an inert (non-active) gas under pressure to prevent the mercury from boiling.

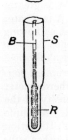

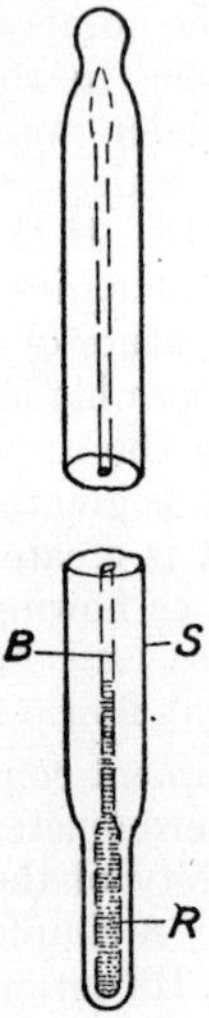

When the thermometer is at normal temperature the mercury level is low down the stem. If the thermometer be placed in contact with a hot body the mercury receives heat and therefore it expands. There is only one direction in which this expansion, or increase in volume, can take place and that is along the fine bore tube. Thus the mercury rises in the tube when the thermometer is placed in hotter surroundings. When transferred to colder surroundings the mercury falls in the tube. Thus the statement that the temperature is rising or falling means that certain surroundings are becoming hotter or colder as the case may be, and suggests that the mercury column in the bore of a thermometer, situated in those surroundings, is rising or falling to suit the circumstances.

Amongst other forms of temperature-measuring instruments are, the mercury-in-steel thermometer, the thermo-couple and special Pyrometers.

FIG. 113.

A Pyrometer is a special instrument for measuring high temperatures up to about 4,000° F. For temperatures such as these the mercury-in-glass thermometer is unsuitable.

Temperature measurements are made by the engineer when testing engines and boilers, and when he is engaged in manufacture where heat treatment of materials is necessary.

The determination of the heating value of fuels depends upon the accurate measurement of small temperature increases.

139. Graduation of Thermometers. A thermometer is said to be graduated when it has its scale marked upon it. The marking of the scale must be done by the aid of some well-known and definite temperature, which can be used as a starting-point in the graduation. As a result of long-continued observation it is now well known that the temperature of melting ice under atmospheric pressure is constant and, to establish this reading, all that is necessary is to procure ice and allow it to melt at atmospheric pressure. This knowledge enables the thermometer maker to obtain one point on the temperature scale. This point is called the lower fixed point. It is also common knowledge that the temperature of steam which is formed from water at the normal atmospheric pressure is also constant. This temperature can be repeated as often as desired by taking water and boiling it at atmospheric pressure. The piece of apparatus used for marking this point is shown in fig. 114 and is called a Hypsometer. If the thermometer is inserted in the steam so that the stem as well as the bulb is in the steam the level of the mercury will register a constant temperature. The arrows show the path of the steam and it will be noted that it has free outlet to the atmosphere through the pipe O. As a precaution that the pressure is atmospheric when the mark is located, a manometer gauge G is fitted. This gauge must show no difference of pressure or the temperature will be uncertain and the barometric reading must be 760 millimetres of mercury.

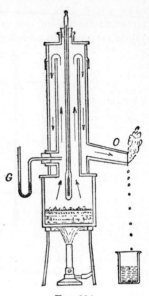

Fig. 114.

The temperature which is fixed in this way is called the upper fixed point. The difference between these two temperatures is known as the *temperature interval*. The temperature interval plays an important part in the process of conversion from one scale of temperature to another. The lower fixed point is known as the freezing point and the upper fixed point as the boiling point. The pressure is atmospheric in both cases.

140. Division of Temperature Interval. Let three thermometer tubes A, B, and C, fig. 115, be taken and suppose that the bore of each is the same diameter, and that the volume of the bulb is the same in each case. If an equal amount of

mercury be put into each bulb and the tube sealed off, the
thermometers will be identical in all respects. Now let them
be placed first in melting ice and then in steam at atmospheric
pressure. The level of the mercury in all the thermometers will
be the same at the two fixed points and therefore the length of
the interval, I, will be the same. Having made marks on the
stems at the fixed points, it now remains to divide the distance
between the two marks on each of the three stems. The
important feature of this step is that *any number of divisions
may be adopted*. In addition to this the number opposite to the

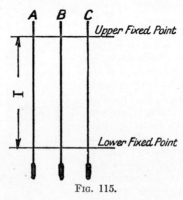

Fig. 115.

lower fixed point may be any number which is found to be
suitable. Thus the number representing the upper fixed point
will depend on the number chosen to represent the lower fixed
point and on the number of divisions into which it has been
decided to divide the interval. The numbers on thermometer
scales are entirely a matter of choice and thus it happens that
different numbers on different temperature scales represent the
same temperature.

141. Conversion of Temperatures. The two principal
temperature scales in use, (a) the Centigrade scale and (b) the
Fahrenheit scale, are shown in fig. 116 for identical thermometers.
It will be noted that the freezing point on the Centigrade scale
is marked 0°, whilst that on the Fahrenheit scale is 32°. These
numbers represent the same temperature. It will also be noted
that the boiling-point on the Centigrade scale is numbered 100°,
that on the Fahrenheit scale being numbered 212°. The interval

on the Centigrade scale is therefore $(100 - 0) = 100°$ C. The interval on the Fahrenheit scale is $(212 - 32) = 180°$ F.

From what has gone before it will be observed that these figures represent the *same* temperature rise.

Therefore 180° F. are equal to 100° C.

or   9° F. „   „   „   5° C.

„   1·8° F. „   „   „   1° C.

„   1° F. is „   „ $\frac{5}{9}$° C.

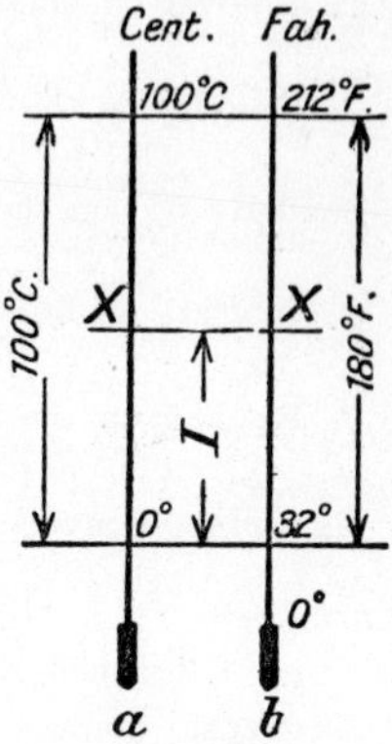

Fig. 116.

No matter what numbers are used for the fixed points, the interval values can be equated in this way and the value of a degree on one scale found in terms of a degree on another. This is the first step in the process of conversion of temperatures. Let the line XX, fig. 116, denote a definite temperature, F° Fahrenheit and C° Centigrade.

Let I be the interval.

Then $I = (F - 32)$ degrees Fahrenheit.

Also $I = (C - 0)$ degrees Centigrade.

But C degrees Centigrade $= \frac{9}{5}$ C degrees Fahrenheit.

∴ The interval C degrees Centigrade becomes $\frac{9}{5}$ C degrees Fahrenheit, and since the intervals are equal in both scales,

$$\frac{9}{5} \text{ C degrees} = (F - 32) \text{ degrees.}$$

There are now Fahrenheit degrees on both sides of the equation

∴ Reading in Centigrade degrees $= (F - 32) \times \frac{5}{9}$
and reading in Fahrenheit degrees $= \frac{9}{5}$ C $+ 32$.

It must be remembered that all thermometers, no matter how they are graduated, will indicate the same temperature if put into the same substance. The different readings (numbers) can be found if the upper and lower fixed points are known for the thermometers and if one temperature reading is known.

EXAMPLE. A Centigrade thermometer indicates a temperature rise of 20° when inserted in a liquid. What rise would be shown on the Fahrenheit thermometer ?

Since one degree C. is equivalent to $\frac{9}{5}$ degrees F., the given rise will be equivalent to a rise of

$\frac{9}{5} \times 20°$ F., or 36° F.

EXAMPLE. The upper fixed point of a thermometer is numbered 96 and the lower fixed point is numbered 30. What would be the reading on this thermometer corresponding to (a) 60° C., (b) 60° F. ?

Total interval on the given thermometer = 96 − 30 = 66°.   Therefore 66° on this thermometer are equal to 100° C.

$$\therefore \ 1° \ C. = \tfrac{66}{100}$$
$$= 0\cdot66° \text{ on the thermometer.}$$

∴ Interval on given thermometer corresponding to 60° C.
$$= 0\cdot66 \times 60 = 39\cdot6°.$$

∴ Reading on the thermometer corresponding to 60° C.
$$= 39\cdot6 + 30 = 69\cdot6°.$$

Similarly 66° on the given thermometer are equal to 180° F.

$$\therefore \ 1° \ F. = \tfrac{66}{180} = 0\cdot366° \text{ on the thermometer.}$$

∴ Interval reading corresponding to 60° F. = 0·366 (60 − 32)
$$= 0\cdot366 \times 28 = 10\cdot25°.$$

∴ Reading on the thermometer corresponding to 60° F.
$$= 10\cdot25 + 30 = 40\cdot25°.$$

EXAMPLE.   Convert 65° C. into a Fahrenheit reading.
$$\text{Interval} = \frac{65 \times 9}{5}° \ F. = 117° \ F.$$

∴ Fahrenheit reading = 117° F. + 32° = 149° F.

EXAMPLE.   Convert 203° F. into a Centigrade reading.
$$\text{Interval} = (203 − 32)° \ F.$$
$$= 171° \ F. = (171 \times \tfrac{5}{9})° \ C.$$

∴ Centigrade reading = 95° C.

When converting from Fahrenheit to Centigrade, subtract 32 and multiply the remainder by $\tfrac{5}{9}$.

When converting from Centigrade to Fahrenheit, multiply by $\tfrac{9}{5}$ and add 32.

In certain cases of low temperatures the readings may fall below the ordinary zero on the thermometer.

When this occurs the readings are given with a negative sign prefixed.   The temperature is then said to be a negative temperature.

The same zero is used with negative temperatures as with ordinary positive temperatures and the method of converting the negative temperatures, from one scale to the other, is the same as the method given above.

EXAMPLE.   Convert a temperature of − 10° C. to Fahrenheit reading.
Interval = − 10° C., or 10° C. below the lower fixed point
$$= (− 10 \times \tfrac{9}{5})° \ F., \text{ or } 18° \ F. \text{ below the lower fixed point.}$$

∴ The Fahrenheit reading = − 18° + 32° = 14° F.

EXAMPLE.   Convert a temperature of − 18° F. to Centigrade reading.
Interval = − 18° − 32°
$$= − 50° \ F., \text{ that is, } 50° \ F. \text{ below the lower fixed point.}$$

∴ Centigrade reading = − 50 × ⅝
= − 27·7° C. or 27·7° C. below the lower fixed
point.

EXAMPLE. Convert a temperature of −80° C. to Fahrenheit reading.
Interval = − 80° C.
= (− 80 × ⅝)° F. = − 144° F.
∴ Fahrenheit reading = − 144 + 32 = − 112° F.

See also art. 224 for explanation of the Absolute temperature
scale.

142. Effects of Heat on Dimensions. When heat is applied
to any substance, the rise of temperature is accompanied by
increase of dimension. This is true for most materials. There
are, however, certain alloys which retain their original dimensions
over a considerable range of temperature. Increase in dimension
is called *expansion*. Reduction in dimension is called *contraction*.
The expansion resulting from the application of heat may be
linear, superficial or *cubical* expansion. When only the increase
in length is considered then the expansion is called *linear*.
When the increase in area only is taken into account, the expansion is *superficial*, and, similarly, when increase in volume takes
place, *cubical* expansion is the name given to it. A few moments,
consideration will lead to the conclusion that all expansion is
cubical. If, however, it is necessary to consider the expansion
of long objects, as for example wires, rods, etc., the expansion in
the direction of the diameters is so small compared with the
expansion in the direction of the length that the lateral expansion
is neglected. The problem is now reduced to the consideration
of expansion of one dimension only and is called linear expansion.
The expansion of metals is easily shown by means of Gravesand's
ring and ball experiment, fig. 117 (*a*). When heated the ball
will not pass through the ring. If it is allowed to cool it passes
through the ring quite easily.

Different metals expand different amounts for the same temperature rise. If two different metals are riveted together to
form a strip, and then heated, the different expansion which
takes place in the two metals will cause bending of the strip,
fig. 117 (*b*). This effect is referred to as *differential* expansion.

Differential expansion of two pieces of the same metal may
occur as a result of the form taken by the two parts. A practical
instance of this arises in connection with double beat valves for
engines. A double beat valve is shown in fig. 118 and the arrows
show the path of the hot fluid. The expansion of the bars

B, supporting the seat S, is unrestricted, whilst that of the valve is affected by the ribs R, and the form of the valve itself.

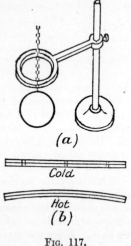

No matter whether the valve or seat expands most, one or other of the valve faces will open slightly. If the valve increases in length more than the seat the top faces will separate, and vice-versa. To overcome this difficulty these

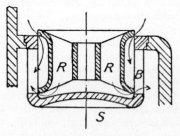

Fig. 117.

Fig. 118.

valves are frequently " ground in " at their correct working temperature.

Provision must be made for expansion in steam pipe ranges. This is done by providing expansion bends, fig. 119 (*a*) or expansion joints, fig. 119 (*b*).

The flanges A and B of the expansion bend can approach each other and thus allow for the expansion of the pipes bolted to the flanges.

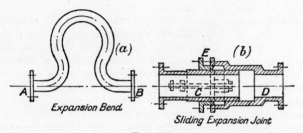

Fig. 119.

The expansion joint shown at b is of the sliding type. The end C slides inside the portion D. A gland is provided at E to enable the joint to be "packed," or made leak-proof.

In steam turbines one end of the casing containing the rotor is bolted down, whilst the other is free to expand along a slide provided for this purpose. The shaft expands also, and any differential expansion as between the shaft and the casing must be allowed for by the turbine builder. To reduce the forces on the turbine casing, flexible pipes are used for oil and steam connections.

Gaps must be left between the adjacent ends of railway metals to allow for expansion when the temperature rises from winter to summer values, and expansion joints have to be provided in long steel bridges.

A valuable application of expansion occurs in the shrink fits frequently made in the manufacture of engines and machines. The part to be shrunk is bored smaller than the part which has to receive it. The difference in dimension is then overcome by heating the portion which is shrunk, a suitable margin being allowed for the cooling which occurs whilst the parts are being fitted together. An example on this application occurs in the next article.

143. Calculation of Amount of Expansion. Coefficient of Expansion. If a rod of any metal be heated uniformly throughout its length it will increase in length by an amount which depends on (1) the kind of metal, e.g. brass, copper, aluminium, etc., (2) the temperature rise, (3) the original length when cold. It must be remembered that the temperature rise may be stated in degrees Fahrenheit or in degrees Centigrade, and also that a rise of 10° Fahrenheit will not produce the same total expansion as a rise of 10° Centigrade. In the latter case the rise in temperature is 1·8 times the rise in temperature in the former case as shown in art. 141. Fig. 120 shows the method of measuring the extension E. The original length is L units. The final length is $L + E$ units. Therefore extension = final length when hot − initial length when cold, or $E = (L + E) - L$.

Now let t_1 = highest temperature to which whole length L is raised

$\qquad t_2$ = temperature when the rod is of length L.

It is found that for any metal the ratio $\dfrac{E}{(t_1 - t_2)L}$ is practically constant and this ratio is called the *coefficient of linear expansion*. The coefficient is different for different metals as shown in table I. It will also be noticed that the number representing $(t_1 - t_2)$ will be larger on the Fahrenheit scale than the number on the Centigrade scale for the same real difference in temperature.

The coefficient of linear expansion is defined as the increase

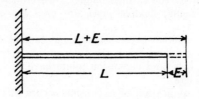

Fig. 120.

in length per unit of original length for each degree of temperature rise. It has two numerical values for each metal, one for Fahrenheit degrees and one for Centigrade degrees. The latter value is 1·8 times the former value. If the original length L is measured in inches the extension E must also be measured in inches. In other words, both E and L must be measured in the same kind of units of length, but any convenient unit of length, centimetres, inches, feet, etc., may be used.

TABLE I

COEFFICIENTS OF LINEAR EXPANSION

Substance.	Linear coefficient per degree C.	Linear coefficient per degree F.
Cast Iron	0·00001113	0·00000618
Wrought Iron and Steel .	0·00001181	0·00000656
Copper	0·00001719	0·00000955
Mercury	0·00005994	0·0000333
Water	0·00015858	0·0000881

EXAMPLE. A rod of copper is carefully measured at a temperature of 15° C. and its length is found to be 26·256 in. It is then placed in a steam jacket which covers its entire length, the ends only being accessible for the purposes of measurement. The steam temperature is 100° C. and the length of the rod after attaining this temperature is found to be 26·294 in. What is the mean coefficient of linear expansion of copper ?

$$\text{Extension} = 26 \cdot 294 - 26 \cdot 256 \text{ in.}$$
$$= 0 \cdot 038 \text{ in.}$$

Extension per inch of orginal length $= \dfrac{0 \cdot 038}{26 \cdot 256}$ in.

$$= 0 \cdot 001447 \text{ in.}$$

[This may also be written $\dfrac{\text{Extension}}{\text{Original length}} = \dfrac{0 \cdot 038}{26 \cdot 256}$

$$= 0 \cdot 001447.$$

It is now a ratio. It is possible and advisable to keep the units attached as in the first statement.]

$\therefore$ Coefficient of expansion $= \dfrac{0 \cdot 001447}{(100 - 15)}$

$$= \dfrac{0 \cdot 001447}{85} = 0 \cdot 00001704 \text{ per } °C.$$

EXAMPLE. A copper pipe is 8 ft. 3 in. long at a temperature of 60° F. What increase in length will take place if the temperature of the whole pipe is raised to 400° F. ? Take the coefficient of linear expansion as 0·0000109 for Fahrenheit degrees.

Length at 60° F. = 99 in.
Increase in length per degree F. = $99 \times 0 \cdot 0000109$ in.
$$= 0 \cdot 0010791 \text{ in.}$$
Temperature rise $= (400 - 60)°$ F. $= 340°$ F.
$\therefore$ Increase in length for this temperature rise $= 0 \cdot 0010791 \times 340$ in.
$$= 0 \cdot 367 \text{ in.}$$

EXAMPLE. A crank is bored to a diameter of 12 in. and it is required to shrink it on to a shaft which is 12·025 in. diameter. If a margin of 0·03 in. is to be allowed, determine the temperature to which the crank must be raised. The initial temperature is 15° C. Coefficient of linear expansion 0·0000118.

Total increase in diameter $= 0 \cdot 025 + 0 \cdot 03$ in. $= 0 \cdot 055$ in.
Increase in diameter per inch per degree C. $= 0 \cdot 0000118$ in.
$\therefore$ Increase in diameter per degree C. rise $= 12 \times 0 \cdot 0000118$ in.
$$= 0 \cdot 0001416 \text{ in.}$$

$\therefore$ Required number of degrees rise in temperature $= \dfrac{0 \cdot 055}{0 \cdot 0001416}$

$$= 388° \text{ C.}$$

Hence the temperature of the crank $= 388° + 15° = 403°$ C.
This temperature will be ample for the purpose of shrinking.

The above examples illustrate the application of the coefficient of linear expansion. The coefficients of superficial (or surface) expansion and of cubical (or volume) expansion are similarly applied.

144. Superficial Expansion. From observation of the effects of heat on the lengths of rods, it will be noticed that a surface or sheet of material will extend in two directions and thus the area increases when the temperature is raised. Fig. 121 shows this increase in area.

Let the original length of each side be L, and let E be the extension of each side when the temperature is raised an amount $(t_1 - t_2)$ degrees.

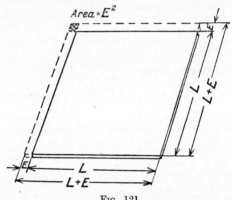

FIG. 121.

Then $E = LC(t_1 - t_2)$ where C is the coefficient of linear expansion.

Therefore the final length of each side $= L + E$.

$$\text{and the final area} = (L + E)^2$$
$$= L^2 + 2EL + E^2.$$

The quantity E^2 is very small and is shown at the top of the figure. Neglecting this small quantity we have

$$\text{final area} = L^2 + 2EL.$$
$$\therefore \text{ Increase in area} = L^2 + 2EL - L^2$$
$$= 2EL$$
$$= 2LC(t_1 - t_2)L$$
$$= 2L^2C(t_1 - t_2).$$

But L^2 is the original area and writing $L^2 = A$ we have,

$$\text{Increase in area} = A \times 2C(t_1 - t_2).$$

Thus final area = original area + original area $\times$ $2C(t_1 - t_2)$.

It will be seen that the expression for the increase in area contains the quantity 2C which may be written S, this being the coefficient of superficial expansion.

$\therefore$ The coefficient of superficial expansion is *twice* the coefficient of linear expansion.

With this modification the calculations on superficial expansion are set out as for calculations on linear expansion, using areas instead of lengths.

145. Cubical or Volume Expansion. It has already been pointed out that all expansion is cubical and that superficial and linear expansion are modifications arrived at by neglecting expansion in one or two directions respectively.

By an extension of the process used in the last article to obtain the coefficient of superficial expansion, it can be shown that the coefficient of cubical expansion is three times the coefficient of linear expansion for any particular material. The coefficient derived in this way may be used for solids. For liquids and gases the coefficient of volume expansion can be measured directly by means of suitable apparatus.

EXAMPLE. Find the increase in volume which occurs when a prism of zinc, originally 3 in. $\times$ 4 in. $\times$ 6 in., is raised in temperature from 67° F. to 400° F. Coefficient of linear expansion for zinc is 0·0000172 for degrees F.

Coefficient of cubical expansion $= 3 \times 0·0000172 = 0·0000516$
Original volume $= 3 \times 4 \times 6 = 72$ cu. in.

$\therefore$ Increase in volume

    $=$ original volume $\times$ coefficient $\times$ temperature rise.

Increase in volume $= 72 \times 0·0000516 \times (400 - 67)$
    $= 72 \times 0·0000516 \times 333 = 1·238$ cu. in.

$\therefore$ Final volume $= 72 + 1·238 = 73·238$ cu. in.

It is of interest to note that, since the weight of zinc contained in the block is not altered, the density of the zinc has been reduced. This always occurs when increase in volume takes place.

146. Transfer of Heat. Heat can be transferred from one substance to another, and from one part of a substance to another part of the substance. There are three ways by means of which heat transfer can be effected : (1) by Radiation, (2) by Conduction, and (3) by Convection.

Heat which is transferred by radiation is called "radiant heat" and is very effective. A person warming himself at a fire avails himself of the radiant heat. He does not touch the source of heat. The heat is transmitted by vibratory action in the medium between the fire and himself. A glowing or incandescent fire throws off enormous amounts of radiant heat, and it is necessary to use caution when approaching such a source of heat. Radiant heat is transferred from one body to another without contact between the bodies.

Heat which is transferred by conduction requires the bodies to be in contact. The more close and intimate the contact the more readily is the heat transferred. The automobile engineer makes use of this fact when he makes dry cylinder liners a push fit into the cylinder block. The steam engineer arranges that hot gases shall " scrub " or " scour " the boiler plates, and that steam shall scrub the condenser tubes. By this means the hot furnace gases are brought into intimate contact with the boiler plates and give up heat more readily to the metal. Similar action takes place when steam is condensing on a condenser tube.

Conduction is the means of transferring heat from one part of a solid to another part of the same solid. If any part of a body is at a higher temperature than another part, conduction will occur and tend to equalize the temperatures of all parts. Metals, particularly copper, are good conductors of heat. They have high thermal conductivity.

When heat is transferred by convection it is necessary that the substance shall be in motion. Thus convection sets up definite currents, known as " convection currents," and by movement and consequent " mixing " of the substance, the heat is transferred from point to point. Convection is encouraged in boiler design and a rapid steaming boiler must be arranged to give maximum movement to the water. Fig. 122 shows the principle of the well-known Babcock, Stirling, and Yarrow boilers. See also figs. 131 and 136. The vertical arrows indicate the path of the radiant heat. The water receives heat and, expanding, becomes less in density. The hotter water moves to the top end of the inclined tubes with the result that a circulation is set up. When steam bubbles are formed they rush to the top and a very vigorous circulation

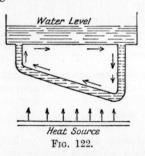

Water Level

Heat Source

Fig. 122.

is thus set up. A very simple apparatus can be constructed from glass tubes to show convection currents in liquids.

From what has been stated it will be noted that convection can only take place in liquids or gases. It is possible, however, for conduction and radiation as well as convection, to take place in these substances. Convection is the basis of the circulation in the thermo-syphon cooling systems in automobiles as well as domestic hot water and general heating systems.

The transfer of heat in a boiler represented by fig. 122 may be summarized as follows. The heat is carried from fire to tube by radiation, conduction and convection. The gases come in contact with the tube and since the gases are in motion convection in the gas will bring fresh hot gas to replace that cooled by contact. The transfer of the heat from the outside to the inside of the tube is effected by conduction. The transfer of the heat to the water is by conduction and convection.

EXAMPLES XIV

Section A

1. What are the direct effects of heat on substances ? Give illustrations from your own experience.

2. What do you understand by the terms " thermometry," " calorimetry " and " temperature scale " ?

3. Describe the construction and graduation of a mercury-in-glass thermometer. What is meant by " fixed points " and how are these points located ?

4. Give instances where the engineer must make provision for expansion on heating. What is meant by " differential expansion " ?

5. Describe an expansion joint suitable for use with long steam pipes.

6. Define the three coefficients of expansion.

7. Convert a temperature of 320° F. into Centigrade degrees.

8. Convert a temperature of 180° C. into Fahrenheit degrees.

9. The upper and lower fixed points on the Réaumur temperature scale are numbered 80 and 0 respectively. What is the value of 1 degree Réaumer in terms of Fahrenheit and Centigrade degrees ?

10. Convert a temperature of 60° Réaumer to Fahrenheit degrees, and also to Centigrade degrees.

11. What amount of expansion will take place in a steam pipe 120 ft. long, the temperature of the steam being 350° F. ? Take the atmospheric temperature to be 50° F. and the coefficient of linear expansion 0·00000656.

12. A block of steel measures 3 in. × 3 in. × 4½ in. at a temperature of 15° C. At this temperature it weighs 10·53 lb. It is raised to a temperature of 600° C. Find the density of the block at this temperature. Take the coefficient of linear expansion to be 0·0000125 per degree C.

13. A locomotive wheel centre is turned to a diameter of 5 ft. 6 in. The tyre which is to be shrunk on the centre is bored to a diameter of 5 ft. 5·8 in. at 15° C. The temperature of the tyre when placed on the centre is 435° C. What is the margin allowed for cooling of the tyre whilst it is being placed in position ? Coefficient of expansion 0·0000118.

14. Define coefficient of linear expansion of a solid.

A copper wire is 60 yd. long in winter. How much longer will it be in summer if the change in temperature is 45° C. ? Coefficient of linear expansion of copper = 0·000017. Give your answer in inches. U.L.C.I.

15. The coefficient of linear expansion of a metal is 0·000011 per degree C. By how much will a bar 5 ft. long extend when the temperature is raised from 15° C. to 125° C. ? N.C.T.E.C.

16. Explain clearly the meaning of the terms " temperature " and

" degree Centigrade."   Convert 10° F. and 192° F. to the Centigrade scale ; and — 20° C. and 60° C. to the Fahrenheit scale.   N.C.T.E.C.

17. (a) Explain why two strips of different metals riveted together tend to bend when heated.

(b) Describe some industrial application of the force exerted by a metal as it contracts on cooling.   N.C.T.E.C.

18. A copper pipe is 50 ft. long.   Find the increase in length in inches if the temperature of the pipe rises by 150° C.   Coefficient of expansion of copper 0·000017 per degree C.   N.C.T.E.C.

19. (a) Explain briefly the Centigrade and Fahrenheit scales and obtain an equation for converting readings from one to the other.

(b) What is the distinction between *temperature and quantity of heat* ?
          N.C.T.E.C.

CHAPTER XV

HEAT AND ITS MEASUREMENT

147. Quantity of Heat.   The amount of heat contained in a body will depend first upon the temperature, second, upon the amount of substance in the body, and third, upon the kind of substance of which the body is made.   Temperature alone does not indicate the amount of heat in a body.   For example, if a pint of water be taken from a vessel originally containing five pints, the temperature of the water in both containers will be the same, but the amount of heat in the smaller container is now only one quarter of the amount in the vessel.   Consideration of this illustration will lead to the conclusion that when the quantity of matter is altered the amount of heat is altered in the same proportion provided the temperature is not altered.

EXAMPLE.   A block of iron weighs 150 lb. and is known to contain 200 heat units at a certain temperature T°.   How much heat would be contained in a block of iron weighing 450 lb. and at the same temperature T° ?

Since there is three times as much iron at the stated temperature in the second case there will be three times as much heat, namely 600 heat units.   It should be noted that the same substance is at the same temperature and therefore the amount of heat is proportional to weight because weight indicates amount of substance.   If we take 150 lb. of iron and give it a temperature rise 2T, it will take twice the amount of heat required to raise the temperature T (see also art. 154).   Hence, if the 450 lb. of iron are raised in temperature 2T the number of heat units would be 600 × 2 = 1,200, or six times the 200 heat units.

It will thus be seen that the product of weight and temperature rise is in some way involved in the calculation of quantities of heat.

148. Specific Heat. It now remains for us to examine the effect of the kind of substance on the heat contained at any given temperature.

The effect of kind of substance on amount of heat is very easily demonstrated by experiment and will be understood with a little reasoning.

If several spheres of different metals, for example lead, tin, copper, aluminium, iron, etc., all weighing the same, are taken and placed in boiling water until all have attained the temperature of the water, then they will *not* have absorbed the same amount of heat. This is easily shown by removing the spheres, quickly drying them, and placing them on a thick cake of wax. It will be found that some spheres sink further into the wax than others. That is, they melt more wax than others. Therefore they must have carried more heat than those which do not sink so far into the wax. They reached the wax at the same temperature, they cooled to the same temperature and they all have the same weight. (The spheres are not the same size because the densities of the substances mentioned are not the same.) The different amounts of heat are due entirely to the physical property of each substance known as its heat appetite or heat capacity. Weight for weight, some substances are able to absorb more heat than others for the same temperature rise.

The property of a substance which denotes its heat capacity is called its *specific heat* and it is a most important property.

Water is capable of absorbing more heat per unit mass for the same temperature rise than any other substance. For this reason the specific heat of water is taken as unity.

Because water has great capacity for heat it is slow in reaching boiling-point, slow in cooling, and a good quencher for hardening steels, for subduing accidental fires, and for condensing steam. In the hardening of steel the glowing mass of steel is dropped into the water tank, and although the steel is at very high temperature a given quantity of water can quench a lot of steel without showing any considerable rise in temperature. The water has high specific heat, whilst the steel has low specific heat.

Specific heat can be defined as the *amount of heat required to raise unit mass of the substance through one degree temperature rise.* The heat value of the specific heat as defined here, will depend

N

on the temperature scale employed. The specific heat of a
substance is also frequently defined as the ratio (less than unity)
of the amount of heat required to raise a quantity of the substance
through a stated temperature, to the amount of heat required
to raise the same weight of water through the same temperature
rise.

Thus Specific Heat

$$= \frac{\text{Heat required to raise W lb. of substance T degrees}}{\text{Heat required to raise W lb. of water T degrees}}.$$

TABLE II

SPECIFIC HEATS OF SUBSTANCES

Substance.	Specific Heat.	Substance.	Specific Heat.
Water . .	1·000	Wrought Iron .	0·113
Cast Iron . .	0·130	Copper . .	0·100
Steel . .	0·118	Mercury . .	0·033

149. Heat Units. The units of heat in common use are the
British Thermal Unit, the Gram-Calorie, and the Therm.

*The British Thermal Unit is defined as $\frac{1}{180}$th part of the amount
of heat required to raise one pound of water from 32° F. to 212° F.
at atmospheric pressure.* It is sometimes defined as the amount
of heat required to raise one pound of water through one degree
F., and it is called " one B.Th.U."

*The Gram-Calorie is $\frac{1}{100}$th part of the amount of heat required
to raise one gram of water from 0° C. to 100° C.* It is often called
the *minor calorie*.

The Therm is 100,000 B.Th.U. and is largely used by gas
engineers when payment is to be made for energy supplied.

Another heat unit may be met with in technical literature.
This is the Centigrade Heat Unit which is defined below.

*The Centigrade Heat Unit (sometimes called the Pound-Calorie)
is the $\frac{1}{100}$th part of the heat required to raise one pound of water
from 0° C. to 100° C. at atmospheric pressure.* It is written
" one C.H.U."

The British Thermal Unit is used by British engineers and
the Gram-Calorie by scientists of most nations. It is interesting
to note how many gram calories are equal to one B.Th.U.

EXAMPLE. Given that there are 453·6 grams to one pound, find the
number of gram calories in one B.Th.U.

Heat required to raise 1 gram of water through 1° F. = $\frac{5}{9}$ gram-calorie.
Heat required to raise 1 lb. of water through 1° F.

$$= 453 \cdot 6 \times \tfrac{5}{9} \text{ gram-calories.}$$
$$= 252.$$

Thus 252 gram-calories = 1 B.Th.U.

EXAMPLE. The amount of heat available in 1 cu. ft. of gas is found by experiment to be 436 B.Th.U. How many therms are stored in a gasholder 40 ft. mean diameter and 20 ft. high ?

$$\begin{aligned} \text{Area of section of gasholder} &= 0 \cdot 7854 \, D^2 \\ &= 0 \cdot 7854 \times 40 \times 40 \text{ sq. ft.} \\ &= 1{,}256 \cdot 64 \text{ sq. ft.} \\ \text{Volume of gasholder} &= 1{,}256 \cdot 64 \times 20 \text{ cu. ft.} \\ &= 25{,}132 \cdot 8 \text{ cu. ft.} \\ \text{Total heat contained} &= 25{,}132 \cdot 8 \times 436 \text{ B.Th.U.} \\ &= 10{,}957{,}900 \cdot 8 \text{ B.Th.U.} \end{aligned}$$

$$\therefore \text{ Number of therms stored} = \frac{10{,}957{,}900 \cdot 8}{100{,}000}$$
$$= 109 \cdot 58 \text{ therms.}$$

150. Measurement of Heat. We have noticed that the amount of heat given out by or received by a quantity of matter depends on :

(1) the weight of matter,
(2) the fall or rise in temperature,
(3) the temperature scale used in (2),
(4) the specific heat of the substance.

A simple equation based on observation of experimental data is used in straightforward cases of heat measurement. The equation is :

Heat received = weight of body × specific heat of substance
                                    × rise in temperature.

If heat is removed the equation becomes :

Heat removed = weight of body × specific heat of substance
                                    × fall in temperature.

Let W = weight of body in lb.
  w =   „   „   „   „ grams.
  C = specific heat of substance.
  t_1 = higher temperature.
  t_2 = lower temperature.
  H = Heat given or received.

Then H = W × C × $(t_1 - t_2)$.

The equation will give B.Th.U.s when t_1 and t_2 are Fahrenheit temperatures and C.H.U.s when t_1 and t_2 are Centigrade temperatures.

It will be remembered that the Centigrade scale only is employed when gram-calories are required.

Thus, $H = w \times C \times (t_1 - t_2)$ gram-calories
$= 453 \cdot 6 WC(t_1 - t_2)$ gram-calories.

EXAMPLE. The specific heat of iron is $0 \cdot 118$; how much heat will be required to raise the temperature of half a ton of iron from 65° F. to 750° F.

$$\begin{aligned}
\text{Heat required} &= W \times C \times (t_1 - t_2) \\
&= 0 \cdot 5 \times 2{,}240 \times 0 \cdot 118 \times (750 - 65) \text{ B.Th.U.} \\
&= 1{,}120 \times 0 \cdot 118 \times 685 \text{ B.Th.U.} \\
&= 90{,}529 \cdot 6 \text{ B.Th.U.}
\end{aligned}$$

EXAMPLE. Find the amount of heat required to raise the temperature of half a ton of water from 65° F. to 750° F.

$$\begin{aligned}
\text{Heat required} &= 1{,}120 \times 1 \times (750 - 65) \\
&= 1{,}120 \times 685 \text{ B.Th.U.} \\
&= 767{,}200 \text{ B.Th.U.}
\end{aligned}$$

EXAMPLE. A copper vessel contains $8 \cdot 75$ lb. of water and the vessel itself weighs $2 \cdot 2$ lb. The temperature of water and vessel is raised from 60° F. to 142° F. Find the amount of heat received by the " system."
From the table II we note that the specific heat of copper is $0 \cdot 1$.

$\therefore$ Heat taken in by the copper $= 2 \cdot 2 \times 0 \cdot 1 \times (142 - 60) = 18 \cdot 04$ B.Th.U.

Heat taken in by the water $= 8 \cdot 75 \times 1 \times (142 - 60) = 717 \cdot 5$ B.Th.U.

$\therefore$ Total heat taken in by system $18 \cdot 04 + 717 \cdot 5 = 735 \cdot 54$ B.Th.U.

It will be noted that we are frequently concerned with changes of heat quantity and that the calculation of a total heat would require the adoption of a zero temperature at which we could say that the heat was zero. See also art. 154.

151. Heat Content of Mixtures. By mixtures, we mean mixtures of different liquids, mixtures of different gases, or mixtures of solids and liquids. Specific heat values are often determined experimentally by the method of mixtures. If two liquids or a solid and a liquid are placed together in a vessel and allowed to come to the same temperature, the amount of heat in the " mixture " will be the same as the sum of the heats in the separate portions before mixing.

Suppose that a quantity of a liquid contains 15 B.Th.U. and that a quantity of another liquid contains 25 B.Th.U. When one liquid is poured into the other, the heat contained by the mixture will be $15 + 25 = 40$ B.Th.U. This is true even if the temperatures are different before and after mixing. Calculations based on this statement are made on the assumption that no heat is lost to outside bodies during the mixing. In all experiments involving mixtures and heat contents great care is necessary to reduce the heat losses to outside bodies. Heat losses always occur if the temperature of the substance experimented upon is greater than that of the room in which the experiment is conducted. In important investigations the heat losses likely to occur are themselves made the subject of separate experiments.

EXAMPLE. A quantity of water weighs $2\frac{1}{2}$ lb. and is at a temperature of 62° F. It is poured into a vessel containing $3\frac{1}{2}$ lb. of water at 92° F. and quickly mixed. Assuming that the water has no heat at a temperature of 32° F., find the heat content of the mixture and its final temperature immediately after mixing.

Taking the specific heat of water to be unity, we have

Total heat of $2\frac{1}{2}$ lb. of water at 62° F. $= 2\frac{1}{2} \times 1 \times (62 - 32)$
$$= 75 \text{ B.Th.U.}$$
Total heat of $3\frac{1}{2}$ lb. of water at 92° F. $= 3\frac{1}{2} \times 1 \times (92 - 32)$
$$= 210 \text{ B.Th.U.}$$

∴ Total heat of mixture $= (75 + 210)$ in 6 lb. weight
$$= 285 \text{ B.Th.U.}$$

To find the final temperature we write the heat equation again and remember that the heat is zero at a temperature of 32° F.

Thus   Heat content = mass × specific heat × (temperature rise),

i.e. $285 = 6 \times 1 \times (t - 32)$,

where t is the temperature which we require to find.

From this, t is found to be 79·5° F. This is the temperature which would be produced by supplying 285 B.Th.U. to 6 lb. of water initially at 32° F.

EXAMPLE. In an experimental determination of the specific heat of copper the following readings were taken : Weight of water in calorimeter, 250 grams ; initial temperature of water and calorimeter, 16° C. ; final temperature, 20° C. ; weight of copper calorimeter, 64 grams ; weight of copper heated in steam bath to 100° C. = 132·6 grams. Calculate the specific heat of the copper.

[*Note.* The copper is usually cut into small pieces and heated in a tube suspended in steam at atmospheric pressure. The tube is arranged with a chute in order to deposit the hot copper bits into the vessel without loss of heat. This vessel is called the calorimeter.]

Let C = required specific heat of copper.
Then
Heat lost by 132·6 grams of copper = Heat gained by water and calorimeter, i.e.

$$132\cdot6 \times C \times (100 - 20) = 250 \times 1 \times (20 - 16) + 64 \times C \times (20 - 16)$$
$$10,608C = 1,000 + 256C$$
∴ $$10,608C - 256C = 1,000$$
$$10,352C = 1,000$$

$$\therefore \ C = \frac{1,000}{10,352} = 0\cdot0965.$$

EXAMPLE. A mixture of gases is composed of 0·2 lb. of oxygen, 1·6 lb. of carbon dioxide, 0·35 lb. of steam, and 2·8 lb. of nitrogen. Given that the respective specific heats are 0·211, 0·198, 0·56, and 0·241, and that the heat content is zero at 32° F., find the heat content of this mixture at

232° F., and also find the average specific heat of the mixture.   Heat content from—

32° F.=0·2 ×0·211×(232−32)= 8·44 B.Th.U. for the oxygen.
  „   =1·6 ×0·198×(232−32)= 63·36   „   „   „ carbon dioxide.
  „   =0·35×0·56 ×(232−32)= 39·2   „   „   „ steam.
  „   =2·8 ×0·241×(232−32)=134·96   „   „   „ nitrogen

∴ Total heat content of 4·95 lb. of gas at 232° F. = 245·96 for mixture.

Let C = mean specific heat of the mixture.

Then $245·96 = 4·95 \times C \times (232 - 32)$

$$\therefore C = \frac{245·96}{4·95 \times 200} = 0.248.$$

The total heat of the mixture is the sum of the heats of the several constituents present.   Each constituent gas has its own specific heat and weight.

152. Water Equivalent of a Body.   This is the weight of water which would take up as much heat as the body when the temperature rise of water and body is the same amount.   It is the product of specific heat and weight of body.

EXAMPLE.   Find the water equivalent of 3·6 lb. of copper.
Now heat taken up by the copper = Heat taken up by the water.

∴ $3·6 \times 0·0965 \times (t_1 - t_2)$ = Weight of water $\times 1 \times (t_1 - t_2)$

∴ $3·6 \times 0·0965$ = Water equivalent of 3·6 lb. of copper

i.e. 0·3474 lb. of water are equivalent to 3·6 lb. of copper in ability to absorb heat.

The water equivalent of a body is sometimes called its heat capacity.

EXAMPLE.   A heat storage tank (sometimes called a thermal flywheel) consists of 250 tons of cast iron (specific heat 0·126) and 100 tons of water. What is the water equivalent of the system ?

Water equivalent of cast iron = 250 × 0·126
                             = 31·5 tons of water
        Water equivalent of water = 100 tons of water

∴ Total water equivalent of the system = 131·5 tons of water.

153. Sensible and Latent Heats.   We have pointed out that several things may happen when heat is supplied to a substance.   When the temperature of a body rises on being supplied with heat a thermometer in contact with the body would convey, by the sense of sight, the information that the heat was being supplied.   When heat makes its effect evident *by rise of temperature* it is said to be sensible heat.   The word sensible means " evident to the senses."   Briefly, *sensible heat may be defined as heat which produces rise in temperature* when supplied to a body and which requires a fall in temperature when removed.   If, for example, a thermometer placed in a vessel of hot water shows a falling temperature we know that the water is losing sensible heat to the surrounding atmosphere.

On the other hand, if the supply of heat does not cause rise of temperature, but causes the substance to change its state (i.e. to go from solid to liquid, or to go from liquid to gas), the heat supplied is said to be *latent*. The word latent means " hidden " or " not shown." The latent heat is not shown by means of a thermometer. That it has been supplied, or removed as the case may be, is quite evident from the change of state which takes place. The change of state most often takes place with the temperature of the substance remaining constant. In this case ordinary methods of heat calculation cannot be used and we are compelled to turn to the results of experiments in order to obtain knowledge of the amounts of heat involved in such changes. For example, if ice melts at atmospheric pressure, each pound will have been supplied with 144 B.Th.U. and if water freezes at atmospheric pressure each lb. of water will have been deprived of 144 B.Th.U. *Meanwhile the temperature of the ice and water will have been constant at 32° F.*

Latent heat may be defined as heat which changes the state of a substance. *The latent heat of a substance is the latent heat necessary to change the state of unit mass of the substance.* The latent heat of a substance has a different value for each substance and its amount will depend on the kind of unit employed when stating the mass.

EXAMPLE. The latent heat of ice is 80 C.H.U. per lb. What is the latent heat of ice in B.Th.U. per kilogramme ? [1 kilogramme = 1,000 grams.]

$$1 \text{ Kg.} = \frac{1,000}{453 \cdot 6} \text{ lb.} = 2 \cdot 22 \text{ lb.}$$

∴ Latent heat per Kg. = $2 \cdot 22 \times 80$ C.H.U. = $177 \cdot 6$ C.H.U.
= $177 \cdot 6 \times \frac{9}{5}$ B.Th.U. = 355 B.Th.U. per Kg.

The latent heat which is used up in melting a solid is known as the latent heat of fusion of that solid, whilst the latent heat which is employed in evaporating a liquid to the vapour state, is called the latent heat of evaporation of the vapour.

EXAMPLE. The latent heat of fusion of a certain solid is 76 B.Th.U. Latent heat is actually supplied to a quantity of the solid to the extent of 890 B.Th.U. What is the least amount of the solid present and how much is melted ?

Since the heat supplied is latent heat it must have been employed in changing the state.

∴ Least amount of solid present = $\frac{890}{76}$ lb. = $11 \cdot 7$ lb.

This is also the amount of solid which has been melted. If there had been less than 11·7 lb. of substance present it would have been impossible to supply 890 B.Th.U. of latent heat, although 890 B.Th.U. of heat could have been supplied. Some portion of this heat would have had to be sensible heat which would have produced a rise in temperature.

EXAMPLE. With the same substance as in the last example 890 B.Th.U. are supplied to 9·2 lb. of substance. If the resulting liquid has a specific heat of 0·95, find the rise in temperature above the melting-point.

$$\text{Amount of heat which is latent} = 9\cdot2 \times 76 \text{ B.Th.U.}$$
$$= 699\cdot2 \text{ B.Th.U.}$$

∴ Heat available from supply, for raising temperature $= 890 - 699\cdot2$
$$= 190\cdot8 \text{ B.Th.U.}$$

This heat is sensible heat and produces rise in temperature after melting is complete.

$$\text{Heat producing rise in temperature} = W \times C \times (t_1 - t_2)$$
$$\therefore \quad 190\cdot8 = 9\cdot2 \times 0\cdot95 \times (t_1 - t_2)$$
$$\therefore \quad \text{Temperature rise} = \frac{190\cdot8}{9\cdot2 \times 0\cdot95} = 21\cdot83° \text{ F.}$$

154. Base or Datum Temperature. In certain examples given above reference has been made to a base or zero temperature.

The total heat contained in a body at a temperature T can only be stated by reference to a low temperature at which the heat in the body is nil. The value of the low temperature is chosen to suit the convenience of calculators. In the case of water and steam the base temperature is 32° F. (i.e. 0° C.) and at this temperature the heat of the water is considered to be nil. In the case of gases in gas-engine cylinders the zero temperature is frequently taken as 100° C. Sometimes it is taken as 27° C. The actual value taken for the base temperature is not very important because we are more frequently concerned with *changes in amount of heat* rather than with *total amount of heat*. It should be remembered, however, that the difference in the amounts of total heat before and after any supply is the amount of heat supplied.

EXAMPLE. How much heat is contained in $1\frac{1}{2}$ lb. of gas at a temperature of 300° C. (a) if the base temperature is 100° C., (b) if the base temperature is 27° C. ? Take the mean specific heat of the gas to be 0·17.

$$\text{Heat content at } 300° \text{ C.} = 1\cdot5 \times 0\cdot17 \times (300 - 100)$$
$$= 51 \text{ C.H.U. from } 100° \text{ C.}$$
$$\text{Heat content at } 300° \text{ C.} = 1\cdot5 \times 0\cdot17 \times (300 - 27)$$
$$= 69\cdot615 \text{ C.H.U. from } 27° \text{ C.}$$

The two quantities of heat are different because we have used two different base temperatures. This example shows clearly the need for stating the base temperature from which a quantity of heat is reckoned. Otherwise a statement of heat content at a temperature T is meaningless.

155. Latent Heats of Substances. The latent heats of substances differ according to circumstances. For example, the latent heat of fusion of a substance differs from its latent heat of evaporation. Again, both these latent heats would alter if the pressure, at which the changes take place, were altered. The latent heats of evaporation of different vapours are different at the same pressure.

Therefore it is necessary to state (a) the kind of substance, (b) the pressure (or temperature), (c) the kind of change of state, (d) the kind of heat unit, and (e) the kind of mass unit before a latent heat quantity can be properly specified. For example, a complete statement would be as follows, " The latent heat of evaporation of steam at a pressure of 90 lb. per sq. in. absolute is 895·5 B.Th.U. per pound." At 100 lb. per sq. in. absolute the latent heat of steam is 889·7 B.Th.U. per lb.

The engineer needs latent heats of substances other than steam and the following example is used to show the general nature of latent heat.

EXAMPLE. The latent heat of ammonia vapour (not the solution of ammonia in water) at 106 lb. per sq. in. absolute is 548 B.Th.U. How much water will be required to condense 3·5 lb. of ammonia vapour at this pressure if the water is initially at 59° F. and finally at 80·6° F. ?

Total amount of heat to be removed $= 3·5 \times 548$ B.Th.U.
$$= 1,918 \text{ B.Th.U.}$$

Amount of heat taken up by 1 lb. of condensing water $= 1 \times 1 \times (80·6 - 59)$
$$= 21·6 \text{ B.Th.U.}$$

$$\therefore \text{ Weight of water required} = \frac{1,918}{21·6}$$
$$= 88·78 \text{ lb.}$$

or (since 10 lb. of water = 1 gallon) $= 8·878$ gall.

Similar examples will occur in the steam section of the book.

156. Evaporation and Condensation. If Latent heat of evaporation is being supplied the substance must be boiling, i.e. evaporating, whilst if the latent heat of evaporation (or condensation) is being removed, the substance must be condensing. Condensation is the exact opposite of evaporation. Both processes take place at constant temperature if the pressure remains the same.

EXAMPLES XV

SECTION A

1. What information would you need in order to calculate the amount of heat possessed by a quantity of matter ?

2. Define the term " specific heat." Why is the specific heat of water taken as unity in approximate calculations ?

3. The specific heat of iron is 0·113 and 12 lb. of iron at a temperature of 1,832° F. are plunged into a " bosh " of water containing 30 gall. at a temperature of 64° F. Calculate the final temperature of the water after thorough " mixing " and assuming no loss of heat.

4. A quantity of lead weighing 2·75 lb. is heated from a temperature of 15° C. to a temperature of 156° C. How much heat has been supplied ? Express the answer in minor calories. Specific heat of lead = 0·031.

5. Steam flows through a tube which is in contact with a source of heat and in its passage it is raised in temperature 125° F. If 30 lb. of steam pass through the tube and the mean specific heat of steam is 0·5, how much heat passes through the tube wall ?

6. What is meant by the term " water equivalent " of a body ? Calculate the water equivalent of a steel boiler which weighs $3\frac{1}{2}$ tons. If the boiler contains $4\frac{1}{2}$ tons of water, what is the water equivalent of the system ?

7. What happens when (a) sensible heat, (b) latent heat, is supplied to a body ? Distinguish between latent heat of fusion and latent heat of evaporation.

8. The latent heat of a pound of steam entering a condenser is 420 C.H.U. If 300 lb. of steam enter the condenser and pass out as water at the same temperature as the entering steam, how much latent heat has been removed from the steam ? If this heat is removed by water initially at 18° C. and finally at 30° C., how much water will be needed to condense this quantity of steam ?

9. What is the specific heat of a substance ?

If 100 grams of water at 212° F. are poured into 120 grams of turpentine at 48·2° F. and the resulting temperature found to be 158° F., what is the specific heat of the turpentine ? What reason have you for supposing that the result you give may not be correct ? U.L.C.I.

10. The heat produced by burning 1·26 grams of fuel oil is passed into 3,000 grams of water and raises the temperature of the latter 4·6° C. Find how much heat in British Thermal Units would be given out in burning 1 lb. of the oil. 1 lb. = 453·6 grams. N.C.T.E.C.

11. A piece of metal weighing 2 lb. is heated to 216° F. and dropped into 6 lb. of water at 59° F. Neglecting losses, determine the final temperature of the water. Specific heat of metal = 0·11. N.C.T.E.C.

12. A piece of copper of weight 1·25 lb. is suspended in a current of hot gas and then immersed in 5 lb. of water at temperature 60° F. If the water is raised in temperature to 65° F., calculate the temperature of the copper. Assume the water to receive all the heat lost by the copper. Specific heat of copper = 0·094. N.C.T.E.C.

13. Four pounds of wrought iron at some unknown temperature, which we may call $t°$ F., were dropped into 10 lb. of water at 62° F., and the water was given time to absorb heat from the iron so that both were eventually at the same temperature, which, when measured, was found to be 75° F. Find the original temperature t of the iron. The specific heat of iron may be taken as 0·114. Neglect losses due to radiation. N.C.T.E.C.

14. A piece of metal, weight 10 lb., is heated to temperature 175° F. and then immersed in 30 lb. of water at temperature 45° F. Determine the specific heat of the metal if the temperature of the water rises to 50° F. N.C.T.E.C.

15. How much heat is required to raise the temperature of 0·2 lb. of copper through 1,890° F. ?   Assume the specific heat of copper to be 0·1. If this heated copper is plunged into 2·2 lb. of water at 59° F., what will be the final temperature of the water, assuming no losses by radiation ?
U.E.I.

16. In a certain cooling apparatus cold water enters the cooling tank at the bottom and leaves by an outlet near the top of the tank.   The hot liquid passes through a coil, entering near the top and leaving at the bottom of the tank ; 3,000 lb. of liquid, of specific heat 0·42, enter the cooler per hour, the liquid entering at a temperature of 329° F. and leaving at 59° F. How much heat is liberated per hour ?   The cooling water enters at 53° F. and leaves at 143° F.   Calculate the quantity of water, in gallons per hour, passing through the cooling apparatus.   1 gallon of water weighs 10 lb.
U.E.I.

17. Define and show the difference between the terms " capacity for heat " and " specific heat."   Describe with sketches a method of measuring the specific heat of a small copper block.   Give approximate values to the quantities used and the changes that occur.   U.E.I.

18. The metal of a boiler weighs 12 tons and it contains 9 tons of water. How much heat is required to raise the temperature of the boiler and the water from 68° F. to 338° F. ?   Assume that the specific heat of the metal is 0·11 and that of the water is unity.   C.G.L.I.

19. The following materials are mixed together : 10 lb. water at 52° F., 8 lb. copper at 250° F., 5 lb. aluminium at 360° F.   The specific heat of copper is 0·095 and of aluminium 0·214.   Reckoning from 32° F., find the total heat contained in the materials and their common temperature after mixing.   C.G.L.I.

CHAPTER XVI

PROPERTIES OF STEAM

157. Steam.   Steam is the gaseous fluid which is formed when a liquid is evaporated.   The word is usually associated with the vapour formed from water and unless otherwise indicated, this meaning will be implied in this book.   The engineer is, however, frequently dealing with gaseous substances other than water steam, as, for example, steam from ammonia liquid or mercury liquid, sulphur dioxide liquid, etc.   Gaseous substances which have a temperature not much higher than that at which their evaporation took place are called *vapours*.   This distinguishes them from gases.   Gases are really vapours at a much higher temperature than that at which they were evaporated. All gaseous substances are capable of increasing their volume and of receiving and conveying heat.

158. Properties of Steam.   This term includes the quantities which the steam user and the engine builder employ in their calculations of engine sizes and of cost of running the steam plant. A simple list of the properties of steam includes, (a) Pressure, (b) Temperature, (c) Volume of 1 lb. of steam, (d) Liquid heat, (e) Latent heat, (f) Total heat. A more complete list would include internal energy, external energy and entropy. The properties of steam are now widely known and accepted, and are embodied in a table known as the steam table.

The steam table is reproduced on page 320 and the data in the following exercises have been taken from it. It has been compiled as a result of long and costly experiments and it is indispensable to the modern power engineer. The student should remember that the table is based on actual measurements. Therefore it is eminently a practical table and it is widely used.

159. Relationship between the Boiling Temperature and the Pressure of Steam in contact with its Liquid. When water boils in the atmosphere the pressure on the surface of the boiling water is normally 14·7 lb. per sq. in. above absolute zero pressure. Under these conditions the temperature of the water and also the temperature of the steam which is formed, is 212° F. This temperature has already been referred to as the boiling point. To be more exact it should be stated as the atmospheric boiling point.

If the pressure on the surface of the boiling water is altered the boiling temperature will alter. If the pressure is increased to a higher value than the atmospheric pressure the temperature at which the water boils is higher than 212° F. This effect is known as the "elevation of the boiling point." On the other hand, if the pressure on the surface of the water is less than atmospheric pressure the temperature at which boiling takes place will be less than 212° F. Boiling at temperatures less than 212° F. occurs in condensing systems, vacuum systems and in de-aerators. The effect of increase of pressure on boiling point is usually shown by means of the arrangement known as the Marcet boiler (fig. 123). It consists of a closed vessel fitted with a pressure gauge G, a thermometer T, a safety valve SV, and a filling plug. A quantity of water is put into the vessel and heat is applied. As the pressure rises the temperature rises. The pressure rises because more steam passes into the steam space SP on application of heat. Therefore the thermometer temperature indicates the boiling point.

Before starting the observations it is necessary to allow steam to displace the air originally in the vessel, since if the air is

PROPERTIES OF STEAM189

allowed to remain it will continue to exert its own pressure.
This pressure would increase with increased temperatures. The
depression or lowering of the boiling point can be shown by
means of the same apparatus but it will be necessary to connect
a vacuum pump to the steam space in order to remove the air
and vapour. The boiling of water at lower temperatures can
be shown by taking a glass flask fitted with a cork and a tube
which can be closed as desired (fig. 124). A quantity of water
is placed in the flask and heated until steam issues freely from

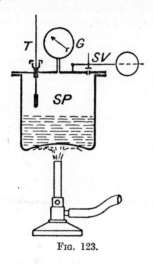

the tube. The flask is then
removed from the source of
heat and the tube closed
immediately. The water
ceases to boil. If the flask
is cooled by placing it in
cold water or under the tap,
the water boils vigorously
even though it has been
removed from the source of
heat for some considerable
time. This boiling will not

Fig. 123.

Fig. 124.

take place if air leaks in after removal of the heat source.
The action is as follows: when the flask is removed from the
heat source the water carries away a quantity of sensible heat
and the flask is full of steam at atmospheric pressure. Closure
of the tube prevents air from passing into the flask and therefore
there can be nothing but steam on the surface of the water.
Heat is removed by the application of cold water and the steam
is condensed. The condensation of the steam would leave
nothing in the space above the water and this space would
become very nearly a perfect vacuum if no boiling occurred.
Nature abhors a vacuum and all matter tends to destroy a
vacuum. Thus the reduction of pressure on the surface of the
water in the flask lowers the boiling point and enables the water

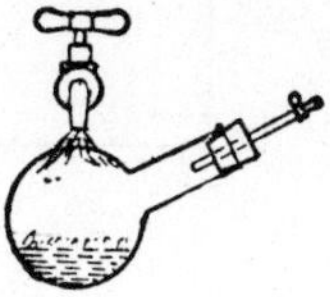

to boil and produce steam to fill the space. During the process of this low-pressure boiling a portion of the sensible heat of the water becomes latent and the water cools very rapidly. The thermal storage tanks (see example, art. 152) used in connection with low-pressure steam turbines in collieries and steelworks depend upon this action.

The relationship between the temperature and the pressure of steam in contact with its liquid does not follow a simple law. It is therefore advisable to consult steam tables or the graph plotted from the data if the pressure or temperature is required. Such a graph is shown in fig. 125 with the co-ordinates of a given

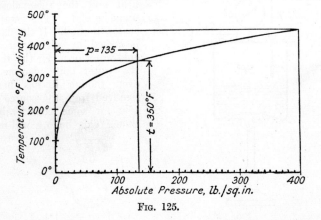

Fig. 125.

state drawn upon it. There is only one boiling-point temperature at a given pressure and this temperature is called the *saturation* temperature at that pressure. It is also called the *evaporation* temperature as well as the boiling point. It must be remembered that the steam and the water are both supposed to be at the same temperature. The graph shows that above the region of 250° F. the temperature does not increase as rapidly as the pressure, particularly in the higher pressure region. The slope of the graph at any point is a factor used later in the calculation of steam volumes.

EXAMPLE. What is the saturation temperature of steam at a pressure of 140 lb. per sq. in. abs. ?

By consulting steam tables the temperature is found to be 353·0° F. ordinary scale.

EXAMPLE. At what pressure will water boil when its temperature is 79·6° F.

From the table the pressure is found to be 0·5 lb. per sq. in. abs., or 14·2 lb. per sq. in. less than the pressure of the atmosphere.

EXAMPLE. What elevation of boiling-point will occur when the pressure on the surface of water is raised from 20 lb. per sq. in. abs. to 200 lb. per sq. in. abs. ?

By consulting the table—

Saturation temperature at 200 lb. per sq. in. = 381·8° F.
,,   ,,   ,,   20 ,,   ,,   ,,   = 228·0° F.
∴ Temperature elevation = 381·8 — 228·0 = 153·8° F.

EXAMPLE. The temperature in a condenser containing steam only in 101·7° F. What is the pressure in the condenser ?

From the tables the pressure is found to be 1 lb. per sq. in. abs.

160. Sensible Heat of Steam. This quantity is the amount of heat contained in one pound of the liquid at the saturation temperature. The steam tables give values of the sensible heat at various temperatures (and pressures) reckoned from 32° F. ordinary temperature. The sensible heat is often called the *liquid* heat and also frequently called the " total heat of water." The amount of the liquid heat depends on the temperature of the liquid. Therefore the *maximum* liquid heat at any given pressure will be fixed by the saturation temperature at that pressure. In elementary calculations it is usual to assume that the liquid heat is equal in numerical value to the saturation temperature if steam tables are not available. This assumes that the specific heat of the liquid is constant through a wide range of temperature and that its value is equal to unity. The quantity should be taken direct from the steam table when available. The liquid heat is denoted by the letter h and its value is zero at 32° F.

EXAMPLE. What is the sensible heat of 1 lb. of water at 250° F., assuming the specific heat of water to be constant and equal to unity ?

h = mass × specific heat × temperature rise
= 1 × 1 × (250 — 32) = 218

because we are reckoning heat amounts from 32° F.

Note that the ordinary heat equation of art. 150 is used and also that the true value of the liquid heat at 250° F. is 218·7 B.Th.U. and can be obtained by plotting the temperatures and liquid heats in the region of 250° F. to scale, the values being taken from the steam table.

EXAMPLE. What is the true value of the sensible heat of steam at a temperature of 347·3° F. ?

From the steam tables h is found to be 318·8 B.Th.U. at 347·3° F.

EXAMPLE. Feed water enters a boiler at a temperature of 126·1° F.
The working pressure in the boiler is 140 lb. per sq. in. abs. Find the
increase in liquid heat which must occur before evaporation can begin.
From the steam table—

Liquid heat at 140 lb. per sq. in. abs. and 353·0° F. =   324·9 B.Th.U.
      ,,   ,,   126·1° F. =   94·0 B.Th.U.
      ∴ Increase in liquid heat, by difference =   230·9 B.Th.U.

Note that the temperature 126·1° F. of the feed water does
not imply that the pressure of the feed water is 2 lb. per sq. in. abs.
In other words, the pressure of the water may be higher than
the saturation value corresponding to the temperature. In this
case the water cannot boil. In the above example the pressure
of the feed water is suddenly increased by the feed pump to the
value 140 lb. per sq. in., but the temperature of the water does
not rise immediately from 126·1° F. to 353·0° F. A certain
time must elapse to enable the heat to enter the water. This
calculation is important when boiler and engine trials are dealt
with.

EXAMPLE. The steam pressure in a condenser is 0·8 lb. per sq. in.
absolute, and the condensed steam (condensate) leaves the condenser at
a temperature of 79·6° F. What is the temperature in the condenser and
how much liquid heat is withdrawn from the condensate per lb. ?
From the steam table the temperature corresponding to 0·8 lb. per sq. in.
is 94·4° F. and this is the temperature in the condenser.
Liquid heat per lb. of water at temperature of condensation
                                       = 62·4 B.Th.U.
Liquid heat per lb. of water at exit temperature 79·6° F.
                                       = 47·6 B.Th.U.
      ∴ Liquid heat removed per lb. of condensate = 14·8 B.Th.U.
The change in liquid heat depends on change in temperature.

The above examples show how the liquid heat is found and
also how the quantity is used in two important types of calculation, such as frequently occur later in the work of an engineering
course.

161. Latent Heat of Steam. This is the amount of heat
required to evaporate one pound of water. Its numerical value
decreases as the temperature of evaporation is raised and therefore the latent heat of steam decreases as the pressure at which
the steam is produced increases. If steam is being produced
then *latent* heat is being supplied. Any heat supplied *before* or
after the *actual production of the steam* is not latent heat. The
heat supplied before evaporation goes to increase the liquid heat,
and any heat supplied after completion of evaporation raises
the temperature of the steam and is therefore " sensible." This

heat goes to produce superheat and the steam temperature increases whilst the pressure of the steam remains the same. If steam is condensing then latent heat is being removed. The processes involving latent heat supply or removal are carried out at constant temperature and pressure in steam power plants. The latent heat of steam is denoted by L.

EXAMPLE. The amount of latent heat supplied to a vessel containing water at atmospheric pressure is 370·1 B.Th.U. How much water is evaporated ?

From steam table the boiling temperature is 212° F., and the latent heat at this temperature is 970·7 B.Th.U. per lb.

$\therefore$ since 1 lb. requires 970·74 B.Th.U. $\dfrac{370\cdot1}{970\cdot7}$ lb. will require 370·1 B.Th.U.

$\therefore$ the weight of water evaporated $= 0\cdot381$ lb.

EXAMPLE. Steam enters a condenser at the rate of 800 lb. per hr. and at a pressure of 6 lb. per sq. in. abs. Assuming each pound of steam to possess only $\frac{9}{10}$ of its full quota of latent heat, find the amount of latent heat removed per hour in the condenser.

From tables latent heat of 1 lb. of steam at 6 lb. per sq. in. $= 996\cdot6$ B.Th.U. This is the full quota of latent heat per pound at this pressure.

Therefore latent heat actually contained per pound of steam

$$= \tfrac{9}{10} \times 996\cdot6 \text{ B.Th.U.} = 896\cdot9 \text{ B.Th.U.}$$
$$\therefore \text{ Latent heat removed per hour} = 800 \times 896\cdot9$$
$$= 717{,}520 \text{ B.Th.U.}$$

162. Total Heat of Steam. This is the total heat content of one pound of steam reckoned from 32° F. It is the sum of the liquid heat at saturation temperature and the latent heat at that temperature. The total heat of steam is frequently called the "Total heat of Evaporation" of the steam. The total heat is denoted by H.

Thus $H = h + L$.

This equation can be transposed so as to give L if h, and H, are given, and to give h if L, and H, are given. The total heat increases as the pressure increases.

EXAMPLE. The total heat of steam at 110 lb. per sq. in. abs. pressure is 1189·9 B.Th.U. The liquid heat at saturation temperature is 305·7 B.Th.U. What is the latent heat at this pressure ?

$$L = H - h$$
$$= 1189\cdot9 - 305\cdot7 = 884\cdot2 \text{ B.Th.U.}$$

EXAMPLE. The total heat of steam at 20 lb. per sq. in. is 1156·7 B.Th.U. The latent heat at this pressure is 960·4 B.Th.U. What is the value of the liquid heat at saturation temperature ?

$$h = H - L$$
$$= 1156\cdot7 - 960\cdot4 = 196\cdot3 \text{ B.Th.U.}$$

O

163. Quality of Steam. The quality of steam is a measure of the amount of heat carried by one lb. of steam. The steam is the vehicle conveying the heat from point to point and the more heat each pound is made to carry the better will be its quality. Steam may be in one of three states, namely (1) Wet steam, (2) Dry steam, and (3) Superheated steam. Thus the word " quality " applied to steam means either wet, dry, or superheated. The steam table values of latent heat and of total heat are those for dry steam only. For both wet steam and superheated steam the total heats require to be corrected from the values given in the table and for wet steam the latent heat also requires correction. These corrections are fully set out in the examples to follow.

164. Process of Formation of Steam at Constant Pressure. Suppose that one pound of water is introduced into a cylinder (fig. 126) under a weightless piston which fits the cylinder perfectly so as to prevent any leakage of water or steam. Then we shall have 1 lb. weight of substance below the piston throughout the whole of the process of producing steam. Let a weight of W lb., including the atmospheric pressure, be placed on the piston. This weight will produce a pressure of $\frac{W}{A}$ lb. per sq. ft. when A is the area of the piston in square feet. Let this pressure be P lb. per sq. ft., or $\frac{P}{144}$ lb. per sq. in. This pressure is the constant pressure at which the steam is produced and in practice is fixed by the load on the boiler-safety valve. Now let heat be applied. The temperature of the water at once rises and sensible heat is supplied. The rise in temperature will continue until

FIG. 126.

the temperature reaches the saturation value corresponding to the pressure, when it will remain constant. For example, if the pressure on the water is 170 lb. per sq. in. abs., the limiting temperature will be 368·4° F., whilst if the pressure is 40 lb. per sq. in. abs. the temperature will be 267·2° F.[1] The water will expand slightly during the rise in temperature and the piston will move upwards to allow for this expansion. The amount of this expansion will be neglected in this book.

[1] Consult steam table for these figures.

This completes the first stage of steam production, and the amount of sensible heat supplied will be the difference in the values of the liquid heats at the final and initial temperatures. Fig. 127a represents the condition before this stage commences and fig. 127b represents the condition at the end of the stage. It will be noted that the piston is slightly higher at the end of the operation.

The next stage is the actual production stage and now the hot water is turned into steam. The heat taken in is latent heat and the supply of latent heat begins at the moment when the supply of sensible heat ceases.

Fig. 127c shows the second stage half completed, and fig. 127d shows it almost completed. The water is diminishing in amount and the steam is increasing in amount and also in volume.

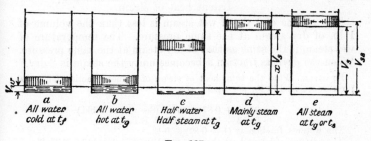

a	b	c	d	e
All water cold at t_f	All water hot at t_g	Half water Half steam at t_g	Mainly steam at t_g	All steam at t_g or t_s

Fig. 127.

Fig. 127e shows the process of formation completed. The water is entirely evaporated and the volume below the piston is V_s and is the value entered in the steam tables and known as the " specific volume " of the steam.

If the supply of heat is stopped when the state is as shown in fig. 127d there will be a little of the water remaining, and at this stage the water may be considered to be spread uniformly through the mass of vapour in the form of mist. Such steam is said to be wet steam. It has not received its full quantity of latent heat.

165. Dryness Fraction of Wet Steam. The amount of steam actually existing, fig. 127d, expressed as a fraction of the total quantity of water and steam present is called the " dryness fraction " of the steam. It is usually denoted by x or q. Suppose that 0·92 lb. of water has been evaporated. There will remain 0·08 lb. of water unevaporated. Thus the original pound of water has become 0·92 lb. of steam and 0·08 lb. of residual water. In this case the dryness fraction is $\dfrac{0·92}{1} = 0·92$, and the "wetness" fraction is $\dfrac{0·08}{1}$ or 0·08. Since the heat supply is cut off during the actual process of evaporation, it follows that the latent heat supplied is not that found in the tables. The amount supplied is xL heat units. Therefore, the total heat of wet steam of dryness fraction x is $(h + x$L$)$ heat units reckoned from 32° F. It must be remembered that all the sensible heat must be present if there is any steam at all. The dryness fraction is best defined as the ratio

$$\frac{\text{Latent heat actually supplied per lb. of steam}}{\text{Latent heat of steam}}.$$

The volume of 1 lb. of wet steam is less than the volume of 1 lb. of dry steam at the same pressure. The temperature of wet steam is the same as that of dry steam at the same pressure. When the dryness fraction x becomes unity the steam is "dry."

EXAMPLE. Find the total heat of steam of dryness fraction 0·87, the pressure being 130 lb. per sq. in. abs.

$$H_{wet} = h + x\text{L}$$
$$= 318·8 + 0·87 \times 874·0 \text{ (See steam table.)}$$
$$= 318·8 + 760·4 = 1079·2 \text{ B.Th.U.}$$

The wetness fraction is $(1 - 0·87) = 0·13$.

The amount of latent heat shortage is $0·13 \times 874·0 = 113·6$ B.Th.U. and the steam would not become dry until this amount of latent heat was supplied. The total heat would then be $1079·2 + 113·6 = 1192·8$ B.Th.U., which is the steam table value.

166. Dry Steam. This quality of steam contains no water in suspension and it is at the temperature of generation t_g. The temperature of generation is the saturation temperature corresponding to the pressure. The heat quantities of dry steam are those given in the steam tables. Dry steam is frequently referred to as "Saturated" steam or "Dry Saturated" steam. The term "dry" embraces these alternative descriptions.

167. Superheated Steam. If, after we have completed the evaporation of the last drop of water, we continue to supply heat to the steam at the same pressure, we shall observe a rise of temperature and a further increase of volume as shown by the dotted piston, fig. 127e. The amount of heat supplied after evaporation is complete will be $w \times C_p \times (t_s - t_g)$ heat units, where w is 1 lb. of steam, C_p is the specific heat of the steam, t_s is the actual steam temperature after superheating and t_g is the temperature at which the steam was generated. Thus, steam at a higher temperature than that corresponding to its pressure is superheated steam. The total heat of superheated steam is the steam table total heat *plus* the amount added after completion of evaporation.

Thus $H_s = h + L + C_p (t_s - t_g)$ heat units per lb. where H_s is the total heat of 1 lb. of superheated steam.

EXAMPLE. The temperature of steam is 482° F. and the pressure is 120 lb. per sq. in. abs. Find the state of this steam and the heat content of 1 lb. from 32° F. Take $Cp = 0.5$.

Whenever a steam pressure and temperature are given together we suspect superheat conditions.

From tables the temperature corresponding to 120 lb. per sq. in.

$$= 341.3° \text{ F.}$$
$$\therefore (t_s - t_g) = 482 - 341.3$$
$$= 140.7° \text{ F.}$$

This is sometimes called the " temperature elevation," " superheat " or " superheat range." It should be noted that although the word " superheat " is used to denote this temperature range, the quantity is not a heat quantity but a rise in temperature.

Total heat per lb. of the superheated steam

$$= h + L + C_p(t_s - t_g)$$
$$= 312.5 + 878.9 + 0.5 \times 140.7 \ (C_p = 0.5)$$
$$= 1261.75 \text{ B.Th.U.}$$

The state of the steam is superheated 140.7° F.

168. General Examples involving Quality of Steam.
These examples include latent heat experiments, dryness fraction experiments, boiler problems and condenser exercises.

EXAMPLE. One quarter-pound of dry steam at an absolute pressure of 100 lb. per sq. in. abs. is condensed in 5 lb. of water contained in a non-conducting tank. Find the resulting temperature of the water if the initial temperature is 100° F.

To simplify the solution assume that the change in liquid heat will be numerically equal to the change in temperature on the scale, in other words the specific heat is unity. Also note that we need not include the heat taken up by the tank since this heat will be zero, the tank being non-conducting.

Then by the principle of art. 151 we have :

Heat gained by the water = Heat lost by the steam.

The heat lost by the steam will be made up of the whole latent heat and some sensible heat. Let t_1 = initial temperature and t_2 = final temperature of water.

Then $5(t_2 - t_1) = \frac{1}{4}[L + h - h_2]$. The quantity h_2 is the liquid heat remaining in the condensed steam itself at the temperature t_2, and we have assumed $h_2 = t_2 - 32$. The liquid heat $h_1 = t_1 - 32$.

∴ From tables and the data given in the example:

$$5(t_2 - 100) = \tfrac{1}{4}[889 \cdot 7 + 298 \cdot 5 - (t_2 - 32)]$$
$$\therefore\ 20t_2 - 2,000 = 889 \cdot 7 + 298 \cdot 5 - (t_2 - 32)$$
$$\therefore\ 21t_2 = 889 \cdot 7 + 298 \cdot 5 + 32 + 2,000$$
$$= 3,220 \cdot 2.$$
$$\therefore\ t_2 = \frac{3,220 \cdot 2}{21} = 153 \cdot 3° \text{ F.}$$

EXAMPLE. The temperature of the water entering a boiler is 126·1° F., and the pressure of steam in the boiler is 190 lb. per sq. in. abs. How much heat will be required to produce 1 lb. of steam, (a) of dryness 0·97 ; (b) dry ; (c) superheated 72° F. ? Take the specific heat of steam to be 0·5.

(a) Total heat of wet steam at 190 lb. per sq. in. from 32° F.

$$= 350 \cdot 9 + 0 \cdot 97 \times 847 \cdot 9 \text{ B.Th.U.}$$
$$= 350 \cdot 9 + 822 \cdot 5$$
$$= 1,173 \cdot 4 \text{ B.Th.U.}$$

The liquid heat of the water
entering boiler, from 32° F. = 94·0 B.Th.U.
∴ Heat required in the case of
the wet steam = 1,173·4 − 94·0 = 1,079·4 B.Th.U.

(b) Total heat of dry steam at 190 lb. per sq. in. from 32° F.

$$= 350 \cdot 9 + 847 \cdot 9$$
$$= 1,198 \cdot 8 \text{ B.Th.U.}$$

∴ Heat required in this case = 1,198·8−94·0=1,104·8 B.Th.U.

(c) The superheated steam contains more heat than the dry steam.

∴ Total heat of superheated steam at 190 lb. per sq. in. and 449·5° F. from 32° F., taking the specific heat as 0·5,

$$= 350 \cdot 9 + 847 \cdot 9 + 0 \cdot 5 \times 72$$
$$= 1,198 \cdot 8 + 36 = 1,234 \cdot 8 \text{ B.Th.U.}$$

∴ Heat required per pound = 1,234·8 − 94·0 = 1,140·8 B.Th.U.

The heat content of 1 lb. of the superheated steam is 36 B.Th.U. more than that of the dry steam, and 61·4 B.Th.U. more than that of the wet steam of dryness 0·97.

EXAMPLE. During an experiment to determine the dryness fraction of steam 0·453 lb. of steam were blown into and condensed in a copper vessel weighing 2·2 lb. and containing 11·53 lb. of water originally at 51·1° F. The steam pressure at the point from which the steam supply was taken was 190 lb. per sq. in. abs., and the temperature of the water after blowing in the steam was 91·4° F. Find the quality of the steam assuming no loss of heat from the vessel.

From table II, art. 148, we find the specific heat of copper to be 0·1.

∴ Water equivalent of the copper vessel = 0·1 × 2·2
$$= 0 \cdot 22 \text{ lb. of water.}$$

∴ Total water equivalent = 0·22 + 11·53 lb. = 11·75 lb. of water.

This water receives the heat from 0·453 lb. of steam. Thus we have, Heat lost by the steam = Heat gained by the total water equivalent.

Heat gained by water equivalent = 11·75 × (91·4 − 51·1)
$$= 11 \cdot 75 \times 40 \cdot 3 = 473 \cdot 5 \text{ B.Th.U.}$$

The heat received by the water is from 0·453 lb. of steam.

∴ Heat received by the water per lb. of steam $= \dfrac{473 \cdot 5}{0 \cdot 453} = 1{,}045$ B.Th.U.

Heat remaining in actual condensate at $91 \cdot 4°$ F. $= 59 \cdot 4$ B.Th.U. per lb.

∴ Total heat of 1 lb. of steam $= 1{,}045 + 59 \cdot 4$ from $32°$ F.

$= 1{,}104 \cdot 4$ B.Th.U.

Comparing this value with that of dry steam given in the tables opposite to 190 lb. per sq. in. abs., we find that there is not sufficient heat to make the steam dry. The amount of the shortage is $1{,}198 \cdot 8 - 1{,}104 \cdot 4 = 94 \cdot 4$ B.Th.U.

This shortage is latent heat shortage. Thus the latent heat actually possessed by 1 lb. of steam is $847 \cdot 9 - 94 \cdot 4 = 753 \cdot 5$

∴ The state of the steam is wet and its dryness fraction is

$$\frac{753 \cdot 5}{847 \cdot 9} = 0 \cdot 888.$$

Careful study of the above example will make formulæ unnecessary.

EXAMPLE. A surface condenser receives 1,200 lb. of steam per hour at a pressure of 4 lb. per sq. in. abs. and $0 \cdot 86$ dry. The water supplied for condensing purposes enters the condenser at a temperature of $54°$ F. and leaves at $81°$ F. Find the amount of condensing water required per hour if the temperature of the condensate is $61°$ F. as it leaves the condenser.

The steam deposits all its latent heat from $0 \cdot 86$ dry and also liquid heat between $153 \cdot 0°$ F. and $61°$ F. The saturation temperature corresponding to 4 lb. per sq. in. abs. is $153 \cdot 0°$ F. and the liquid heat at this temperature is $121 \cdot 0$ B.Th.U., i.e. $(153 - 32)$ taking specific heat of water as $1 \cdot 0$.

∴ Heat removed from each pound of steam

$= h_1 + x_1 L_1 - h_2$

$= x_1 L_1 + h_1 - h_2$

$= 0 \cdot 86 \times 1{,}006 \cdot 7 + 121 - (61 - 32)$

$= 865 \cdot 8 + 60 + 32$

$= 957 \cdot 8$ B.Th.U.

∴ Heat removed per hour $= 1{,}200 \times 957 \cdot 8 = 1{,}149{,}360$ B.Th.U.

Heat taken up by one pound of condensing water $= [81 - 54]$

$= 27$ B.Th.U.

∴ Weight of condensing water required per hour $= \dfrac{1{,}149{,}360}{27}$

$= 42{,}569$ lb.

If the answer had been required in gallons this number would be divided by 10, giving $4{,}256 \cdot 9$ gall. per hr.

EXAMPLE. The absolute pressure of the steam entering a jet condenser is 2 lb. per sq. in. and its dryness fraction is $0 \cdot 9$. The condensing water enters at $59°$ F. and 99 lb. of condensing water are supplied per pound of steam. Find the resulting temperature of the mixture (see fig. 133, art. 189).

Heat lost by steam $=$ Heat gained by condensing water.

$1 \times [x_1 L_1 + t_1 - t_2] = 99[t_2 - 59°]$ Sp. ht. of water $= 1 \cdot 0$.

i.e. $0 \cdot 9 \times 1{,}022 \cdot 2 + 126 \cdot 1 - t_2 = 99 t_2 - 5{,}841$

$920 \cdot 0 + 126 \cdot 1 = 99 t_2 - 5{,}841 + t_2$

$1{,}046 \cdot 1 + 5{,}841 = 100 t_2$

$$t_2 = \frac{6{,}887 \cdot 1}{100} = 68 \cdot 87° \text{ F.}$$

169. Specific Volume of Steam. This quantity is tabulated, for dry steam, in the third column of the steam tables. It is the volume of steam in cubic feet per pound weight. The specific volume is very large at low pressures and diminishes rapidly as the pressure is increased.

Let V_T = total volume of space containing steam at pressure p lb. per sq. in. abs.

V_s = specific volume of steam at pressure p lb. per sq. in. abs.

w = weight of steam in space V_T in lb.

Then $w = \dfrac{V_T}{V_s}$ lb. Both volumes are in cubic feet.

EXAMPLE. A steam vessel is 6 ft. diameter and 20 ft. long. The steam pressure is 90 lb. per sq. in. abs., and the steam is dry. What weight of steam is present in the vessel ?

At 90 lb. per sq. in. the specific volume = 4·896 cu. ft.

$$\text{Volume of steam in vessel} = \frac{\pi \times 6 \times 6}{4} \times 20 = 565\cdot488 \text{ cu. ft.}$$

$$\therefore \text{ Weight of steam present} = \frac{565\cdot488}{4\cdot896} = 115 \text{ lb.}$$

EXAMPLE. A steam-engine piston 24 in. diameter is subjected to a pressure of 150 lb. per sq. in abs. The dryness of the steam is 0·98. How much steam is supplied whilst the piston moves 2 ft. if the pressure is maintained at 150 lb. per sq. in. ?

$$\text{Volume of steam taken} = \frac{3\cdot1416}{4} \times \frac{24}{12} \times \frac{24}{12} \times 2 = 6\cdot2832 \text{ cu. ft.}$$

Specific volume of dry steam at 150 lb. per sq. in. = 3·015 cu. ft.
The specific volume of wet steam at „ „ „ „ „ = 0·98 × 3·015
= 2·955 cu. ft.

$\therefore$ Weight of steam supplied during the movement,

$$= \frac{6\cdot2832}{2\cdot955} \text{ lb.} = 2\cdot123 \text{ lb.}$$

EXAMPLES XVI

SECTION A

1. Explain the terms " sensible heat," " latent heat," " saturation temperature," and " total heat " as applied to steam.

2. What is taking place (a) if latent heat is being supplied, (b) if latent heat is being removed ?

3. What is the greatest amount of latent heat which can be supplied to $1\frac{1}{4}$ lb. of water at a pressure of 100 lb. per sq. in. abs. ?

4. How much heat would be required to produce one pound of steam at a pressure of 180 lb. per sq. in. from feed water originally at 170·1° F. (a) if the steam is dry, (b) if the steam is 0·95 dry ?

5. What additional heat would be required to superheat the steam in exercise 4 to a temperature of 464° F. in each case ? Take $Cp = 0·5$.

6. The steam conditions at the stop valve of an engine are : pressure, 120 lb. per sq. in. abs.; temperature, 482° F. If Cp is 0·5, how much heat reaches the engine per pound of steam ?

7. If the feed-water temperature in exercise 6 is 212° F., how much heat is actually supplied per pound of steam at the stop-valve conditions ?

8. The following data are extracted from a steam table :

p lb. per sq. in.	$t°$ F.	h, B.Th.U. per lb.	H, B.Th.U. per lb.
100	327·8	298·5	1,188·2
200	381·8	355·5	1,199·5
300	417·3	394·0	1,203·8
400	444·6	424·2	1,205·5
500	467·0	449·6	1,205·4

On a base of " pressures per square inch," plot curves of " sensible heat," " total heat," and " latent heat," and from the curves estimate the value of the latent heat at a pressure of 250 lb. per sq. in.   U.L.C.I.

9. The feed temperature in a boiler working at atmospheric pressure is 212° F. How many pounds of water will be evaporated by a supply of heat of 10,890 B.Th.U. ?

10. 10 lb. of dry steam at atmospheric pressure are blown into and condensed by 200 lb. of water in a tank. The original temperature of this water was 50° F. Calculate the final temperature of mixture assuming the latent heat of the steam to be 967 B.Th.U.   U.E.I.

11. Explain the meaning of the terms " sensible heat " and " latent heat." 5 lb. of dry steam at a pressure of 190 lb. per sq. in. absolute are passed into a tank containing 60 lb. of water at 50° F. Assuming no loss of heat and neglecting the water equivalent of the tank, what will be the final temperature of the water ? Steam at a pressure of 190 lb. per sq. in. abs. has a temperature of formation of 377·5° F., a sensible heat of 350·9 B.Th.U. per lb., and a latent heat of 847·9 B.Th.U. per lb. and water at 50° F. has a sensible heat of 18 B.Th.U. per lb.   U.E.I.

12. The following figures have been taken from steam tables. Complete the table and then find the amount of heat required to completely convert 5 lb. of water at 26·4° C. into steam at a pressure of 115 lb. per sq. in. abs.

Pressure, lb. per sq. in. abs.	Temperature ° C.	Heat of the liquid C.H.U. per lb.	Heat of evaporation C.H.U. per lb.	Total heat of evaporation C.H.U. per lb.
0·5	26·4	—	580·4	606·7
50	138·3	138·3	515·3	—
115	170	171·7	—	663·4

U.E.I.

13. Explain the meaning of the following quantities found in steam tables : " Heat of the liquid, or sensible heat " ; " Heat of evaporation, or latent heat " ; " Total heat of evaporation." If the heat of the liquid is 283·8 B.Th.U. per lb. and the total heat of evaporation is 1,182·8 B.Th.U. per lb., what is the heat of evaporation in British Thermal Units per pound ? If the initial temperature of the water is constant, does the heat of the liquid

(as quoted in steam tables) increase or decrease as the pressure to which the water is subjected increases ? Give a reason for your answer. U.E.I.

14. Calculate the amount of heat required to convert 10 lb. of water at 68° F. into steam at 212° F. Express your answer in Centigrade heat units and British Thermal Units.

Latent heat of steam at 212° F. = 961 B.Th.U. per lb. N.C.T.E.C.

15. A gas-heated boiler generates steam at temperature 212° F. at the rate of 100 lb. per hr. from feed water at temperature 60° F. How much heat does the water receive in one hour ?

If the heating value of the gas is 480 B.Th.U. per cu. ft. and 30 per cent. of this heat is wasted, calculate the gas consumption in cubic feet per hour. Latent heat of steam at 212° F. = 961 B.Th.U. per lb. N.C.T.E.C.

16. The following information was taken from a steam table :

Pressure, lb. per sq. in.	Temperature ° F.	Latent Heat B.Th.U. per lb.	Total Heat B.Th.U. per lb.
50	281·0	924·6	1,174·8
150	358·4	864·5	1,195·1
260	404·4	822·6	1,202·5
360	434·4	792·3	1,205·1
480	462·8	760·7	1,205·5

On a base of " pressure per square inch," draw graphs of latent heat and total heat. From these graphs, obtain the sensible heat of dry saturated steam at 300 lb. per sq. in. pressure. U.L.C.I.

17. The following data were extracted from a steam table :

Absolute Pressure, lb. per sq. in.	Temperature ° F.	Sensible Heat B.Th.U. per lb.	Total Heat B.Th.U. per lb.
250	401·0	376·1	1,202·1

Determine the total quantity of heat that must be added to 10 lb. of feed water at 59° F., to turn it into dry steam at a pressure of 250 lb. per sq. in., and indicate how much of the total represents sensible heat and how much latent heat. U.L.C.I.

18. If steam at 45 lb. absolute pressure per sq. in. is 90 per cent. dry, how much heat has to be given per pound to produce steam at a pressure of 100 lb. per sq. in. abs. and of 0·95 dryness ? Assume that the specific heat of water is unity. Latent heat of steam at 45 lb. pressure is 930 B.Th.U. at temperature 275° F., and that for steam at 100 lb. pressure is 893 B.Th.U. at 327° F. C.G.L.I.

19. A steel ball weighs 5 lb. and has a specific heat of 0·116. The ball is placed, at a temperature of 600° F., in 1 lb. of water at 62° F. and at atmospheric pressure. What weight of the water will be evaporated ? Specific heat of water = 1, latent heat of steam = 970 B.Th.U.

SECTION B

20. In an experiment to determine the heat of evaporation of water, steam is generated in a small boiler. The steam passes through a separator and the dried steam is then condensed in water contained in a well-lagged calorimeter. Using such an apparatus, the following figures were obtained

Temperature of steam	230° F.
Weight of water in calorimeter	20 lb.
Initial temperature of water	59° F.
Weight of water and condensed steam	20·5 lb.
Final temperature of water	86° F.

Determine the heat of evaporation of the water.

This figure was not accepted and the following additional data was obtained :

Weight of calorimeter . . . . . . 5 lb.
Specific heat of metal of calorimeter . . . . 0·10

Re-calculate the heat of evaporation of the water. Assume that 1 B.Th.U. is required to change the temperature of 1 lb. of water 1° F. throughout the temperature range. U.E.I.

21. What do you understand by " wet saturated " and " superheated steam " ? Find the number of heat units required to produce 1 lb. of steam at 361° F. from feed water at 120·2° F., (a) when the steam contains 5 per cent. of moisture ; (b) when the steam is superheated to 400° F., assuming the specific heat of superheated steam to be 0·5.

EXTRACT FROM STEAM TABLES.

Temperature °F.	Heat of the liquid B.Th.U. per lb.	Total heat of evaporation. B.Th.U. per lb.
120·2	88·0	1,022·9
361·0	332·9	1,193·9

U.E.I.

22. A condensing engine uses 20 lb. of steam per indicated horse-power per hour. The temperature of the hotwell is 122° F., and the pressure of the exhaust steam 8 lb. per sq. in. abs. The inlet and outlet temperatures of the circulating water are 55° and 60·4° F. respectively. What weight of circulating water would be required per horse-power during a run of 5 hr. ?

At a pressure of 8 lb. per sq. inch abs. the temperature of evaporation is 182·9° F. and the latent heat of evaporation 987·9 B.Th.U. per lb. You may assume that water at 122° F. has a sensible heat of 90 B.Th.U. per lb. U.E.I.

23. Heat is supplied to 1 lb. of water at 32° F. until all the water is converted into steam, the steam then being further heated, the pressure remaining constant throughout. Describe, in order, the changes that take place. Show by means of a neatly drawn graph, plotting temperature vertically and heat units supplied, horizontally, the connection between temperature and heat units supplied for 1 lb. of water at 32° F. converted into steam at 212° F. and then further heated under the above conditions. You should indicate on your graph the approximate number of heat units contained by the fluid at any point where the slope of the graph changes suddenly. U.E.I.

24. Waste steam from the exhaust of a steam engine is sometimes used to pre-heat the feed-water on its way to the boiler. In such a case feed-water at 55° F. is raised to a temperature of 175° F. on leaving the pre-heater. The exhaust steam is at 16 lb. per sq. in. pressure and may be considered dry. What is the greatest weight of feed-water which can be heated by 1 lb. of steam ?

At 16 lb. per sq. in. the temperature of steam is 216° F. and its latent heat 968 B.Th.U. C.G.L.I.

CHAPTER XVII

FUELS AND COMBUSTION

170. A fuel is a substance which gives out heat when certain requirements are satisfied. These requirements are, (1) there must be a supply of oxygen available, (2) the temperature of the fuel and the oxygen must be high enough to enable burning to commence. The process of burning is called combustion. When burning takes place certain substances contained in the fuel combine with the oxygen to form new substances called the products of combustion. The products of combustion of any fuel are gases. The lowest temperature at which burning begins to take place is known as the "ignition" temperature of the fuel. The ignition temperatures of different fuels vary considerably. For coal an average value is 750° F., for oil values from 522° F. to 892° F., depending on the kind of oil, are required, and for gaseous fuels the ignition temperatures range from 1,400° F. to 1,650° F. A more exact definition of a fuel may now be given. *A fuel is a substance, or combination of substances, which, when raised to the temperature of ignition, will unite freely with the oxygen in the atmosphere and give out heat at a rate sufficient to maintain combustion.* There are many substances which will give out heat when combining with oxygen, but the heat is not given out freely. These substances smoulder away and are not classed as fuels.

Fuels may be divided into three main classes :

(1) Solid fuels such as coal, peat, wood and lignite (brown coal with a soft woody structure), (2) Liquid fuels such as petrols, paraffins and heavy oils, (3) Gaseous fuels like acetylene, methane, carbon monoxide, and hydrogen. Town gas is a mixture of several of these gases. We have defined heat as a form of energy, art. 135, and thus it is worthy of note that a fuel is a storehouse of energy. The motorist does not purchase petrol for its own sake but for the number of foot-pounds of energy stored in it. The energy stored in coal, gas, and oil, moves all our traffic on road and rail, and provides almost all the power needed by our manufacturing industries.

171. Composition of Air. Air is the mixture of gases composing the atmosphere. It plays a very important part in the process of combustion of fuels. It serves as the source and carrier of the essential oxygen. Oxygen is a gas very much above its evaporation temperature and a supply of this gas must be available before any fuel can be utilized. For ordinary combustion processes the oxygen supply is taken from the air. If the supply of air is cut off from a petrol engine, or from any space where combustion is taking place, the combustion will cease, no matter how much fuel is present. This fact is made use of in patent fire extinguishers for oil and petrol fires where water would be useless unless emulsified or atomised. From this fact it is evident that air supply is just as important as fuel supply, and that the one is no use for combustion processes without the other. It is therefore necessary to know something of the properties of air from which the oxygen supply is obtained before proceeding to study fuels and combustion in greater detail.

Air is mainly composed of Oxygen, Nitrogen and Carbon dioxide. There are other gases present but they are of negligible quantity. For our purposes we shall also neglect the carbon dioxide which is present only in comparatively small amount. Thus we can regard air as consisting of oxygen and nitrogen. It is usual in elementary calculations to regard the nitrogen as taking no part in the process of combustion. Thus it is assumed that the nitrogen in the air passes through the internal combustion engine or furnace unchanged.[1]

The composition of the atmosphere may be stated on the basis of weight or on the basis of volume. In passing, the student may be reminded that it is the weight of the air which causes the barometric or atmospheric pressure. On the basis of weight, air contains 23 per cent. of Oxygen and 77 per cent. of Nitrogen, and on the basis of volume it contains 21 per cent. of Oxygen and 79 per cent. of Nitrogen. Thus 1 lb. of air will contain 0·23 lb. of Oxygen and 0·77 lb. of Nitrogen, and 1 cu. ft. of air will contain 0·21 cu. ft. of Oxygen and 0·79 cu. ft. of Nitrogen. In addition to this data the volume of 1 lb. of air can be accurately obtained if the pressure and temperature of the air are known (see art. 228). Thus the volume of 1 lb. of air (the specific volume) at 14·7 lb. per sq. in. abs. and 32° F. (0° C.) is 12·391 cu. ft. When the pressure is 14·7 lb. per sq. in. abs. and the temperature 62° F. (16·6° C.), the volume of 1 lb. of air is 13·146 cu. ft. Thus a cube of 2·36 ft. side will enclose 1 lb. of air at atmospheric pressure and at 62° F. or 16·6° C.

[1] This is not strictly true for very high temperature combustion. Some part of the nitrogen appears to form compounds during the combustion process.

EXAMPLE. Calculate the weight of air which will contain 1 lb. of oxygen.
Since 0·23 lb. of oxygen is contained in 1 lb. of air

then   1 lb. of oxygen will be „   „ $\dfrac{1}{0·23}$ lb. of air,

i.e. in 4·35 lb. of air.

The weight of nitrogen contained in this weight of air will be

$$0·77 \times 4·35 = 3·35 \text{ lb.}$$

Thus   1 lb. of oxygen + 3·35 lb. of nitrogen = 4·35 lb. of air.

EXAMPLE. How many cubic feet of air will be required to supply 1 cu. ft. of oxygen at the same pressure and temperature as the air ?

0·21 cu. ft. of oxygen exists in 1 cu. ft. of air

∴   „ „ „   „   will exist in $\dfrac{1}{0·21}$ cu. ft. of air.

That is, in 4·77 cu. ft. of air.

Thus there will be 3·77 cu. ft. of nitrogen and 1 cu. ft. of oxygen in 4·77 cu. ft. of air.

EXAMPLE. A gas-engine piston is 10 in. diameter and its stroke is 21 in. Assuming air to be drawn in during the suction stroke at 62° F. and at atmospheric pressure, find the weight of oxygen entering the cylinder per stroke.

$$\text{Area of piston} = \frac{\pi D^2}{4} = \frac{3·1416 \times 10 \times 10}{4 \times 144}$$

$$= 0·546 \text{ sq. ft.}$$

∴ Volume of air drawn in per stroke $= 0·546 \times \dfrac{21}{12}$ cu. ft.

$$= 0·955 \text{ cu. ft.}$$

∴ Weight of air drawn in $= \dfrac{0·955}{13·146}$ lb. $= 0·0726$ lb.

∴ Weight of oxygen entering the cylinder per stroke
$$= 0·0726 \times 0·23 = 0·0167 \text{ lb.}$$

EXAMPLE. One pound of carbon burning completely requires 2·66 lb. of oxygen to combine with it. Find the weight of air necessary to burn 0·76 lb. of carbon.

Weight of oxygen required $= 0·76 \times 2·66$ lb. $= 2·02$ lb.
∴ Weight of air required $= 2·02 \times 4·35 = 8·8$ lb.

For methods of calculating weights of air at different pressures and temperatures, see art. 228.

172. Chemistry of Fuels. Combustion is a process which obeys the laws of chemistry. All substances can be divided into two classes, namely " Elements " and " Compounds." An element is a substance which cannot be split up into two substances having different properties. Iron, Gold, Lead, Oxygen, Hydrogen and Nitrogen are elements. There are about 92 elements known to chemical science. All substances not included in the list of elements are compounds or compositions of two or more elements. For example, water is a compound of the elements hydrogen and oxygen. It resembles neither element in appearance nor in properties. When two or more elements combine chemically an entirely new substance is formed and in the process of combination heat is generated or absorbed. In some cases the heat generated is small in amount. In others it is a very considerable quantity. The actual " attack " of one element on another is called a " reaction." Reactions which give out heat are called " exothermic " reactions and those which absorb heat are called " endothermic " reactions. The reactions of the fuel elements are exothermic in character.

173. Laws of Chemical Combination.

(1) *When two elements unite to form a new substance, they combine in definite proportions.*

(2) *The total weight of the substance formed is always equal to the sum of the weights of the elements which combine.*

The first law enables us to determine the amount of oxygen required for any fuel element and the second law enables us to decide the amount of the products of the combustion. All elements are regarded as being composed of particles called *atoms* which are chemically indivisible. The atoms of any one element are all alike in weight and properties, but they differ from those of other elements. Chemical compounds are made by the union of atoms and two or more atoms together form a molecule. Even with elements the atoms seldom exist alone. They frequently go about in pairs and in this case two similar atoms form a molecule. For example, most of the gases possess atoms which pair together and in such a case the gas is said to be di-atomic. We may therefore have molecules made of the same kind of atoms and molecules made of different kinds of atoms.

Thus a molecule may be defined as the smallest portion of any substance capable of separate existence, whilst the atom is the smallest amount of any element that can enter into the formation of a molecule.

174. Atomic and Molecular Weights. It is not possible to determine the actual weight of atoms and molecules because they are so small as to be invisible even under the most powerful microscope. It is, however, possible by means of careful experiments to determine the relative weights of atoms and molecules. The element Hydrogen is a gas and bulk for bulk it is the lightest substance known. Therefore the weight of the atom of hydrogen is taken as unity, and the molecular weight of hydrogen is twice unity since two atoms of hydrogen make up the molecule. All other substances have atomic and molecular weights greater than unity.

Table III gives values of atomic and molecular weights of the principal substances encountered in combustion problems, and also gives the symbol used to denote that substance. The small figure 2, at the bottom right-hand corner, denotes a two-atom molecule in the case of the elementary gases.

TABLE III

ATOMIC AND MOLECULAR WEIGHTS OF FUEL CONSTITUENTS

Substance.	Symbol.	Atomic Weight.	Molecular Weight.
*Hydrogen	H_2	1	2
Oxygen	O_2	16	32
Nitrogen	N_2	14	28
*Carbon	C	12	—
*Sulphur	S	32	—
Steam	H_2O	—	18
*Carbon monoxide . .	CO	—	28
Carbon dioxide . . .	CO_2	—	44
Sulphur dioxide . .	SO_2	—	64
*Methane or Marsh gas . .	CH_4	—	16

The first five substances in the table are elements whilst the remainder are compounds. The compounds have no atomic weights because the least amount of a compound must be the molecule. The substances marked with the asterisk are the fuel elements or compounds. The other substances are not regarded as giving out heat although they take part in the combustion process. It will be noted that the elements Carbon and Sulphur have no molecular weight stated. This is because these elements exist in different forms each of which has a different molecular weight. In calculations on fuels and combustion the symbols are invaluable, and are freely used to indicate the substances taking part in the process and also to show the amounts of substance present. The use of symbols saves time and serves as a guide to the products, and checks the amount of substance reacting.

175. Composition of Fuels. The principal constituent elements in any fuel are carbon and hydrogen, and for this reason, many fuels are called *hydrocarbon fuels*. When carbon such as coke or charcoal burns in a plentiful supply of oxygen the product resulting from the combustion is carbon dioxide gas. The carbon is unable to take into combination any further oxygen. If, however, the carbon burns in a restricted oxygen supply the product of the combustion is the gas called carbon monoxide and this gas is itself a fuel. This gas is highly poisonous. Any carbon monoxide passing away in the gases from a boiler plant represents a loss of fuel which is not detected by ordinary methods of observation.

When hydrogen burns the resulting product is water-steam, which ultimately condenses. Other constituents in fuels include sulphur, oxygen, and ash. Sulphur is undesirable in a fuel since its product SO_2 is easily further oxidized to SO_3 which with water forms the corrosive sulphuric acid, and which causes corrosion and wasting of the boiler plates. The ash is that portion of the fuel which remains after all the combustible portion of the fuel has been burned. When the ash fuses (melts) it flows into the air passages in the grates and greatly interferes with the combustion. When fused ash solidifies it is known as clinker. For ordinary boiler furnaces a fuel whose ash has a high fusing temperature is desirable, but with powdered fuel low-temperature fusing ash can be dealt with conveniently.

Table IV gives typical analyses of fuels, the figures for solid and liquid fuels being stated on a weight or gravimetric basis, and those for the gases being on a volumetric basis.

TABLE IV

COMPOSITION OF FUELS. PERCENTAGES

Constituent Fuel.	Constituent.							Calorific Value.
	C	H	S	O	N	Ash.	Water.	
Average steam coal	80	5	1	8	1·5	4·5	—	12,500 B.Th.U./lb.
Anthracite coal	85·7	2·97	0·62	2·1	1·8	3·66	3·15	15,000 B.Th.U./lb.
Wood (dry)	49·5	6	—	44	—	0·5	—	9,000 B.Th.U./lb.
Petrol	85	15	—	—	—	—	—	11,086 cal./gram.
Heavy oil	86·89	13·11	—	—	—	—	—	10,913 cal./gram.
Town Gas	CH_4 29·3	45·0	CO 10·1	0·5	10	Other hydrocarbons 5·1		Lower 538 B.Th.U./cu. ft.
Mond Gas	3·5	22·65	16·05	0	44·55	—	CO_2 13·25	Lower 147·3 B.Th.U./cu. ft.

P

176. Combustion Equations. These equations are the means of finding the weight of oxygen required for, and the amount of substance produced by, the combustion of fuel.

When carbon burns completely to CO_2 the combustion equation is $\qquad C + O_2 = CO_2$
and, writing weights, $\quad 12 + 32 = 44.$
Dividing by 12, $\qquad 1 + 2 \cdot 66 = 3 \cdot 66.$

From this equation we find that 1 lb. of carbon requires 2·66 lb. of oxygen and produces 3·66 lb. of carbon dioxide. Each pound of carbon following this reaction gives out 14,540 B.Th.U.

If the carbon is incompletely burned to CO the equation is
$$2C + O_2 = 2CO$$
or by weight $\qquad 24 + 32 = 56.$
Dividing by 24, $\qquad 1 + 1 \cdot 33 = 2 \cdot 33.$

That is, 1 lb. of carbon requires 1·33 lb. of oxygen and produces 2·33 lb. of carbon monoxide. The heat given out by 1 lb. of carbon in this case is 4,400 B.Th.U. There is therefore heat to the amount of 10,140 B.Th.U., per lb. of carbon in the original fuel, still available in the fuel gas CO.

The combining equation for sulphur shows that 1 lb. of sulphur requires 1 lb. of oxygen and forms 2 lb. of SO_2. The calorific value of sulphur is 4,000 B.Th.U. per lb.

The next elementary fuel to be considered is hydrogen.

The combustion equation is $2H_2 + O_2 = 2H_2O$
or, writing weights, $\qquad 4 + 32 = 36$
dividing by 4, $\qquad 1 + 8 = 9.$

In other words, " one pound of hydrogen requires 8 lb. of oxygen and produces 9 lb. of steam when burnt, and gives out 61,520 B.Th.U. in the process."

In all the above equations the plus sign should be read " combining with," and the equality sign should be read " produces." The above ratios are always the same no matter how the various elements are arranged in any fuel.

EXAMPLE. A sample of coal when analysed gave the following composition by weight : C, 53 per cent.; H_2, 14 per cent.; O_2, 20 per cent.; N_2, 3 per cent.; and S, 4 per cent.; remainder ash. Calculate the weight of air required for complete combustion of 1 lb. of the coal.

The substances requiring oxygen are C, H_2 and S.

$\therefore$ Oxygen required for C $= 0 \cdot 53 \times 2 \cdot 66 = 1 \cdot 409$ lb.
,, ,, ,, S $= 0 \cdot 04 \times 1 \quad = 0 \cdot 04$,,
,, ,, ,, $H_2 = 0 \cdot 14 \times 8 \quad = 1 \cdot 12$,,

$\therefore$ Total oxygen required per lb. of coal $= 2 \cdot 569$,,

Oxygen already present in 1 lb. of coal = 0·2   lb.
∴ Oxygen to be supplied from air by difference = 2·369 „

∴ Air required per lb. of coal = 2·369 × 4·35 lb.
                              = 10·305

This is the least amount of air which will suffice for the combustion to be completed. It is known as the " minimum " air supply.

177. Excess Air. If the exact theoretical minimum amount of air is supplied to a furnace very careful precautions are necessary in order to ensure that the oxygen will come into contact with the fuel particles. This ideal condition is difficult to attain and consequently an extra quantity of air is supplied in addition to the minimum amount. This increases the possibility of complete combustion. The extra air is known as " excess " air. In older boiler plants and industrial furnaces the excess air was from 50 per cent. to 70 per cent. of the minimum requirements. The modern practice is to reduce the excess air as much as possible, generally about 25 per cent. to 50 per cent. excess is allowed, and to arrange for the complete mixing of fuel and air in the furnace. This reduces the heat losses through the chimney and increases the efficiency of the combustion, that is, it increases the amount and intensity of heat actually produced in the furnace.

178. Density and Volume of Gases. The density of a gas is the weight per unit volume (generally one cubic foot) at a stated temperature and pressure. The temperature usually employed is 32° F. and the pressure is 14·7 lb. per sq. in. abs. These values are known as *normal temperature and pressure* (N.T.P.), see art. 227.

The weight of hydrogen is 0·00559 lb. per cu. ft. at N.T.P.

The weight of one cubic foot of any other gas at N.T.P. will be weight of hydrogen × relative density of gas.

The relative density of a gas is the ratio,

$$\frac{\text{Molecular weight of gas}}{\text{Molecular weight of hydrogen}}$$

∴ Weight of 1 cu. ft. of any gas in lb.

$$= 0{\cdot}00559 \times \frac{\text{Molecular weight}}{2}$$

because the molecular weight of hydrogen is **2.**

EXAMPLE. What is the volume of 1 lb. of nitrogen at N.T.P. ?

Density of $N_2 = 0.00559 \times \dfrac{28}{2}$

$= 0.07826$ lb. per cu. ft. at N.T.P.

$\therefore$ Volume of 1 lb. $= \dfrac{1}{0.07826}$ cu. ft. $= 12.77$ cu. ft. at N.T.P.

The molecules of all gases occupy the same space at the same pressure and temperature.

Thus the volume of one molecule of hydrogen is the same as the volume of one molecule of oxygen or nitrogen or any gas when at the same temperature and pressure. This is Avogadro's Law.

This law enables us to state that the relative density of a gas is equal to the ratio of the molecular weights as shown above. It also enables us to find the volume of air necessary to burn gaseous fuels.

179. Combustion of Gaseous Fuels.

The combining equations for gas fuels are written in the same way as for solid and liquid fuels.

EXAMPLE. Find the amount of air required to burn $1\frac{1}{2}$ cu. ft. of hydrogen gas.

Equation is

$$2H_2 + O_2 = 2H_2O$$
$$\therefore 2 \text{ mol.} + 1 \text{ mol.} = 2 \text{ mol.}$$

All molecules are the same size

$$\therefore 1 \text{ cu. ft.} + 0.5 \text{ cu. ft.} = 1 \text{ cu. ft.}$$

Hence $1\frac{1}{2}$ cu. ft. of H_2 would require 0.75 cu. ft. of O_2 and would produce $1\frac{1}{2}$ cu. ft. of steam. Therefore there is a shrinkage or contraction on combustion of 0.75 cu. ft.

The volume of air required is $0.75 \times \dfrac{100}{21} = 0.75 \times 4.77$

$$= 3.58 \text{ cu. ft.}$$

EXAMPLE. A fuel gas consists of marsh gas and carbon monoxide in equal amounts by volume. Find the volume of air required to burn 1 cu. ft. of the mixture.

The equation for the marsh gas combustion is

$$CH_4 + 2O_2 = CO_2 + 2H_2O$$

i.e. $$1 \text{ mol.} + 2 \text{ mol.} = 1 \text{ mol.} + 2 \text{ mol.}$$
$$\therefore 1 \text{ cu. ft.} + 2 \text{ cu. ft.} = 1 \text{ cu. ft.} + 2 \text{ cu. ft.}$$
or $$0.5 \text{ cu. ft.} + 1 \text{ cu. ft.} = 0.5 \text{ cu. ft.} + 1 \text{ cu. ft.}$$

$\therefore$ For the marsh gas portion 1 cu. ft. of oxygen is required.

The equation for the combustion of the carbon monoxide is

$$2CO + O_2 = 2CO_2$$
$$\therefore 2 \text{ mol.} + 1 \text{ mol.} = 2 \text{ mol.}$$
$$\therefore 2 \text{ cu. ft.} + 1 \text{ cu. ft.} = 2 \text{ cu. ft.}$$
$$\therefore 0.5 \text{ cu. ft.} + 0.25 \text{ cu. ft.} = 0.5 \text{ cu. ft.}$$

∴ Volume of oxygen required for the carbon monoxide portion is 0·25 cu. ft.

∴ Total volume of oxygen required for the cubic foot of mixture is

$$1 + 0·25 = 1·25 \text{ cu. ft.}$$

∴ Volume of air required is $1·25 \times 4·77$ cu. ft.

$$= 5·96 \text{ cu. ft. for 1 cu. ft. of mixture.}$$

180. Calorific Value of Fuels. This is the amount of heat given out by unit quantity of the fuel when it is completely burned. For solid fuels the calorific values are stated in B.Th.U. or C.H.U. per lb. It is frequently stated in gram calories per gram. In the case of liquid fuels the calorific value may be stated in heat units per lb., or per pint, or per litre. The calorific value of gaseous fuel is stated in B.Th.U. or C.H.U. per cubic foot at *normal temperature and pressure*, i.e. N.T.P. (see art. 227).

181. Determination of Calorific Values. The calorific value of a fuel is best found by the direct method of calorimetry. In this method a small quantity of the fuel is burned in oxygen to ensure complete combustion. The amount of heat liberated by the combustion is taken up by the calorimeter and the water surrounding it.

The calorific value of a fuel can be calculated approximately if its composition is known. In this case the total heat given out by unit mass of the fuel is regarded as being equal to the sum of the heats given out by each constituent element. The heat given out by each constituent element is the product, weight of element × calorific value of element. The calorific value of each element is found by actual experiment.

The heat given out by 1 lb. of hydrogen in a calorimeter is 61,520 B.Th.U. per lb. and 1 lb. of carbon gives out 14,540 B.Th.U., and 1 lb of sulphur, 4,000 B.Th.U. under the same conditions. We may use these values to calculate the calorific value of a fuel of given composition.

EXAMPLE. Calculate the calorific value of 1 lb. of coal having the following composition by weight : C, 80 per cent. ; H_2, 5 per cent. ; Oxygen, 8·5 per cent. ; Ash, 4 per cent. ; N_2, 1·5 per cent. ; S, 1 per cent.

Note that there is oxygen and hydrogen present in the fuel. Hence we may assume that the oxygen is already combined with a portion of the hydrogen.

Thus the hydrogen still available

$$= \left[0·05 - \frac{0·085}{8} \right] = [0·05 - 0·0106]$$

$$= 0·0394 \text{ lb. per lb. of fuel.}$$

∴ Heat evolved by available hydrogen $= 0.0394 \times 61,520$
$$= 2,423.8 \text{ B.Th.U. per lb. of fuel.}$$
Heat evolved by the carbon $= 0.8 \times 14,540$
$$= 11,632 \text{ B.Th.U. per lb. of fuel.}$$
Heat evolved by the sulphur $= 0.01 \times 4,000$
$$= 40 \text{ B.Th.U. per lb. of fuel.}$$
∴ The calorific value of 1 lb. of coal $= 2,423.8 + 11,632 + 40$
$$= 14,095.8 \text{ B.Th.U.}$$

or $\dfrac{14,095.8 \times 5}{9}$ C.H.U. $= 7,831$

If we substitute the symbols for the figures we can write an equation for the calorific value. This equation is—

$$\text{Calorific value} = 14,540 \text{ C.} + 61,520 \left[H_2 + \frac{O_2}{8} \right] + 4,000 \text{ S.}$$

The symbols now represent the weight in lb. of each constituent respectively in 1 lb. of fuel.

182. Higher and Lower Calorific Values. When a fue contains hydrogen it has a lower calorific value as well as a higher one. The higher calorific value is that which would be obtained in a calorimeter. It is higher because it includes the latent heat of the steam formed by the hydrogen and also part of the sensible heat of the resulting water. When the fuel is burned in a boiler this latent heat and the part of the sensible heat cannot be given up because the furnace gases are at a temperature too high for condensation of the steam to take place.

Thus the *lower* calorific value $=$ *higher* calorific value $-$ wt. of steam $\times (L + h - h_0)$. The values of L and h are those corresponding to 14.7 lb. per sq. in. abs. and h_0 is the sensible heat at room temperature, i.e. about 62° F.

EXAMPLE. What is the lower calorific value of the fuel in the last exercise ?
The total weight of steam formed per lb. of fuel $= 9 \times 0.05$
$$= 0.45 \text{ lb.}$$
∴ Heat carried away per lb. of coal $= 0.45 [970.7 + 180 - 30]$
$$= 0.45 \times 1,120.7$$
$$= 504.3 \text{ B.Th.U.}$$
∴ Lower calorific value $= 14,095.8 - 504.3$
$$= 13,591.5 \text{ B.Th.U.}$$

183. Fuel Calorimeters. The principle of all fuel calorimeters is the same, namely, that the heat given out by a known weight of fuel is absorbed by a known weight of water the temperature rise of which is accurately observed. Fig. 128 shows the arrangement of the " Simplex " calorimeter for solid fuels. A carefully weighed quantity of fuel is placed in the crucible C, a glowing splinter, or touch cord, is placed beside the fuel and the whole closed in the glass container G. Oxygen at approximately atmospheric pressure is introduced through the

regulating valve V, until the combustion is complete. During the process of combustion the products of combustion escape at the bottom of the spiral tube HT, through holes provided for the purpose. The weight of calorimeter and its water content is obtained carefully and the temperature rise noted. The calculation will be understood from the following example.

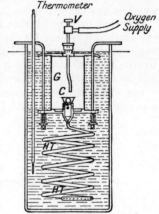

FIG. 128.

EXAMPLE. In a determination of the calorific value of a sample of coal the following data were taken, using a simplex calorimeter: Weight of coal burnt, 1·1 grams; water contained in calorimeter, 2,186 grams; water equivalent of calorimeter, 296 grams; initial temperature of the water, 18·2° C.; final temperature (maximum) of water and calorimeter, 21·5° C. Deduce the calorific value of the fuel.

$$\text{Total water equivalent of system} = 2{,}186 + 296$$
$$= 2{,}482 \text{ grams}$$
$$\therefore \text{Heat evolved by 1·1 grams of coal} = 2{,}482 \times [21·5 - 18·2]$$
$$= 2{,}482 \times 3·3$$
$$= 8{,}190·6 \text{ gram-calories.}$$
$$\therefore \text{Heat evolved per gram} = \frac{8{,}190·6}{1·1}$$
$$= 7{,}446 \text{ gram-calories.}$$
$$\therefore \text{Heat evolved per lb.} = 453·6 \times 7{,}446 \text{ gram-calories.}$$
$$= \frac{453·6 \times 7{,}446}{453·6} \text{ pound-calories.}$$
$$\text{or C.H.U.}$$
$$\therefore \text{Calorific value} = 7{,}446 \text{ C.H.U. per lb.}$$
$$= 13{,}403 \text{ B.Th.U. per lb.}$$

It should be noted in the above example that the calorific value of the fuel is numerically the same in gram-calories and in C.H.U.s. If the initial and final temperatures of the water had been read in Fahrenheit degrees the temperature difference would have been

$$3·3 \times 1·8 = 5·94.$$

Then

$$\frac{2{,}482 \times 5 \cdot 94}{1 \cdot 1} = 13{,}403$$

which is the calorific value in B.Th.U.s.

It is thus immaterial what units of weight are used so long as the same unit is used for the sample of fuel and the water. If temperatures are on the Fahrenheit scale the result will be British Thermal Units, but if on the Centigrade scale the result will be gram-calories or Centigrade Heat Units.

184. The Bomb Calorimeter. This calorimeter consists of a strong steel vessel or bomb B which is provided with a screw-on cover. The bomb is illustrated in fig. 129 whilst the calorimeter assembly is shown in fig. 130. The fuel to be tested is placed in the container C, which is suspended from the cover. Touching the fuel is a fuse wire F, fastened across two leads LL, which are also secured to the cover and pass through it to terminals TT, outside the cover. The cover is provided with a screw-down valve V, and a pipe-union U. The essential feature of this calorimeter is that the combustion takes place in oxygen at a pressure of about 360 lb. per sq. in. The oxygen is drawn from a steel bottle or cylinder which has been charged at an oxygen-producing plant.

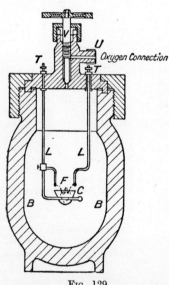

Fig. 129.

The container, fuel, and fuse wire are carefully adjusted, and the cover is securely screwed down on to the bomb so as to make a gas-tight joint. Oxygen is then charged in and the valve screwed down. The oxygen supply is then disconnected, and the whole bomb immersed completely in the water in the calorimeter. The terminals are connected to an electric battery with a firing key in the circuit and readings of temperature are taken at equal intervals of time. When the temperature is steady the key is closed and the fuel is ignited. The calorific value is calculated in the manner indicated in the last example.

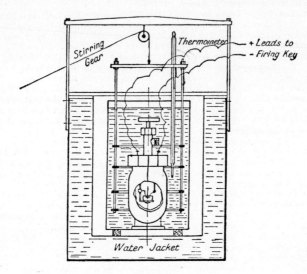

Fig. 130.

In exact determinations corrections are made for heat losses, heat evolved by complete oxidation of the sulphur, and the heat given out by the fuse wire. A special thermometer is used to read small fractions of a degree.

EXAMPLES XVII

1. What are the principal constituents of fuels ?
2. Define the terms, " ignition temperature," " calorific value," and " products of combustion."
3. State the approximate composition of air (a) by weight, (b) by volume.
4. Explain what is meant by " minimum air " and " excess " air. Why is excess air usually supplied ?
5. What amount of air will be sufficient to burn 1 lb. of carbon, 1 lb. of hydrogen and 1 lb. of sulphur ?
6. What is meant by the term relative density of a gas ? Find the weight of 3 cu. ft. of CO at N.T.P.

7. What are the higher and lower calorific values of a fuel oil of percentage composition, C 82 per cent., H 15 per cent., residue 3 per cent. ?

8. Find the minimum air for 1 lb. of the fuel oil in example 7.

9. A fuel oil contains 85·5 per cent. C, 13 per cent. H, 1·5 per cent. S. Find its calorific value and the air supply per lb. if the excess air is 25 per cent. of the minimum amount.

10. A sample of boiler coal yields the following analysis : Carbon 80 per cent., Hydrogen 5 per cent., Oxygen 8 per cent., Sulphur 1·25 per cent., Nitrogen 1·2 per cent., and Ash 4·55 per cent. How much air would be theoretically required per lb. of coal to ensure complete combustion ? How much might actually be required in practice ?   U.E.I. (2)

11. The minimum air required for the combustion of a certain fuel is 14 lb. per lb. of fuel. Assume the gas temperature at the base of the chimney to be 730° F. and that of the air in the boiler house to be 75° F. ; also assume that all the fuel goes into the flue gas. Find the heat carried away in the flue gases per lb. of coal. Assume the specific heat of the gases to be 0·24. What heat would be carried away per lb. of fuel if the excess air is 30 per cent. ?

12. In a test to determine the calorific value of a sample of coal the following data were recorded using a simplex calorimeter : water in calorimeter 2,200 grams, water equivalent of calorimeter 293 grams, initial temperature of the water 54° F., final temperature 61·4 F., weight of coal burned 1·38 grams. Find the calorific value in B.Th.U. per lb.

13. Determine the minimum weight of air required for the complete combustion of 1 lb. of fuel which contains 85 per cent. carbon and 4 per cent. hydrogen by weight, the remainder being incombustible matter. Work from the atomic weights of the substances involved.

Air contains 23 per cent. oxygen by weight.   N.C.T.E.C.

14. Carbon burns in air to form (a) carbon monoxide and (b) carbon dioxide according to the amount of oxygen present.

The equations representing the above actions are respectively:

$$(a)\ 2C + O_2 \longrightarrow 2CO$$
$$(b)\ \ C + O_2 \longrightarrow CO_2.$$

Calculate the weight of air necessary to form carbon monoxide from 8 lb. of carbon and the weight of carbon monoxide formed. How much more air would be required to form carbon dioxide ?   N.C.T.E.C.

15. Calculate the minimum weight of air required for the combustion of 1 lb. of coal containing 87·0 per cent. carbon and 4·4 per cent. hydrogen by weight.

Air contains 23 per cent. oxygen by weight.   N.C.T.E.C.

16. The percentage composition of a sample of coal is 89 per cent. carbon, 3·1 per cent. hydrogen, and 3 per cent. oxygen. Calculate the minimum weight of air required for the complete combustion of 1 lb. of this coal. If 50 per cent. of excess air is supplied, find, assuming complete combustion, the weights of the respective flue gases per lb. of coal burnt.

(*Atomic weights :* Carbon 12, hydrogen 1, oxygen 16. The atmosphere contains 23 per cent. by weight of oxygen.)   U.L.C.I.

17. Make an outline sketch of a calorimeter used for determining the calorific value of a sample of coal.

The following data were recorded during an experiment with a calorimeter : weight of coal burnt 1 gram, weight of water in calorimeter 1,020 grams, water equivalent of calorimeter 170 grams, initial temperature of water 16·2° C., final temperature of water 23·3° C.

Determine the calorific value of one pound of the sample of coal used, in Centigrade heat units, and in British Thermal Units.   U.L.C.I.

18. Determine from first principles the weight of air required to burn completely one pound of carbon and one pound of hydrogen respectively.

Estimate the weight of air required for the complete combustion of one pound of oil consisting of 87 per cent. carbon and 13 per cent. hydrogen.

What weights of steam and carbon dioxide are formed during combustion ? (See also data at end of No. 16.)   U.L.C.I.

CHAPTER XVIII

THE PRODUCTION OF POWER

185. Power Production. Power may be produced by animals, water, wind, and fire. Elementary engineering science is concerned with the principles underlying the production of power from water and fire, and this chapter deals with the production from fuels by means of fire.

A heat engine is an engine which does work when supplied with heat energy. The heat energy is initially liberated by combustion. The substance carrying the heat to the engine and doing the work in the engine is called the working substance. The working substance flows into and out of the cylinder in which the work is done. The amount of working substance leaving any engine is exactly the same as the amount entering the engine. *The substance is not destroyed in passing through the engine.* The essential feature of any heat engine is the conversion of heat energy into mechanical work in the cylinder. *There is no destruction of energy in the engine.*

These two italicized statements are based upon " the principle of the conservation of matter " and " the principle of the conservation of energy " respectively.

186. Conversion of Energy. Energy is apparent in various forms. For example, it occurs as heat, mechanical, electrical and chemical energy. Each form can be converted into any other form. Thus arises the need for conversion factors in order to express a quantity of energy in one form in terms of a quantity in another form.

187. Mechanical Equivalent of Heat. As a result of careful experiment it has been found that 778 ft.-lb. of mechanical work are needed to raise the temperature of 1 lb. of water one degree Fahrenheit. This heat quantity is the British Thermal Unit. Hence we say that 778 ft.-lb. of work is the "mechanical equivalent" of 1 British Thermal Unit. If a new heat unit is taken a new number for the mechanical equivalent of heat will be required. For example, 1,400 ft.-lb. is equivalent to 1 Centigrade Heat Unit. To honour the memory of the eminent scientist, Dr. Joule, who did a great deal of work to arrive at a correct value for this equivalent, it has been decided to call this quantity "Joule's equivalent of heat." It is denoted by the letter J. Thus the value of Joule's mechanical equivalent of heat is

$$778 \text{ ft.-lb.} = 1 \text{ B.Th.U.}$$
$$\text{or} \qquad 1,400 \text{ ,, ,, } = 1 \text{ C.H.U.}$$

In testing engines we measure the work in foot-pounds, but the heat supply is always measured in heat units. Thus one or the other of these quantities must be converted before they can be compared.

EXAMPLE. In an experiment using the friction between two discs to generate heat, it was found that 10 lb. of water was raised in temperature 7·56° F. The work was put into the apparatus by means of a force of 6 lb. moving through a distance of 10,000 ft. Find the value of Joule's equivalent.

Both heat and work quantities are measured in the same period of time.

Heat developed $= 10 \times 1 \times 7·56 = 75·6$ B.Th.U.
Work expended $= 10,000 \times 6$ ft.-lb.

∴ Mechanical equivalent $= \dfrac{60,000}{75·6} = 793$ ft.-lb. per B.Th.U.

EXAMPLE. The specific gravity of petrol is 0·725 and its calorific value is 11,150 minor calories per gram. Find the energy in ft.-lb. stored in one pint of petrol. One gallon of water weighs 10 lb. and there are 8 pints to the gallon.

Weight of 1 gallon of petrol $= 0·725 \times 10 = 7·25$ lb.

,, ,, 1 pint ,, ,, $= \dfrac{7·25}{8} = 0·906$ lb.

The calorific value is 11,150 minor calories per gram or 11,150 C.H.U. per lb.

∴ Heat per pint $= 0·906 \times 11,150$ C.H.U. $= 10,101·9$ C.H.U.
∴ Energy in ft.-lb. per pint $= 10,101·9 \times 1,400 = 14,142,760$ ft.-lb.

188. Thermal Energy. In this country thermal energy is the source of almost all the power produced for industrial and communal needs. If the heat is liberated by combustion inside the engine cylinder, the engine is said to be an internal combustion engine, whilst if the heat is liberated in a space (called the furnace or combustion chamber) outside the engine cylinder, the engine is said to be an external combustion engine.

Gas, oil and petrol engines are internal combustion engines, whilst steam engines of all kinds are external combustion engines. We have already learned that 1 B.Th.U. is equivalent to 778 ft.-lb. and 1 C.H.U. is equivalent to 1,400 ft.-lb. In practice we find it impossible to convert the whole of the heat produced by the fuel into work. A good internal combustion engine will convert about 40 per cent. of the heat in the fuel into work, whilst the steam turbine converts from 20 per cent. to 25 per cent. and in some cases over 30 per cent.

Using values of these ratios we can now illustrate, by means of examples, the relationship between rate of combustion and power.

The rate of combustion may be expressed in British Thermal Units, in cubic feet, or in lb. per minute. Alternatively the rate may be stated on the basis of one hour.

EXAMPLE. A gas engine consumes 25·3 cu. ft. of gas per hour, of calorific value 437 B.Th.U. per cu. ft. If 26 per cent. of the heat supplied to the engine is converted into work, find the horse-power of the engine.

$$\text{Gas consumed per minute} = \frac{25\cdot3}{60} = 0\cdot4216 \text{ cu. ft.}$$

Heat supplied to engine per minute
$$= 0\cdot4216 \times 437 = 184\cdot24 \text{ B.Th.U.}$$

$$\text{Heat converted into work} = \frac{26}{100} \times 184\cdot24 = 47\cdot9 \text{ B.Th.U.}$$

$$\therefore \text{Work done per minute} = 47\cdot9 \times 778 = 37,266 \text{ ft.-lb.}$$

$$\therefore \text{Horse-power developed} = \frac{37,266}{33,000} = 1\cdot129 \text{ H.P.}$$

EXAMPLE. The heat supplied to an engine per lb. of steam is 1,224 B.Th.U. The engine converts ¼ of this heat into work and develops 560 horse-power. How much steam is flowing to the engine per minute ?

Work done per minute = 560 × 33,000 = 18,480,000 ft.-lb.

$$\text{or in Heat Units} = \frac{18,480,000}{778} = 23,760 \text{ B.Th.U. per minute.}$$

Now 1 lb. of steam does work to the extent of ¼ × 1,224 B.Th.U.
$$= 306 \text{ B.Th.U.}$$

$$\therefore \text{Required weight of steam per minute} = \frac{23,760}{306} = 77\cdot64 \text{ lb.}$$

189. The Steam Engine Plant. The word plant includes all the arrangement of boilers, furnaces, chimneys, pipes, engines. condensers, cooling towers, etc., which are necessary in order to develop power by use of steam. A diagram of a simple condensing steam engine plant is shown in fig. 131. It includes the following main sections :

(1) *A source of water supply*, W. This may be a river, canal, well, tank, or reservoir. If the engine is a condensing engine, and if the condensed steam is returned to this feed tank, then the tank itself is called the *hotwell*. The water in it is at a higher temperature than raw water from an outside source. The term hotwell is of long-standing use, dating from the days of the Newcomen engine, which was a condensing engine. The water from the cylinders was drained to a well below the engine and the boiler feed water was taken from the well.

(2) *A boiler feed pump* to draw the water from the hotwell and force it into the boiler. Feed pumps are steam driven in most cases although there are frequent cases where electrical drives are employed.

(3) *The boiler or steam generator*. This part of the steam plant occupies about one-half of the total space and demands great skill in manufacture, maintenance and control, particularly when very high pressures are in use. The combustion takes place in the boiler casing, heat is liberated, and is encouraged to pass through the tubes and plates of the boiler structure into the water space. The greater the amount of heat which passes into the water space the greater the amount of steam generated. Fuel and air are fed to the furnace, water is pumped into the water space and steam leaves the boiler. The function of the boiler is to produce steam.

(4) *The main steam pipe*. The steam leaves the steam space in the boiler through the main stop valve and enters the steam pipe. At the engine end of the steam pipe is another valve known as the engine stop valve. This valve is used to start and stop the engine.

(5) *The engine cylinder*. Here the steam does work. It is for this purpose that it has been generated, and conveyed to the cylinder of the engine. This part of the plant is called the working cylinder.

(6) *The exhaust pipe*. This pipe, denoted EP on the diagram, conveys the steam from the cylinder after it has done its work. It may lead the steam into the open air, when the engine is said

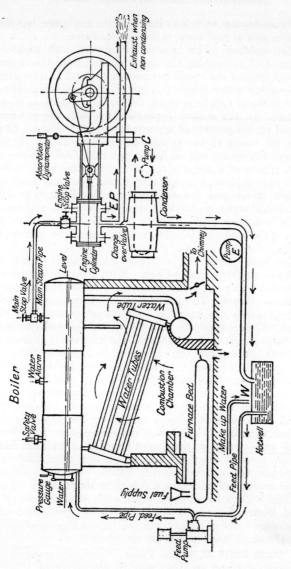

Fig. 132.

to be *non-condensing*, or, it may lead it to the condenser, in which case the engine is said to be a *condensing engine*.

(7) *The condenser.* This is a vessel supplied with water for the purpose of condensing the steam coming from the engine. The latent heat of the steam is removed by, and is transferred to, the cooling water which thereby is raised in temperature. Condensers are of two main types, (*a*) surface condensers, (*b*) jet condensers. In the surface condenser, fig. 132, the steam is condensed on the outside of brass tubes whilst the water flows through the inside of the tubes. In this case the condensed steam and the condensing water do not mix. Jet condensers, fig. 133, consist of a water spray arranged to discharge into a vessel which receives the exhaust steam. In this case the condensed steam and the condensing water intimately mix. The condensed steam is called the *condensate* and the condensing water is known as cooling water or circulating water. The function of the condenser is to create low pressures by condensing the steam.

(8) *Condenser pumps.* If a condenser is used it will be necessary to employ certain pumps. With a surface condenser, an extraction pump E, fig. 131, is necessary to lift the condensate out of the condenser. This pump is sometimes referred to as the air pump because it is frequently used to pump out air as well as water. The air comes in with the steam, and leaks through low-pressure glands, and would spoil the vacuum if allowed to accumulate. A separate air extractor is generally fitted in modern plant. A pump, C, is also necessary to circulate the condensing water. This pump is called the circulating pump. In the jet condenser the circulating pump is also the extraction pump, although a separate air extractor may be employed.

It will be noted that when a surface condenser is used the same feed water can be used over and over again. If all leaks could be prevented no addition need be made to the total water circulating through the plant after it has once been filled. In practice, however, test cocks, safety valves, leaks, etc., pass out a certain amount of substance which must therefore be " made up." This is done by adding a small amount of new water to the feed tank. This new water is known as " make-up feed," or " make-up " water. The circulation of working substance is clearly shown on the diagram of the plant.

190. Main Parts of Steam Plant. The main parts of the steam plant will now be dealt with in greater detail.

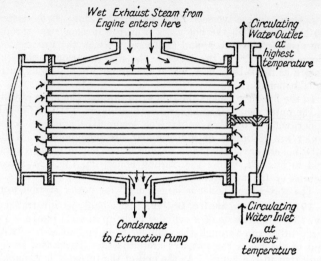

Wet Exhaust Steam from Engine enters here

↑ Circulating Water Outlet at highest temperature

Condensate to Extraction Pump

↑ Circulating Water Inlet at lowest temperature

FIG. 132.

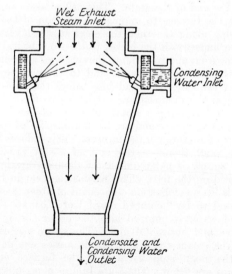

Wet Exhaust Steam Inlet

Condensing Water Inlet

↓ Condensate and Condensing Water Outlet

FIG. 133.

Q

Boilers. These vessels may be divided into two classes : (1) those in which the hot gases from the furnace pass through the inside of the tubes, and (2) those in which the water passes along the inside of the tubes. The first mentioned class are known as fire-tube boilers, whilst the second are known as water-tube boilers.

In the fire-tube boilers the tubes run through the mass of water in the outer shell. The boiler described in art. 191 is a fire-tube boiler with two tubes only. The locomotive and the Scotch boiler are examples of multitubular fire-tube boilers. Water-tube boilers are indicated in outline in the steam plant diagram and in fig. 122, whilst the Stirling boiler, fig. 136, shows more details of the arrangement.

The water-tube boiler is largely used for power station work.

191. The Lancashire Boiler. This boiler is illustrated in fig. 134. It consists of a cylinder built up of steel plates. Two large tubes run through the cylinder from end to end. At one end of the tubes the furnaces are situated. The water level is indicated in the figure. At the end of the furnaces is situated a fire-brick " bridge " for the purpose of preventing the fuel from falling off the end of the grate. This bridge also causes the hot gases from the furnace to impinge on the top of the fire tube. After passing along the tube the gases descend vertically and then return underneath the boiler, to the front of it. The gases divide at the front and rise up into the side flues wherein they pass along to the back of the boiler and to the chimney. At the exit end of the side flues, and just before the gases enter the chimney flue, the dampers are fixed. These are sliding plates controlled by wire ropes from the front of the boiler. The dampers slide vertically and are for the purpose of reducing the rate of flow of air through the furnace. This reduces the rate of combustion and therefore the rate of steam production. If the steam supply is not required the dampers are lowered and fuel is placed on the fires. This retains the heat in the furnace but there is little combustion on account of absence of air. The boiler is said to be " damped down " or " banked."

The feed water is pumped into the boiler through the feed check valve and horizontal pipe. The steam passes from the water to the steam space and thence passes out of the boiler through the main stop valve. On the furnace crowns, the fusible plugs are fitted. These are bronze plugs filled with low melting-point metal F, to give warning when the water level

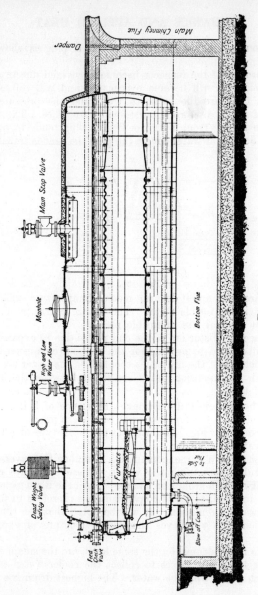

FIG. 134.

is dangerously low. A section of such a plug is shown in fig. 135.

If the crowns of the furnaces become uncovered due to a low water level, they will become overheated and will soften. In this state they are too weak to withstand the pressure and bulging, if not a disastrous burst, will take place. The water and steam issuing from a broken fusible plug tends to quench the fire. So long as water covers the plug the heat is transferred

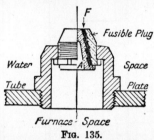

Fig. 135.

quickly through it and it does not reach a temperature sufficiently high to melt the fusible metal. The bronze centre piece, A, is to prevent gradual loss of fusible metal.

To reduce the distortion of the end plates due to expansion of the fire tubes, and to provide for the unequal expansion of the top and bottom of the fire tubes themselves the latter are often corrugated, or expansion joints are fitted between the several lengths of tube.

192. The Water-Tube Boiler. This type of boiler is now widely used and is the representative of modern practice in steam generator design. Fig. 136 illustrates the latest type of Tri-drum Stirling water-tube boiler.

It consists of a large combustion chamber C, traversed by rows of tubes containing the water. These tubes are clearly shown in two main groups or " banks." All the main generating tubes are inclined, to assist convection and therefore to procure vigorous water circulation. It will be noted that the tubes are bent, which largely relieves the boiler structure of expansion stresses.

The two upper drums, on the same level, are the steam drums, whilst the lower one serves to collect the cooler water and the mud which enters with the water. The highest drum is a steam receiver.

The feed water is introduced into the top right-hand drum, through the feed check valve F, from the economizer E. This

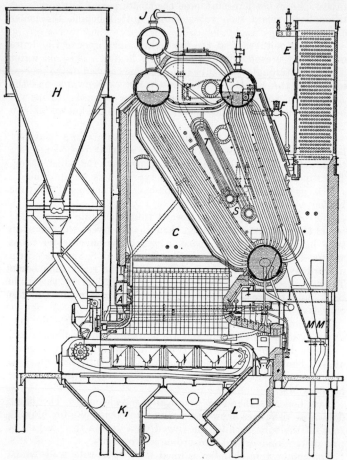

Fig. 136.

feed water assists the circulation, which is clockwise round the boiler, by its greater density.

The steam leaves the boiler at J and passes into the pipe "header" to the right of the letter S.

From this pipe it passes to the other just above the letter S, traversing the hairpin tubes T. These tubes are the super-heater tubes. From the left-hand pipe the steam passes to the engines through the main stop valve shown dotted behind the boiler casing.

The nest of tubes E at the top right-hand corner of the figure comprises the economizer or feed-water heater. The cold water is pumped through these tubes and becomes heated in the process of flowing through them. The water flows downwards and the gases, from which the heat is derived, flow upwards. Thus the hottest water meets the hottest gas. This is known as the " contra-flow " system.

It will be noted that the superheater tubes are in a relatively hot part of the combustion chamber and that the economizer tubes are in the path of the gases as they leave the boiler casing. The superheater is of the inverted type and is self-draining.

The gas baffles are shown crosshatched amongst the tube banks.

The path of the gases is upward from the grate to near the top of the combustion chamber, then down between the two main tube banks, through the space in which the superheater tubes are fixed. Just below the superheater headers S, the gases turn upward again, traversing the left half of the right tube bank. They then descend through the right-hand half of this tube bank, and thence ascend through the economizer tubes to the chimney.

The dampers are arranged close to the induced draught fans at the base of the chimney and are not shown in the illustration.

The fuel hopper is shown at H and the air supply duct is shown at A. The small fuel escaping the grate drops into the hopper K, and the ashes into the hopper L. Flue dust collects in the hoppers MM.

This boiler is therefore practically self-cleaning. The black dots near the tubes show the position of steam jets for blowing soot off the tubes, whilst the ringed dots denote the position of pyrometers and draught recording instruments.

The combustion chamber is lined with water-tube walls called " Bailey " walls to improve the efficiency of the boiler and to lengthen the life of the chamber lining.

The boiler illustrated generates steam at 350 lb. per sq. in. gauge with a final superheat temperature of 585° F. It is capable of producing 65,000 lb. of steam per hour with a feed temperature

to the economizer of 190° F. The normal load efficiency is
85·5 per cent.

193. Boiler Fittings. All boilers are fitted with accessories
in order to ensure safety and complete control of the process of

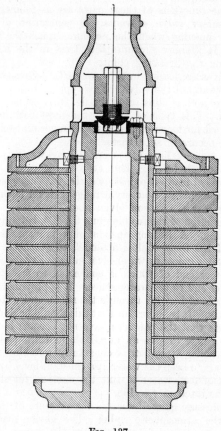

Fig. 137.

steam generation. These accessories are known as fittings or
mountings.

The safety fittings are (*a*) the safety valves, (*b*) the fusible plugs, (c) the water level indicator or water gauge, (d) the high steam and low water alarm valve.

The control fittings are (a) the pressure gauge, (b) the feed water check valve, (c) the blow-off cock, (d) the main stop valve, and (e) the dampers.

Briefly, the functions of these parts are as follows :

(1) The safety valve prevents the generation of excessive pressure, by opening when the pressure equals the load upon the valve. It thereby prevents the stress in the boiler metal from reaching the breaking point.

Safety valves are loaded in three ways, (1) by weights directly applied to the top of the valve. This type is known as the dead weight valve and is illustrated in fig. 137, which shows the construction. This type of load is the most certain type but cannot be used for locomotives or ships on account of the movement which occurs in such cases.

The next type of load (2) is created by weights applied to the valve through levers. This type is illustrated in fig. 51. The third type of load is applied by springs. This type is largely used and is the only satisfactory arrangement for locomotive and ships' boilers for the reason given above.

(2) The function of the fusible plug, fig. 135, is to give warning of overheating. A leaking fusible plug prevents satisfactory operation of the boiler unless attended to at once.

(3) The water gauge or water-level indicator consists of a glass tube the upper end of which is connected to the steam space and the lower end to the water space. It is provided with cocks for the purpose of blowing through the steam and water passages independently. It is important that this should be done periodically to ensure that the passages have not become blocked, thus causing the gauge to give an unreliable indication of the water level. The boiler attendant is constantly watching this gauge. He endeavours to keep the water at a constant level by regulating the amount of feed water to suit the demand for steam. The gauge is illustrated in fig. 138.

(4) The pressure gauge indicates the pressure of the steam in excess of the atmospheric value. The gauge reads zero at atmospheric pressure. In this country the gauges always give pressures in lb. per square inch.

(5) The dampers regulate the draft and thereby control the rate of combustion.

(6) The feed check valve is illustrated in fig. 139. It consists

of a feed-regulating valve which is controlled by the hand wheel.
The amount of opening can be controlled and thus the amount
of feed water is controlled. The feed valve is also a check or
non-return valve. The water can flow up through the valve
but cannot flow downwards because the valve would immediately
close. The valve is not attached to the valve spindle. This

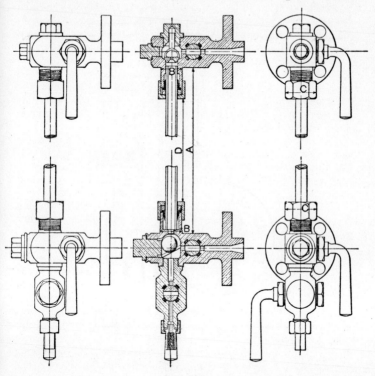

Fig. 138.

arrangement is used to prevent loss of water or steam from the
boiler in the event of a burst feed pipe or disablement of the feed
pump. The pressure in the feed pipe is always more than that
in the boiler. In some cases it may be considerably more than
boiler pressure.

(7) The blow-off cock (see fig. 134) is for the purpose of empty-

ing the boiler when necessary.   It is also used for blowing down
purposes.   The solids in the feed water are left in the boiler when
evaporation takes place and as a result the density of the boiler
water increases.   From time to time a quantity of water is blown

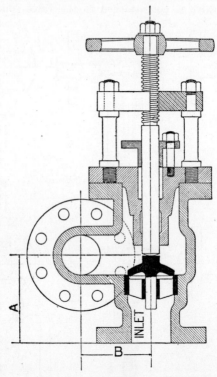

Fig. 139.

out and replaced with fresh feed water.   This removes a large
amount of the solid matter from the boiler.

(8) The stop valve, the position of which is shown in figs. 131,
134 and 136, is for the purpose of shutting off the boiler from the
steam-pipe range.   It is also used to regulate the flow of steam
from any particular boiler.   A non-return valve is usually fitted

close to this valve in order to prevent accidental admission of steam to an empty boiler in which men may be working.

(9) The high steam and low water alarm is illustrated in fig. 140. This device consists of a large valve R, containing a smaller valve shown at the top of the spindle C. An extension B, of the spindle C, carries a collar H and a dead weight O. This weight O loads the small valve for high steam and this, together

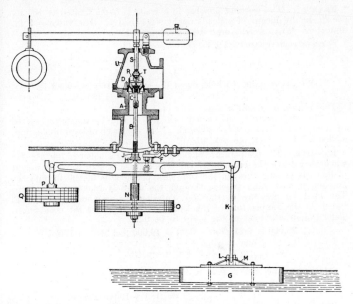

Fig. 140.

with the lever and weight outside the boiler, loads the outer valve R for high steam.

If the water level falls to a low value the float G also falls and the lever to which this float is attached turns about its fulcrum E in a clockwise direction. This brings the projections on the float lever into contact with the collar H. Further fall in water level will relieve both valves of load when they will open. The steam discharges noisily and the attention of the stoker is at once called to the fact that the water level is too low.

All boilers are fitted with access doors, or manholes for internal inspection purposes. Mud holes are also provided at the bottom of the boilers to remove sludge. To assist in the process of sludge removal wash-out plugs are also fitted through which a hose may be inserted.

194. Exercises on Boiler Calculations. The following exercises will illustrate calculations on various parts of the boiler plant.

EXAMPLE. The working pressure in a boiler is to be limited to 160 lb. per sq. in. by means of a dead weight safety valve. The valve is 3 in. diameter. What weight must be placed on it ?

Force on each square inch of valve area = 160 lb.

$$\text{Area of valve} = \frac{\pi D^2}{4} = \frac{3 \cdot 1416 \times 3 \times 3}{4} = 7 \cdot 0686 \text{ sq. in.}$$

∴ Weight required to hold down the valve = 160 × 7·0686 lb.
$$= 1{,}131 \text{ lb.}$$

This is just over half a ton.

If this valve were spring-loaded then this would be the force exerted by the spring when the valve is closed. For calculation of lever and spring-loaded safety valves, see art. 46.

EXAMPLE. The temperature of the gases leaving a boiler is 700° F., and when they leave the economizer the temperature is 350° F. The weight of flue gas passing through the tube nest per hour is 36,000 lb. and the amount of feed water passing through the tubes is 16,000 lb. per hour. The inlet temperature of the feed entering the economizer is 100° F. Calculate the temperature of the feed water as it leaves the economizer. Take the specific heat of the gases to be 0·24.

∴ 36,000 × 0·24 (700 − 350) = 16,000 × 1 × (t − 100).

$$\therefore \frac{36{,}000}{16{,}000} \times 0 \cdot 24 \times 350 = t - 100,$$

i.e. 2·25 × 0·24 × 350 = t − 100
189 = t − 100

∴ t = 189 + 100 = 289° F.

This is the feed-water temperature.

EXAMPLE. The amount of coal supplied to a boiler furnace is 1,150 lb. per hour and its calorific value is 12,240 B.Th.U. per lb. in the state as fired. The air supply is 18 lb. per lb. of coal and its temperature is 60° F. The ashes withdrawn per hour amount to 92 lb. The temperature of the gases entering the chimney is 348° F. What percentage of the heat fired is carried away by the gases ? Take the specific heat of the gases as 0·25.

Weight of fuel passing into flue gas = (1,150 − 92) = 1,058 lb. per hr.

∴ Weight of fuel passing into flue gas per lb. of coal fired = $\dfrac{1{,}058}{1{,}150}$

$$= 0 \cdot 92 \text{ lb.}$$

∴ Weight of flue gas per lb. of coal fired = 18 + 0·92 = 18·92 lb.
This weight rises in temperature from 60° F. to 348° F.

∴ Heat carried away per lb. of coal fired $= 18 \cdot 92 \times 0 \cdot 25 \times (348 - 60)$
$$= 18 \cdot 92 \times 0 \cdot 25 \times 288$$
$$= 18 \cdot 92 \times 72$$
$$= 1,362 \text{ B.Th.U.}$$

∴ Percentage heat carried away $= \dfrac{1,362}{12,240} = 11 \cdot 13$ per cent.

This assumes that the ashes are cooled to 60° F. before they are withdrawn from the ash hopper.

195. Evaporative Power of Boilers. This is the amount of water which the boiler can evaporate in one hour. It is the steam produced per hour. It is usually stated in pounds. The evaporative capacity of a boiler depends on—

(1) The heat required to produce 1 lb. of steam.
(2) the amount of heat which can be got through the boiler tubes to the water.
(3) the amount of fuel which can be burned per hour in the furnace.
(4) the heating value of the fuel.

The heat required to produce 1 lb. of steam will depend on the working pressure, on the feed-water temperature, and on the quality of the steam as it leaves the boiler. The heat which passes through the tube walls into the water space is a measure of the effectiveness of the boiler. It depends on the difference between the gas temperature and the water temperature, on the material of the tube, and on the thickness and state of the tube wall. The amount of fuel which can be burned in the furnace will depend on the dimensions of the furnace, and the rate of air supply.

EXAMPLE. The combustion chamber of a water-tube boiler measures 10 ft. × 20 ft. × 12 ft. and the heat is released at the rate of 39,600 B.Th.U. per cu. ft. per hr. If the working pressure is 200 lb. per sq. in. abs. and the feed temperature is 212° F., find the evaporation of the boiler. Assume the steam to be dry as it leaves the boiler and that 70 per cent. of the heat released in the furnace is actually used in steam production.

Heat required to produce 1 lb. of dry steam $= 1,199 \cdot 5 - (212 - 32)$
$$= 1,019 \cdot 5 \text{ B.Th.U.}$$

Heat released per hour $= 10 \times 20 \times 12 \times 39,600$ B.Th.U.
$$= 2,400 \times 39,600 = 95,040,000 \text{ B.Th.U.}$$

Heat actually passing through tube wall $= \dfrac{70}{100} \times 95,040,000$ B.Th.U.

$$= 66,528,000 \text{ B.Th.U.}$$

∴ Steam produced per hour $= \dfrac{66,528,000}{1,019 \cdot 5} = 65,250$ lb.

196. Boiler Efficiency. The thermal or heat efficiency of a boiler is the ratio $\dfrac{\text{Heat actually producing steam}}{\text{Heat supplied by the fuel}}$. Both the heat quantities used in this ratio must be in the same kind of heat unit, and also must be for the same period of time. The actual period of time is not important, but it must be the same for both numerator and denominator of the ratio. The usual method is to calculate the weight of steam produced per lb. of fuel and then the ratio becomes

$$\text{Thermal efficiency} = \frac{\text{Heat producing steam per lb. of fuel}}{\text{Calorific value of the fuel}}.$$

EXAMPLE. A boiler produces 8·25 lb. of steam per lb. of fuel. The temperature of the feed water is 170·1° F. and the working pressure is 150 lb. per sq. in. abs. The steam leaving the boiler is 0·98 dry. The calorific value of the fuel is 15,660 B.Th.U. per lb. Find the boiler efficiency.

Heat in 1 lb. of wet steam as it leaves the boiler $= 330\cdot6 + 0\cdot98 \times 864\cdot5$
$$= 330\cdot6 + 847\cdot2$$
$$= 1{,}177\cdot8 \text{ B.Th.U.}$$
Heat in 1 lb. of feed water entering the boiler $= 138\cdot1$ B.Th.U.
∴ Heat supplied for each pound of steam produced $= 1{,}177\cdot8 - 138\cdot1$
$$= 1{,}039\cdot7 \text{ B.Th.U.}$$
Heat used for steam production for each lb. of fuel $= 1{,}039\cdot7 \times 8\cdot25$
$$= 8{,}577\cdot5 \text{ B.Th.U.}$$

∴ Thermal efficiency of boiler $= \dfrac{8{,}577\cdot5}{15{,}660} = 0\cdot547$ or 54·7 per cent.

We may write the expression for the boiler efficiency in general terms as follows :

Let S $=$ weight of steam produced per unit time.

    C $=$ weight of fuel burnt in unit time.

    H $=$ calorific value of fuel.

    H$'$ $=$ heat actually contained in 1 lb. of steam at boiler stop valve reckoned from 32° F.

    h_f $=$ heat in 1 lb. of feed water reckoned from 32° F.

    h_g $=$ heat of the liquid at evaporation temperature reckoned from 32° F.

    t_g $=$ temperature of evaporation.

    t_s $=$ actual temperature of steam if superheated.

    Cp $=$ specific heat of steam if superheated.

    L $=$ latent heat of steam at working pressure.

    x $=$ dryness fraction if steam is wet at boiler stop valve.

Then. Heat supplied per lb. of steam $= [\text{H}' - h_f]$.

Heat passing through boiler tubes in unit time $= \text{S}[\text{H}' - h_f]$

Heat released in furnace in unit time $= C \times H$.

$\therefore$ Boiler Efficiency $= \dfrac{S[H' - h_f]}{C \times H}$

Note that

for wet steam $\qquad H' = h_g + xL.$ } See arts.

„ dry „ $\qquad\qquad H' = h_g + L.$ } 165, 166,

„ superheated steam $\quad H' = h_g + L + Cp(t_s - t_g)$ } 167.

Also note that $\dfrac{S}{C} =$ weight of steam produced per lb. of fuel.

If this is denoted by W, the boiler efficiency becomes

$$= \frac{W(H' - h_f)}{H}.$$

EXAMPLE. During a boiler test of 7 hours' duration, the amount of coal burnt was 12,230 lb. and the weight of water evaporated was 109,440 lb. The boiler pressure was 120 lb. per sq. in. abs. and the feed temperature was 293° F. The calorific value of the coal was 14,670 B.Th.U. per lb. and the steam was dry as it left the boiler. Find the boiler efficiency.

Weight of steam produced per lb. of coal $= \dfrac{109{,}440}{12{,}230}$ lb. $= 8.95$ lb.

Heat required to produce 1 lb. of steam $= [312.5 + 878.9] - 262.5$
$\qquad\qquad = 928.9$ B.Th.U.

$\therefore$ Heat actually producing steam per lb. of coal burnt $= 928.9 \times 8.95$
$\qquad\qquad = 8{,}314$ B.Th.U.

$\therefore$ Boiler Efficiency $= \dfrac{8{,}314}{14{,}670} = 0.567$ or 56.7 per cent.

197. Equivalent Evaporation. This is the evaporation produced under standard conditions by the heat passing through the plates of the boiler under consideration.

The equivalent evaporation forms a means of comparing the performance of boilers which have different feed temperatures and working pressures, and which are fired with the same fuel.

Different boilers have widely varying feed temperatures and working pressures, hence the heat which will produce one pound of steam in one boiler may not be sufficient to produce one pound of steam in another. Thus it is meaningless to say that one boiler produces $7\frac{1}{2}$ lb. of steam and another, when using the same fuel, produces $8\frac{1}{4}$ lb. of steam per pound of fuel, because this gives no indication of the heat necessary to produce one lb. of steam. If, however, we say that the equivalent evaporation of one boiler is $7\frac{1}{2}$ lb. and that of the other is $8\frac{1}{4}$ lb., then the latter is a much better boiler than the former.

The feed water in the standard boiler is at 212° F., which is atmospheric boiling point, and the working pressure is 14·7 lb. per sq. in. Consequently the steam in the standard boiler is produced at 212° F. Under these conditions we are not heating up the water. We are changing its state only, and therefore we need supply latent heat alone. This latent heat is 970 B.Th.U. or 539 C.H.U. per lb. Thus in the standard boiler the heat required to produce 1 lb. of steam is always the same. This amount is known as " the standard evaporation unit " and is the latent heat of steam at atmospheric pressure. Since the feed water is at 212° F. and the steam is formed at this temperature in the standard boiler the steam in the standard boiler is said to be produced " from water at 212° and at 212° F." Thus the words " from and at 212° F." imply the evaporation which requires latent heat only, at atmospheric pressure, to produce 1 lb. of steam.

With the notation in the last article we have equivalent evaporation per lb. of fuel

$$= \frac{\text{Heat passing through boiler plates per lb. of fuel}}{\text{Standard evaporation unit}}$$

$$= \frac{W(H' - h_f)}{970} \text{ when } H' \text{ and } h_f \text{ are in B.Th.U.}$$

$$= \frac{W(H' - h_f)}{539} \text{ when } H' \text{ and } h_f \text{ are in C.H.U.}$$

Note that the difference between this expression and that for the boiler efficiency lies in the denominator.

EXAMPLE. What is the equivalent evaporation of the boiler in the first example of art. 196.

$$\text{Equivalent evaporation} = \frac{8,577·5}{970} \text{ lb. of steam per lb. of coal.}$$

$$= 8·84 \text{ lb.}$$

Thus 8·84 lb. of steam produced in the standard boiler is equivalent to a production of 8·25 lb. of steam in the actual boiler.

EXAMPLE. A boiler working at 130 lb. per sq. in. abs. and supplied with water 140° F. evaporates 7·8 lb. of water per lb. of coal. What is the equivalent evaporation (a) per lb. of coal, (b) per lb. of steam. Assume the steam dry as it leaves the boiler.

Total heat in 1 lb. of steam leaving the boiler = 1,192·8 B.Th.U.
   ,,   ,,   ,, 1 lb. of water entering the boiler =   108 B.Th.U.

∴ Heat supplied to water and steam per lb. = 1,084·8 B.Th.U.
  ∴ Heat producing steam per lb. of coal = 7·8 × 1,084·8
                = 8,461 B.Th.U.

(a) $\therefore$ Equivalent Evaporation $= \dfrac{8,461}{970}$ lb. $= 8\cdot72$ lb. per lb. of coal.

(b) Equivalent Evaporation $= \dfrac{1,084\cdot8}{970}$ lb. per lb. of steam

$$= 1\cdot118 \text{ lb.}$$

That is, 1 lb. of steam produced in the actual boiler has an equivalent production of 1·118 lb. in the standard boiler.

198. The Steam Engine.   The steam engine is manufactured in two forms : (1) the reciprocating piston engine, and (2) the rotary engine without pistons.   This engine is called the turbine engine.   This book deals with the reciprocating type because the principles of the action of this type are more easily understood. A simple engine is illustrated in fig. 141.   It is fitted with drop valves and the valve gear is omitted.   An outline arrangement showing how the valves are operated is shown below the section of the engine.   The cylinder of the engine is the portion in which the work is done.   The action is as follows.   Let the piston P be at the left-hand end of the cylinder with the left-hand exhaust valve V_E closed.   Let the right-hand exhaust valve V_E' be open. Now suppose the right-hand steam valve to be closed and allow the left-hand valve SV to open.   Then any steam on the right-hand side of the piston can leave the cylinder when the piston commences to move.   The opening of the left-hand steam supply valve admits steam to the left of the piston and the steam pressure overcomes the resistance of the piston and the latter moves. When part of the stroke has been completed the left-hand valve SV can be closed without affecting or altering the others.   This action *cuts off* the steam and the steam supply ceases.   The steam now falls in pressure until the piston is near the end of the stroke.   At a convenient point near the end of the stroke the exhaust valve V_E, on the left, opens.   Most of the steam now flows out through this valve and the remainder is pushed out by the piston which returns to the left end of the cylinder owing to the pressure of the steam admitted through the top right-hand valve.   The left-hand exhaust valve remains open almost to the left-hand end of the piston travel.   The action on the right-hand side of the piston is the same as that on the left.   In this case the engine is said to be " double acting."   If the steam had access to one side of the piston only the engine would be " single acting."   In this case the piston is returned to the left-hand end by the energy stored in the flywheel during the out stroke

R

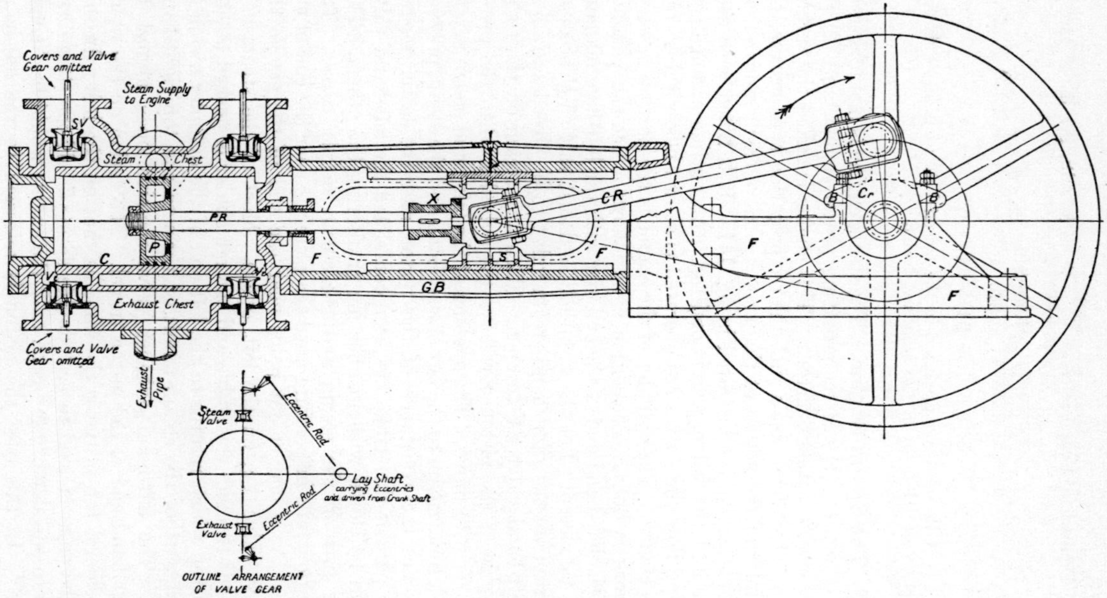
Covers and Valve Gear omitted
Steam Supply to Engine
SV
Steam
Chest
X
CR
Cr
B
B
PR
P
C
F
F
F
F
S
GB
V
Exhaust Chest
Covers and Valve Gear omitted
Exhaust Pipe
Steam Valve
Eccentric Rod
Lay Shaft
carrying Eccentrics and driven from Crank Shaft
Eccentric Rod
Exhaust Valve
OUTLINE ARRANGEMENT OF VALVE GEAR

FIG. 141.

or working stroke. It will now be possible to describe the functions or uses of the various parts of the engine.

The cylinder C constrains the steam (or in the case of gas engines, the gas) and allows its pressure to be effective in producing movement in a definite direction. It is the part of the engine in which the work is done. The piston is really a thick plate forming a movable wall to the cylinder. The force on the piston is the product of its area and the pressure intensity. The piston receives the force and being free to move, allows the steam to do work. The piston rod PR transmits the force from the inside of the cylinder to the outside parts of the engine mechanism. The outer end of the piston rod is attached to the crosshead X. This is really a knuckle joint fitted with smooth slippers S, to support it (see art. 27). The crosshead forms the connection between the piston rod and the connecting rod CR. The slippers slide on the guide bars GB, and thus compel the piston-rod end, and the attached end of the connecting rod, to move in a straight line. The connecting rod, CR, connects the sliding crosshead to the rotating crank, Cr. The crank and the connecting rod are the means of converting the reciprocating motion of the piston into the rotary motion of the shaft. The force exerted by the connecting rod on the crank causes the shaft to rotate.

The shaft is mounted in bearings B, which are securely attached to the bed frame, F, of the engine. The engine frame is for the purpose of connecting the engine parts together in a rigid manner. The guide bars in the engine illustrated also form part of the frame. If the piston force is 5 tons, then the cylinder experiences an equal and opposite force and the frame takes this load. Should the frame break the cylinder would move backward instead of the piston moving forward. The valves already mentioned are for the purpose of admitting and releasing the steam at the right moments. The steam valve admits the steam when it opens and cuts off the steam when it closes. It thus performs two acts. The exhaust valve allows the steam to leave the cylinder when it opens and prevents it from leaving when it closes. Thus this valve also performs two acts. These four actions or " events " will be referred to later (art. 237). The valve operating gear operates the valves at the right time and in correct order. The valve gear is also called the distributing gear and the valves themselves are called the distributing valves since they " distribute " the steam.

There are two other parts of the steam engine which are of

importance. These are the Governor and the Flywheel. If an engine is driving a factory by means of ropes and if the ropes break suddenly the engine will have no resistance to overcome. It would be relieved of "load" and unless the steam were immediately shut off it would increase in speed at an enormous rate. Very high speed would result in high inertia stresses and the engine would ultimately smash to pieces. To prevent such an occurrence, and to limit definitely the speed of the engine to a known value at practically all loads, the governor is fitted. Its action is due to centrifugal force and the outward movement of the flyballs causes the valve gear to supply less steam and, in the event of a complete breakdown of the transmission, so to reduce the steam supply that the speed cannot become excessive. The governor therefore prevents changes in speed for long periods of time. That is, the engine will make N revolutions per minute, for hour after hour, under the control of a good governor.

The action of the flywheel is also that of speed control, but it controls it in a different way and for very short intervals.

When steam is supplied at full pressure and then cut off before the end of the stroke as described on page 241 the piston force is variable during the stroke. Thus the engine tends to increase in speed in the first part of the stroke and to fall in speed when the pressure falls after cut off. This change in speed does in fact occur, and is known as the "cyclic variation in speed." It occurs twice in every revolution in the case of a double-acting engine. The kinetic energy of the flywheel is thus changing during the stroke. When the piston effort is in excess of the mean value needed to overcome the load on the engine, the excess energy developed is stored in the flywheel. This energy increases the speed.

When the resistance of the load is greater than the piston effort the flywheel gives out energy and in so doing slows down. Thus the function of the flywheel is to keep down the cyclic fluctuation in speed and it does this by storing and restoring the excess kinetic energy. The kinetic energy of the governor does not affect the governing action.

199. Internal Combustion Engines. This class of engine includes gas, oil and petrol engines of all kinds. In all cases the air and fuel are supplied to the working cylinder of the engine. Gas and oil engines may be arranged either single-acting or double-acting, but as the former arrangement is most common we shall confine our attention to the single-acting types. Petrol engines are invariably single-acting engines.

All internal combustion engines work on one or other of two cycles. The term cycle is intended to mean a series of processes taking place in a definite unchanging order, as will be understood from art. 242. The two cycles are known as " the Otto or Four-stroke cycle " and the " Clerk " or two-stroke cycle respectively. These cycles are dealt with in arts. 242 and 244. Gas engines and petrol engines are fitted with electrical arrangements for igniting the fuel and air charge, at the correct time in the cycle. This electrical gear is known as the ignition system. By means of a magneto or, alternatively, by means of a battery and coil, a strong electric spark is made to pass across an open gap in the combustion chamber or cylinder head. When this spark passes the gas and air, or petrol vapour and air, are ignited, and combustion is almost instantaneous. The speed of the combustion is so great that petrol engines can run at well over 3,000 r.p.m. Modern type oil engines have no electrical device. They depend for their ignition upon the fact that a gas compressed rapidly rises in temperature, and if the compression is sufficient a very high temperature can be obtained. The fuel oil is sprayed into the compressed air in the cylinder, and combustion takes place at once. These engines are known as self-ignition engines or compression-ignition engines.

200. The Four-Stroke Gas Engine. This engine is illustrated in fig. 142, which shows a sectional view.

The functions of the main parts are similar to those of the main parts of the steam engine. The principal differences between the parts of the steam engine and the gas engine are : (1) The piston of the single-acting gas engine is open at one end and forms the bearing for the crosshead pin. The crosshead pin changes its name to gudgeon pin in the gas engine. The piston also carries the guide thrust which is taken by the crosshead slippers in the steam engine. The piston of the gas engine illustrated thus performs the duties of piston and crosshead together. The second difference is that the cylinder of the gas engine is enclosed by a water jacket, WJ, which is kept full of water flowing slowly upwards through it. This water jacket is necessary to prevent the piston and cylinder from becoming too hot. The flame temperatures are sufficiently high to melt the metals of piston and cylinder if the temperatures were maintained for any considerable period. The cylinder of the steam

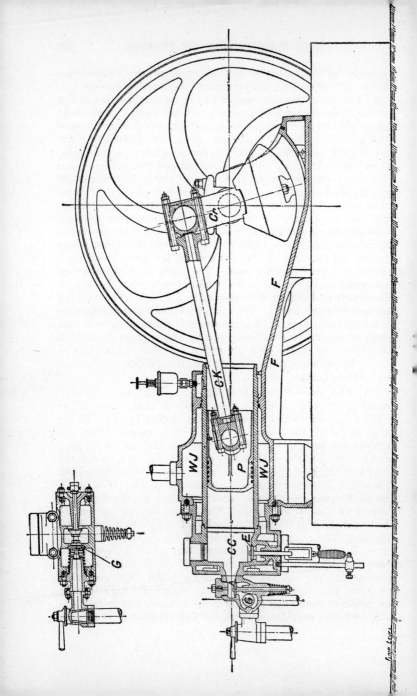

engine is kept as hot as possible and in the case of slow-speed engines the cylinder is often surrounded by a steam jacket. The piston of the gas engine does not approach the end of the cylinder very closely. When the piston is at the extreme left-hand end of its stroke there is a considerable space, CC, enclosed between the valves and the piston face. This space is known as the combustion chamber, or clearance space. It is usually about one-quarter of the space swept by the piston. This clearance space or clearance volume plays a very important part in the working of the gas engine. The three valves opening into this space control the distribution of the gases and are shown diagrammatically in fig. 180, art. 242. They are : (1) The air valve A, which admits air from the atmosphere, together with the gas. (2) The gas valve G (see also fig. 142a), which admits the gas from the gas holder or gas producer. (3) The exhaust valve E, which opens to allow the gases to pass out of the cylinder when they have done their work. The air and gas valve are often operated together on one spindle and the combination is then known as the mixing valve. The series of events comprising the cycle and the method of calculating the power of the gas engine are fully described in arts. 242 and 208 respectively.

EXAMPLES XVIII

SECTION A

1. What is meant by the term mechanical equivalent of heat ? Give the heat value of the work done by an engine of one horse-power when it runs for one hour.

2. One pound of fuel oil has a calorific value of 18,000 B.Th.U. An engine converts $\frac{4}{10}$ of the heat supplied to it into work. Find the amount of oil required per hour if the engine develops 10 H.P.

3. The kinetic energy of a moving vehicle is 160,000 ft.-lb. This energy is wholly absorbed by application of the brakes. How much heat is generated at the brake ?

4. In a steam engine plant each pound of steam carries 1,296 B.Th.U. to the cylinder. If 22 per cent. of this heat is converted into work, how much steam will be required per hour if the engine is 1,000 H.P. ?

5. An oil engine develops 5 H.P. and uses 1·9 lb. of oil per hour of heating value 17,900 B.Th.U. per lb. What is its thermal efficiency ?

6. A combined engine and boiler uses 440 lb. of coal per hour. The engine develops 210 H.P. and the calorific value of the coal is 14,100 B.Th.U. per lb. Find the thermal efficiency of the complete plant.

7. A gas engine uses 3·535 cu. ft. of gas per minute. The calorific value of the gas is 430 B.Th.U. per cu. ft. and the engine develops 5·37 H.P. Find its thermal efficiency.

8. Describe briefly, with the aid of outline sketches, the chief features.

of construction of any boiler with which you are familiar, and show the path of the gases from the furnace to the flues. The fittings need not be described.   U.L.C.I.

9. A motor car is brought to rest in 30 ft. by the application of a constant frictional resistance of 230 lb. Determine the number of foot-pounds of work expended in bringing the car to rest, and calculate the heat equivalent of the work done.   U.L.C.I.

10. One pound of petrol generates 18,200 B.Th.U. when burned completely. If an engine converts 30 per cent. of the heat of combustion into work in the cylinder and its mechanical efficiency is 0·82, what will be the weight of petrol consumed per hour per brake horse-power ? State what becomes of the remainder of the heat.   U.L.C.I.

11. Calculate the mechanical work equivalent of the amount of heat required to raise the temperature of 10 lb. of water from 59° F. to boiling point.   778 ft.-lb. = 1 B.Th.U.   U.L.C.I.

12. What do you understand by " The Mechanical equivalent of heat " ? How much heat is required to raise the temperature of 600 lb. of water from 60° F. to 159° F. ?   What is the mechanical equivalent of this amount of heat ?   If it takes an hour to raise the temperature of the 600 lb. of water, at what rate measured in horse-power is the energy supplied to the water ?   U.L.C.I.

13. State four of the principal fittings to be found on a boiler and give a brief note regarding each.   N.C.T.E.C.

14. The initial temperature of the cooling water of an oil engine is 44·5° F. and the final temperature 165° F.   If 18 lb. of water are circulated per minute, how many British Thermal Units are carried away per minute ? The engine uses per minute 0·246 lb. of oil of a calorific value of 20,100 B.Th.U. per lb.   Calculate the percentage of the total heat carried away by the cooling water.   N.C.T.E.C.

15. In passing through a steam-engine each pound of steam gives up 90 B.Th.U. to be converted into mechanical energy.   How many pounds of this steam will be used in one hour by an engine of 100 H.P.   C.G.L.I.

16. The working pressure in a boiler is to be limited to 200 lb. per sq. in. by means of a dead weight safety valve.   The valve is 3 in. diameter. What weight must be placed on it ?

SECTION B

17. Sketch and describe the general arrangement of a steam engine condenser and air pump.   Explain why the air pump is necessary.   U.L.C.I.

18. Briefly describe, with the aid of an outline sketch, some type of boiler, and indicate the path of the gases from the furnace to the chimney.
                                                                U.L.C.I.

19. A boiler generates 9 lb. of dry saturated steam per lb. of fuel at an absolute pressure of 150 lb. per sq. in. from feed water at 70° F

Temperature of steam at 150 lb. pressure   .   358·4° F.
Sensible heat of steam at 150 lb. pressure   .   330·6 B.Th.U.
Latent heat of steam at 150 lb. pressure   .   864·5 B.Th.U.

If the calorific value of the fuel is 13,500 B.Th.U. per lb., what fraction of the heat of combustion is actually used in generating steam ?   U.L.C.I.

20. A boiler produces 4,800 lb. of steam per hour at a pressure of 190 lb. per sq. in. abs. and 0·95 dry.   The heat given out by the fuel is 14,690 B.Th.U. per lb. and 65 per cent. of this heat passes through the boiler

plates. If the feed water is at 82° F. find the weight of coal required per hour.

21. A boiler generates 7,000 lb. of steam per hour at an absolute pressure of 160 lb. per sq. in. from feed water at 176° F. If the efficiency of the boiler is 75 per cent., and the calorific value of the coal used is 14,580 B.Th.U. per lb., find the number of pounds of steam generated per pound of coal consumed. The total heat of steam at 160 lb. pressure is 1,196 B.Th.U. per lb. U.L.C.I.

22. Distinguish briefly but clearly between the purposes for which governors and flywheels are fitted to engines. U.L.C.I.

23. In the working of a steam engine and boiler explain briefly the functions of the following : slide valve, governor, flywheel, condenser, air pump, and circulating pump. N.C.T.E.C.

24. What do you understand by *jet* and *surface* condensation respectively ? Give a diagrammatic sketch of each arrangement. N.C.T.E.C.

25. A test of a boiler having a grate area of 210 sq. ft. and a heating surface of 4,963 sq. ft. gave the following results: fuel used per hour 4,490 lb., feed water used per hour 40,360 lb., feed temperature 255° F., absolute boiler pressure 164 lb. per sq. in.

Determine (a) The ratio of heating surface to grate area.
    (b) The number of pounds of fuel burnt per square foot of grate surface per hour. What is the object of determining this information ?
    (c) The number of pounds of steam generated per lb. of fuel fired, and
    (d) The equivalent evaporation from and at 212° F. per lb. of fuel fired.

Given temperature of steam at 164 lb. per sq. in. abs. 365·5° F., the sensible heat of water at 365·5° F. is 338 B.Th.U. per lb., the latent heat of steam at 365·5° F. is 858·4 B.Th.U., and the latent heat of steam at 212° F. is 970·7 B.Th.U. per lb. U.L.C.I.

26. What do you understand by the statement, "The mechanical equivalent of heat is 778 ft.-lb. per British Thermal Unit " ?

The combustion of 1 gall. of petrol generates 145,000 B.Th.U. If one-fifth of this energy is available for useful work, how many foot-pounds of work can be done with it ?

If the petrol is used for propelling a 20-H.P. car, for how many minutes can the car be run at full power on 1 gall. ? N.C.T.E.C.

27. In an oil-fired boiler 20 lb. of air are supplied per lb. of oil burnt. The temperature of the gases at the base of the chimney is 700° F., and the temperature of the air in the boiler house is 80° F. Assuming the specific heat of the flue gases is 0·24, find the heat carried up the chimney per lb. of oil burnt. If the calorific value of the oil used is 20,000 B.Th.U. per lb., how many pounds of water would this boiler evaporate per lb. of oil burnt, from and at 212° F., assuming no further heat losses ? Latent heat of evaporation at 212° F. = 967 B.Th.U. per lb. U.E.I.

28. In a jet condenser the condensing water has temperature 50° F. and 12 lb. is supplied per lb. of steam. If the steam is at pressure 115 lb. per sq. in. abs. and has dryness fraction 0·75, calculate the resulting temperature of the mixture. At 115 lb. per sq. in. abs., $h = 309·2$ B.Th.U. per lb., $L = 881·5$ B.Th.U. per lb. N.C.T.E.C.

CHAPTER XIX

MEASUREMENT OF POWER
AND PERFORMANCE OF ENGINES

201. Testing the Engine. Engines of all kinds have been and are still being tested. The information obtained as a result of engine trials has been of the utmost value in enabling the builders and users to determine suitable sizes for their engines. The test figures are consulted when similar engines are to be built.

Another important use of the test is to find exactly how much steam, oil, or gas, the engine will use in order to produce a given amount of power for a given period of time. In all tests measurements are made by means of instruments designed for their especial purpose, and then calculations are made using the results of the measurements.

The measurements include those of temperature, pressure, dryness fraction of steam, weight of steam, forces, and dimensions of wheels and cylinders. Also weight of oil or petrol, and volume of gas are measured, in the case of internal combustion engines These measurements will now be dealt with in detail.

202. Measurement of Power. This involves measurement of forces and also the rate of travel of the forces since power cannot be developed without movement. The power developed in the cylinder of any engine is known as the " cylinder horse-power." It is also commonly known as the " Indicated Horse-Power." Thus the indicated horse-power is the rate of doing work on the moving piston in the cylinder. It is called the " indicated " horse-power because an instrument known as the " indicator " is used in observing data employed later for the purpose of calculating the work done on the piston. The indicator registers pressures of gas in the cylinder, and it may be said to " indicate " pressures.

Another power usually stated for each engine is the quantity known as the Brake Horse-Power. This is so called because it was first measured by means of a brake. When an engine is driving a factory the power developed in the cylinder is divided into two parts, (1) that required to drive the engine itself, i.e. to overcome its friction, and (2) that actually transmitted to the factory. This latter part is the Brake Horse-Power. If a brake is used to measure this power the whole power is converted into heat energy and thus cooling arrangements have to be fitted to brakes for power measurement. It is possible, however, to measure the output of an engine by means of instruments without destroying the power. This is done by means of a *transmission* dynamometer which measures the power whilst it is being transmitted. The brake which absorbs the power is known as an *absorption* dynamometer. All power measuring devices are dynamometers. A well-known transmission dynamometer is based on the principle of Hooke's law as applied to the torsional straining of a shaft.

203. The Indicator. This instrument is illustrated in fig. 143. The indicator consists of three main portions, namely a cylinder C fitted with a piston, a drum D, and a parallel motion PM. Different makes of indicator differ only in the manner in which these three parts are constructed. The drum is driven by means of a non-extensible cord from the crosshead of the engine, or from some point having a to and fro motion similar to that of the crosshead. If the cord were attached to the crosshead directly, the drum would have to be of diameter large enough to give the full travel of the piston in about three-quarters of a revolution of the drum. The drum does not make a complete revolution because it is prevented by means of " stops " at each end of its angular travel. The actual movement of the driving end of the cord must be within the limits of drum travel. Indicator drum diameters range from 1 in. to 3 in. and consequently it is necessary to " reduce " the travel of the engine crosshead to a value suitable for the particular indicator in use. This is done by means of an " indicator reducing gear " described in the next article. The indicator drum carries two spring clips S, one slightly longer than the other, and both close together. The clips are for the purpose of securing the paper, upon which the pressures are to be registered, to the drum. The paper is thus held firmly to the drum without creases or bulges. The clips prevent the drum from making a complete revolution. The drum is returned to one end of its travel by means of a strong spring R. The cord tension therefore varies from point to point in the movement. This variation must be kept small and the driving cord should be as short as possible, otherwise the diagram is not a true indication of the pressure at any point, in the stroke of the engine.

The cylinder of the indicator is attached to the cylinder of the engine by means of connecting pipes. These pipes are provided with cocks so that communication between the engine cylinder and the indicator cylinder may be established when desired. When the cocks are opened the pressure of the steam or gas in the engine cylinder is transmitted to the piston in the indicator

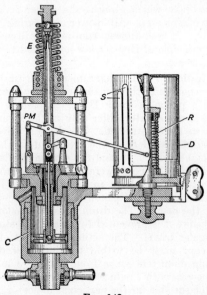

Fig. 143.

cylinder. This piston therefore experiences a force and tends to move. The movement of the indicator piston in the indicator is resisted by means of a spring E the stiffness (i.e. number of pounds required to compress or extend it one inch) of which is known. From art. 4 we know that the force on a spring is proportional to its extension or compression. Thus the movement of the piston depends on the spring stiffness and the pressure of the steam or gas. Therefore the piston movement indicates the pressure upon the piston. The piston travel is limited by two stops, one at each end of its movement.

The parallel motion performs a double purpose. It allows the indicator piston movement to be magnified and it compels the tracing pencil, which operates on the drum, to move in a direction parallel to that of the piston of the indicator. Thus, because the indicator piston is guided in a straight line, the pencil of the indicator is also guided in a straight line. Movement of the pencil in the direction of the drum travel must be prevented, otherwise the pressure will be registered at the wrong point in the stroke.

The indicator must satisfy the following conditions :

(a) The travel of the drum must, at all points in the stroke, be proportional to the travel of the engine piston. That is, if the engine piston moves three-eighths of its stroke, the drum must move three-eighths of its travel.

(b) The indicator pencil must move exactly at right angles to the direction of the travel of the drum.

(c) The movement of the pencil must be proportional to the travel of the indicator piston and therefore proportional to the pressure upon the piston.

(d) The pencil must move in a straight line.

204. The Indicator Spring. Each indicator sent out by the makers is accompanied by a series of springs of different

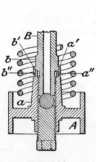

FIG. 144.   FIG. 145.

" rates " or stiffnesses. Each spring will suit the particular indicator but will not suit any other indicator without correction. Upon each spring is stamped two numbers, one which shows the maximum pressure for which that spring is suitable with that

particular indicator, and the other which indicates the pressure
necessary to move the *pencil* of the indicator one inch, when that
particular spring is in use.

This last number is known as the " scale " of the spring. It
is not the actual " rate " of the spring as the following example
will show. The spring is illustrated in fig. 145 and its attachment to the piston rod is shown in fig. 144.

EXAMPLE. An indicator spring is loaded directly by means of weights
and its compression is found to be $\frac{1}{8}$-in. under a load of 60 lb. It is used
in an indicator in which the pencil travel is 4 times the travel of the indicator
piston. The piston of the indicator has a diameter of 0·797 in. Find the
pressure necessary to move the pencil 1 in.

The piston movement for 1 in. pencil movement = $\frac{1}{4}$ in.

$$\therefore \text{ Load on piston} = \frac{\frac{1}{4}}{\frac{1}{8}} \times 60 = 120 \text{ lb.}$$

$$\text{Area of piston} = 0·7854 \times 0·797^2 = 0·5 \text{ sq. in.}$$

$$\therefore \text{ Pressure intensity} = \frac{120}{0·5} = 240 \text{ lb. per sq. in.}$$

This is the spring scale of the indicator. The rate of the
spring is $\dfrac{60}{\frac{1}{8}} = 480$ lb. per in.

From this example it will be evident that the spring scale
takes account of area of indicator piston, stiffness of indicator
spring, and multiplication of piston travel by means of the
parallel motion.

205. The Reducing Gear. The function of this gear is to
reduce the piston travel to a value suitable for the drum of the
indicator. It should move the drum a proportionate amount
of the piston stroke. The arrangement shown in fig. 146 reduces
the motion, but the movement from point to point in the stroke
is not exactly proportional to the movement of the engine piston.
This is because the link, L, does not move over equal angles for
equal movements of the crosshead. This will be quite clear if
example 27, exercises XIX, is carefully set out and the results
tabulated.

In fig. 146, X is the crosshead, L is a swinging link pivoted
at O. C is a connection link, whilst Q is a quadrant. The intro-
duction of the link C and quadrant Q prevents absolute propor-
tionality of movement at all points in the stroke.

If the arrangement is modified to that shown in fig. 147, then
the proportional movement will be secured. The crosshead in this
case drives the link through the pin P, and a pin Q drives a block

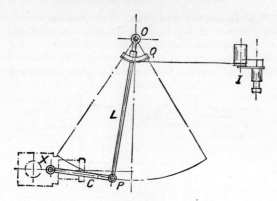

Fig. 146.

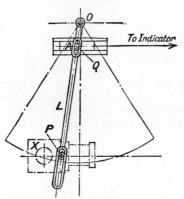

Fig. 147.

A moving in a straight line. The motion of Q is an exact copy of the motion of P.

EXAMPLE. A steam engine of 4 ft. stroke is to be indicated by means of an indicator the drum of which is $2\frac{1}{4}$ in. diameter. If the reducing rig is of the type shown in figs. 146 or 147, and if seven-eighths of a revolution of the drum is available, find the ratio of the lengths, $\dfrac{OQ}{OP}$.

Full circumference of drum $= \pi \times 2 \cdot 25 = 7 \cdot 07$ in

Travel available $= 7 \cdot 07 \times \frac{7}{8} = 6 \cdot 19$ in.

∴ ratio $\dfrac{OQ}{OP} = \dfrac{6 \cdot 19}{48} = \dfrac{1}{7 \cdot 76}$.

∴ The dimension OP must be not less than 7·76 times the dimension OQ.

206. The Indicator Diagram. The diagram traced out by
the indicator is a closed figure composed of straight lines and
curves. If the pencil is at a fixed height (held there by a steady
pressure) and the drum revolves, a straight horizontal line will
be drawn. The height of this line will indicate the pressure when

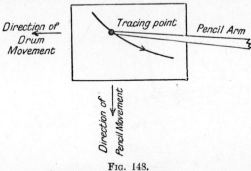

Fig. 148.

it was drawn. If the drum is stopped, and the pressure in the
cylinder increases, a straight vertical line will be drawn.
Similarly when the pressure decreases. If now the drum is in
motion and if the pressure is falling, a curve will be drawn by
the falling pencil as shown in fig. 148. The arrow on the curve
shows the actual path of the pencil on the paper.

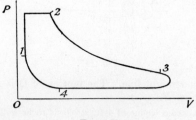

Fig. 149.

The complete diagram for a steam engine is of the form shown
in fig. 149. Further diagrams are illustrated in figs. 177 and 178,
art 241. A typical gas engine diagram is illustrated in fig. 179.

207. The Determination of Power. The power developed
in the cylinder of any engine can be determined if the engine

cylinder dimensions and speed are known and if an indicator diagram with its spring scale is available. The first step is to find the mean effective pressure. The mean effective pressure is the average of the effective pressures on one side of the piston and must be found for both sides of the piston in the double-acting engine. The mean effective pressure is dependent on the mean height of the indicator diagram measured from boundary to boundary. Thus the mean height of the diagram is first deter-

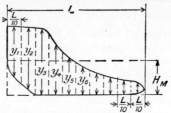

Fig. 150.

mined. The diagram is carefully measured and the length, L is divided into any number of equal divisions as shown in fig. 150 This divides the area into a number of strips. The middle ordinate is then drawn in each strip as shown in full lines. The lengths of the mid-ordinates are measured and the whole of the lengths are added together. This sum is then divided by the number of mid-ordinates giving the mean height of the diagram as a result.

Thus, mean height, $H_M = \dfrac{y_1 + y_2 + \text{etc.}}{\text{number of ordinates taken}}$.

The mean effective pressure is then $= H_M \times$ spring scale.

EXAMPLE. An indicator diagram is divided into 10 equal strips. The mid-ordinates of the strips measure 0·7, 0·8, 0·66, 0·43, 0·32, 0·25, 0·20, 0·14, 0·13, and 0·1 in. respectively. The scale of the spring is 120 lb. per sq. in. per in. Find the mean effective pressure from this diagram.

Total length of mid-ordinates
$= 0·7 + 0·8 + 0·66 + 0·43 + 0·32 + 0·25 + 0·20 + 0·14 + 0·13 + 0·1$
$= 3·73$ in.

∴ Mean length of the 10 mid-ordinates $= \dfrac{3·73}{10} = 0·373$ in.

∴ Mean effective pressure $= 0·373 \times 120$ lb. per sq. in.
$= 44·76$ lb. per sq. in.

Another method of determining the mean height of the diagram is to measure the area and divide the area by the length, L, of the diagram.

S

The area may be measured by counting squares or by planimeter. If the squares method is used the smaller the squares (say down to $\frac{1}{10}$ in. sq.) the more accurate the result.

EXAMPLE. The length of an indicator diagram taken from a gas engine is found to be 1·7 in. The area of the diagram after three determinations by planimeter is noted as 0·63 sq. in. The spring scale is 200 lb. per sq. in. per in. Find the mean effective pressure.

$$\text{Mean height of diagram} = \frac{0 \cdot 63}{1 \cdot 7} \text{ in.} = 0 \cdot 37 \text{ in.}$$

∴ Mean effective pressure = 0·37 × 200 = 74 lb. per sq. in.

208. Calculation of Indicated Horse-Power. The mean effective pressure is a constant pressure which will do the same work as the actual varying pressures. Hence the actual varying pressures encountered in the engine cylinders can be replaced by the mean effective pressure. To find the power we must know the work done per minute. This will be the amount of work done per stroke multiplied by the number of strokes per minute. A stroke is made when the piston travels from one end of the cylinder to the other.

Let P_M = mean effective pressure in pounds per square inch.

L = length of engine piston stroke in feet.

N = number of working strokes per minute.

D = diameter of cylinder in inches.

F = mean piston force in pounds.

S = distance moved by piston in feet per minute, *whilst the pressure is effective.*

$$\text{Then mean force on piston} = P_M \times \frac{\pi D^2}{4} \text{ lb.}$$

$$\text{i.e. } F = 0 \cdot 7854 P_M D^2 \text{ lb.}$$

$$\text{Work done per stroke} = F \times L \text{ ft.-lb.}$$
$$= 0 \cdot 7854 P_M D^2 L \text{ ft.-lb.}$$

$$\text{Work done per minute} = 0 \cdot 7854 P_M D^2 L N \text{ ft.-lb.}$$

$$\therefore \text{ Horse-power} = \frac{0 \cdot 7854 P_M D^2 L N}{33,000}$$

$$\text{i.e. I.H.P.} = \frac{0 \cdot 7854 P_M D^2 S}{33,000}.$$

The unit of power is called the horse-power and its value is 33,000 ft.-lb. per min. The above equation can be used to calculate the indicated horse-power (I.H.P.) of any engine provided that S or N is given its correct interpretation.

EXAMPLE. A double-acting steam engine has a cylinder 12 in. diameter and the stroke of the piston is 18 in. An indicator diagram taken from the engine when the speed was 100 r.p.m. gave an area of 1·5 sq. in. on a length of 2·6 in. The spring scale was 64 lb. per sq. in. per in. Find the indicated horse-power of this engine

(a) neglecting the piston rod

(b) allowing for a piston rod 2¼-in. diameter on one side only.

Mean effective pressure = mean height × spring scale

$$= \frac{1·5}{2·6} \times 64 \text{ lb. per sq. in.}$$

$$= 36·9 \text{ lb. per sq. in.}$$

Case (a). Neglecting piston rod.

Area of 12-in. diameter piston = $\frac{\pi}{4} \times 12 \times 12 = 113$ sq. in.

∴ Mean force on piston = 36·9 × 113 = 4,170 lb.
Work done per stroke = 4,170 × 1·5 = 6,255 ft.-lb.
∴ Work done per minute = 6,255 × 2 × 100 = 1,251,000 ft.-lb.

$$\therefore \text{ Horse-power} = \frac{1,251,000}{33,000} = 38·1 \text{ H.P.}$$

Case (b). Allowing for 2¼-in. piston rod.
Area of 12-in. diameter piston = 113 sq. in.

Area of 2¼-in. diameter piston rod = $\frac{\pi}{4} \times 2·25 \times 2·25$

$$= 3·98 \text{ sq. in.}$$
Effective area of front of piston = [113 − 3·98]
$$= 109·02 \text{ sq. in.}$$

∴ Mean area (front and back) = $\frac{113 + 109·02}{2} = 111·01$ sq. in.

Mean force on piston = 36·9 × 111·01 = 4,095 lb.
Work done per minute = 4,095 × 1·5 × 2 × 100 = 1,228,000 ft.-lb.

$$\therefore \text{ Horse-power} = \frac{1,228,000}{33,000} = 37·2 \text{ H.P.}$$

EXAMPLE. The mean effective pressure from an indicator diagram taken from a gas engine is 74 lb. per sq. in. The engine operated on the four-stroke cycle and the speed was 280 r.p.m. The governor cut out 20 cycles per minute. Find the horse-power of the engine if the cylinder diameter is 6½ in. and the length of the stroke is 12 in.

Effective thrust on piston = pressure × area

$$= 74 \times \frac{\pi}{4} \times 6·5 \times 6·5 \text{ lb.} = 2,452 \text{ lb.}$$

Maximum number of strokes per minute (to and fro) = 280 × 2
$$= 560.$$

Maximum number of cycles per minute = $\frac{560}{4} = 140$

since there is one possible firing cycle for each four strokes. But 20 cycles are not operative,

∴ Number of operative cycles = 140 − 20 = 120 per minute.

∴ Work done per minute = $2,452 \times \dfrac{12}{12} \times 120 = 294,200$ ft.-lb.

∴ Horse-power = $\dfrac{294,200}{33,000} = 8 \cdot 94$ H.P.

Note. In the gas engine the number of working strokes per minute is the number of times a gas charge is fired per minute. It cannot be more than half the number of revolutions per minute in a four-stroke engine but it can be, and often is, less than this figure if the governor is of the type which cuts out the gas supply when the engine is over-speeding.

EXAMPLE. A four-cylinder petrol engine of 3½-in. bore and 5¼-in. stroke runs at a speed of 2,200 r.p.m. The mean effective pressure is 90 lb. per sq. in. Find the horse-power developed in the cylinders.

The engine operates on the four-stroke cycle, therefore each cylinder will take and fire a charge $\dfrac{2,200}{2}$ times per minute. The petrol engine is not governed by cutting out cycles.

∴ Total number of working strokes for four cylinders
$$= 1,100 \times 4 = 4,400 \text{ per minute.}$$

Area of piston 3½-in. diameter = $\dfrac{\pi}{4} \times 3 \cdot 5 \times 3 \cdot 5 = 9 \cdot 63$ sq. in.

Mean force on piston = $9 \cdot 63 \times 90 = 866$ lb.

Work done per stroke = $866 \times \dfrac{5 \cdot 25}{12} = 379$ ft.-lb.

Work done per minute = $379 \times 4,400$ ft.-lb.

and horse power = $\dfrac{379 \times 4,400}{33,000} = 50 \cdot 5$ H.P.

EXAMPLE. A double-acting steam engine develops 22 horse-power at 120 r.p.m. The cylinder diameter is 13 in. and the stroke 20 in. Find the mean effective pressure neglecting the effect of the piston rod.

Work done per minute = $33,000 \times 22 = 726,000$ ft.-lb.

Work done per stroke = $\dfrac{726,000}{120 \times 2} = 3,025$ ft.-lb.

Mean force on piston = $\dfrac{3,025}{\dfrac{20}{12}} = 1,813$ lb.

Area of piston = $\dfrac{\pi}{4} \times 13 \times 13 = 132 \cdot 8$ sq. in.

∴ M.E.P. = $\dfrac{1,813}{132 \cdot 8} = 13 \cdot 64$ lb. per sq. in.

209. The Brake Horse-Power. In order to determine the brake horse-power of an engine it is necessary to apply a resistance which can be measured. A simple arrangement for this purpose is shown in fig. 151 which shows a rope-type brake dynamometer. The rope may be arranged to subtend an arc less than 360° if desired. The rope wheel rotates in the direction shown by the arrow and the friction tends to lift the weight W, at the bottom end of the rope. The top end of the rope is attached

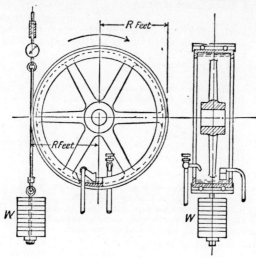

FIG. 151.

to a spring balance B which measures the pull in the upward direction. The difference between the weight W and the spring balance reading is the effective brake load and it acts at the centre of the rope.

Let R = effective radius of brake in feet measured from centre of shaft to centre of rope.

D = diameter of wheel itself in feet.

d = diameter of rope in feet.

Then $R = \dfrac{D + d}{2}$

Let W = dead weight on brake in pounds

S = spring balance reading in pounds

Then E = effective brake load = [W − S] lb.

∴ Brake torque on shaft = [W − S]R lb.-ft.

Let N = revolutions per minute.

Then angular velocity in radians per second = $\dfrac{2\pi N}{60}$

∴ Work done per second = $\dfrac{[W − S]R2\pi N}{60}$

and brake horse-power = $\dfrac{[W − S]R2\pi N}{550 \times 60}$.

If we write T = torque in pound-feet = (W − S)R.

ω = angular velocity in radians per second = $\dfrac{2\pi N}{60}$

Then brake horse-power = $\dfrac{T\omega}{550}$

EXAMPLE. The brake torque on an engine-shaft running at 2,400 r.p.m. was 20 lb.-ft. What was the brake horse-power ?

$$\text{B.H.P.} = \frac{T\omega}{550}$$

$$\omega = \frac{2,400}{60} \times 2\pi = 80\pi = 251 \text{ radians per second.}$$

$$\therefore \text{B.H.P.} = \frac{20 \times 251}{550} = 9\cdot14 \text{ B.H.P.}$$

EXAMPLE. During a test of a gas engine the load on the brake was 92 lb. and the spring balance reading was 14 lb. The path of the rope was 3 ft. 1 in. diameter and the rope itself was 1 in. diameter. The engine speed was 240 r.p.m. Find the brake horse-power and the heat dissipated at the brake in B.Th.U. and in C.H.U. per hour.

Effective diameter of brake path = 3 ft. 1 in. + 1 in.
= 3 ft. 2 in. = 3·166 ft.

$$\therefore \text{Effective radius} = \frac{3\cdot166}{2} = 1\cdot583 \text{ ft.}$$

Effective load on brake = [92 − 14] = 78 lb.

∴ Torque on shaft = 78 × 1·583 = 123·4 lb.-ft.

Angular velocity = $\dfrac{240}{60} \times 2\pi = 25\cdot1$ rad. per sec.

∴ Work done per second = 123·4 × 25·1 = 3,100 ft.-lb.

∴ Brake horse-power = $\dfrac{3,100}{550} = 5\cdot64$ B.H.P.

Energy dissipated per second = 3,100 ft.-lb.

    „   „   „ hour = 3,100 × 3,600

= 11,160,000 ft.-lb.

= $\dfrac{11,160,000}{778}$ B.Th.U.

= 14,340 B.Th.U. per hr.

or = 7,970 C.H.U. per hr.

In order to prevent the brake parts from becoming dangerously hot this heat is usually carried away by cooling water which is led into and out of the channel formed on the inside of the brake ring. A section and elevation of this arrangement is shown in fig. 151.

210. Mechanical Efficiency of an Engine. This is the efficiency of an engine when it is considered as a machine.

There is a certain amount of work needed to overcome the friction of the engine parts and therefore the amount of work available at the shaft is less than that produced in the cylinders.

We may define the mechanical efficiency of any engine as the ratio, $\dfrac{\text{work done at the shaft in unit time}}{\text{work done in cylinder in unit time}}$. The unit time may be the minute, the hour, or any other convenient unit.

EXAMPLE. The work done in the cylinder of an engine in three minutes is 150,000 ft.-lb. and the work absorbed on a brake dynamo-meter is 300,000 ft.-lb. in seven and a half minutes. What is the mechanical efficiency of this engine ?

The first operation is to reduce the work quantities to a common unit of time. In this case the minute is a convenient time unit.

$$\text{Work done in cylinder per minute} = \frac{150,000}{3} = 50,000 \text{ ft.-lb.}$$

$$\text{Work done at brake per minute} = \frac{300,000}{7\frac{1}{2}} = 40,000 \text{ ft.-lb.}$$

$$\therefore \text{ Mechanical efficiency} = \frac{\text{Work done at brake per minute}}{\text{Work done in cylinder per minute}}$$

$$= \frac{40,000 \text{ ft.-lb.}}{50,000 \text{ ft.-lb.}} = 0\cdot8 \text{ or } 80 \text{ per cent.}$$

The amount of work expended in friction in the engine is [50,000 − 40,000] ft.-lb. per min., and the heat equivalent of this friction is $\dfrac{10,000}{778}$ B.Th.U. per min. Note carefully that the work quantities are to be measured in the same units and for the same period of time.

If we divide the two quantities of work in the last example by 33,000 we shall get the Brake Horse-Power and the Indicated Horse-Power in the numerator and denominator respectively.

$$\text{Thus mechanical efficiency} = \frac{\dfrac{40,000}{33,000}}{\dfrac{50,000}{33,000}}$$

$$= \frac{\text{Brake Horse-Power}}{\text{Indicated Horse-Power}}$$

This is not the definition of Mechanical Efficiency. The ratio of the powers is the same as the ratio of the works done at brake and in cylinder respectively.

EXAMPLE. An oil engine develops 20 I.H.P. and its mechanical efficiency is 82 per cent. How much power is available for driving machines other than the engine itself ?

$$\text{Mechanical Efficiency} = \frac{\text{B.H.P.}}{\text{I.H.P.}}$$

$$\therefore \text{ B.H.P.} = 0.82 \times 20 = 16.4 \text{ H.P.}$$

This is the power available for driving external machines.

EXAMPLE. A steam engine indicates 38 H.P. and the brake horse power developed is 30. Find the mechanical efficiency.

$$\text{The mechanical efficiency} = \frac{30}{38} = 0.79 \text{ or } 79 \text{ per cent.}$$

211. The Energy Units. The energy units employed in stating test results are

(1) The Horse-Power Hour.

(2) The Kilowatt Hour or The Board of Trade (B.O.T.) Unit (art. 61).

The horse-power hour is the amount of work done when one horse power is produced continuously for one hour. In other words it is $33,000 \times 60$ ft.-lb.

This product is 1,980,000 ft.-lb.

or 2,545 B.Th.U.

or 1,414 C.H.U.

The horse-power hours may be calculated on the basis of either indicated horse-power or brake horse-power.

EXAMPLE. The engine in the last example runs continuously for 4 hr. and the powers stated are the average values for the 4-hr. period. Find the indicated and brake-horse-power hours worked.

Indicated-horse-power hours $= 38 \times 4 = 152$ H.P.-hr.

Brake-horse-power hours $= 30 \times 4 = 120$ H.P.-hr.

The Kilowatt is a larger unit of power than the horse power. The Watt is a small unit of power and is the energy expended when unit quantity of electrical energy per unit time is made to flow against an electrical pressure of one unit. It is equivalent to 0.7373 ft.-lb. per sec.

The electrical current is rate of flow of electrical energy and this quantity is measured in amperes. The unit of electrical pressure is the volt.

Thus the watt = 1 ampere × 1 volt.
The kilowatt = 1,000 watts.

EXAMPLE. An engine-driven generator gives an output of 200 amperes at 450 volts. What is the electrical power output of the generator ?

$$\text{Watts output} = 200 \times 450$$
$$= 90,000 \text{ watts}$$
$$= 90 \text{ kilowatts.}$$

The horse power is equal to 746 watts (art. 61, Ex. 5), therefore 1 kw. = $\dfrac{1,000}{746}$ H.P., that is 1·34 H.P., and thus the horse-power of the generator = 1·34 × 90 = 120·6 H.P. The kilowatt-hour is the work done in one hour when one kilowatt is developed continuously. It is thus 1·34 times as large as the horse-power hour.

EXAMPLE. The power of a small steam turbine is 500 kw. How many horse-power hours are worked in one day of 24 hr. ?

Kilowatt-hours per hour run = 500 × 1
        „   „   per day   „ = 500 × 24 = 12,000
                since 1 kw.-hr. = 1·34 H.P.-hr.
the horse-power hours worked = 12,000 × 1·34
                             = 16,080 H.P.-hr.

212. Working Substance and Heat carried to the Engines.

The working substance has already been mentioned in art. 185. The function of the working substance is to carry heat to the engine cylinder. Therefore as a first step in ascertaining the amount of heat being carried to the engine it is necessary to know the weight or volume of working substance going to the engine. Thus the amount of working substance going to the engine is always measured in a complete engine trial. The other quantity needed, to find the heat going to the engine, is the heat contained in unit weight or in unit volume of the working substance as the case may be.

EXAMPLE. A gas engine uses 36·2 cu. ft. of gas per hour of higher calorific value 482·4 B.Th.U. per cu. ft. Find the rate of heat supply to the engine in British Thermal Units per minute.

Rate of heat supply per hour = 36·2 × 482·4
                             = 17,462 B.Th.U.

∴ Rate of heat supply per minute = $\dfrac{17,462}{60}$

                                 = 291·03 B.Th.U. per min.

EXAMPLE. A steam engine uses 6,870 lb. of steam per hour. Each pound of steam is supplied with 1,098 B.Th.U. in the boiler. How much heat is carried from boiler to engine in a day of 8 hr. ?   Neglect loss of heat from pipes, etc.

$$\text{Total heat supplied per hour} = 6{,}870 \times 1{,}098$$
$$= 7{,}546{,}000 \text{ B.Th.U.}$$
$$\therefore \text{ Total heat supplied per day} = 7{,}546{,}000 \times 8$$
$$= 60{,}368{,}000 \text{ B.Th.U.}$$

213. The Consumption of an Engine.   This is the amount of working substance or the heat-carrying constituent consumed by the engine in a period of one hour.   It is often referred to as the " total consumption " of the engine or the total hourly consumption.

214. The Consumption Rate of the Engine.   This is the amount of working substance consumed by the engine in one hour, for each horse-power it develops.   It is therefore

$$\frac{\text{Total hourly consumption rate}}{\text{Horse-power}}.$$

The consumption rate may be stated either for the indicated horse power or for the brake horse-power.   It is sometimes called the " specific rate " of the engine.

EXAMPLE.   A steam engine is tested and the steam is condensed and weighed as it leaves the engine.

The amount of condensate passing from the engine was 2,700 lb. in 45 min. and the indicated horse-power was 142.   Find the consumption rate of the engine in pounds per horse-power per hour.

$$\text{Total hourly rate} = \frac{2{,}700 \times 60}{45} = 3{,}600 \text{ lb.}$$

$$\therefore \text{ Consumption rate} = \frac{3{,}600}{142} = 25 \cdot 3 \text{ lb. per H.P. per hr.}$$

EXAMPLE.   If the mechanical efficiency of the above engine is 83 per cent., find the consumption rate per brake-horse-power hour.

$$\text{Brake horse-power} = 0 \cdot 83 \times 142 = 117 \cdot 8.$$

$$\therefore \text{ Consumption rate} = \frac{3{,}600}{117 \cdot 8}$$
$$= 30 \cdot 56 \text{ lb. per B.H.P. per hr.}$$

since total hourly rate is the same.

This result could have been obtained directly from

$$\frac{25 \cdot 3}{0 \cdot 83} = 30 \cdot 56 \text{ lb. per B.H.P. per hr.}$$

because

Brake horse power × consumption per brake-horse-power hour
= Total hourly rate

and

Indicated horse power × consumption per indicated-horse-power hour
= Total hourly rate

$$\therefore \frac{\text{B.H.P.}}{\text{I.H.P.}} = \frac{\text{Consumption per I.H.P. per hour}}{\text{Consumption per B.H.P. per hour}} = \text{Mechanical efficiency.}$$

215. The Thermal Efficiency. We have already pointed out, art. 188, that no engine can convert all the heat supplied to it into mechanical work. The fraction which is converted is the thermal efficiency of the engine. The Indicated Thermal Efficiency of any engine is the ratio :

$$\frac{\text{Heat equivalent of the work done in the cylinders per unit time.}}{\text{Heat supplied to the engine in unit time}}$$

The units of the heats must be the same and the time period for which they are stated must also be the same. This is highly important.

If the work done at the brake is substituted for the work done in the cylinders, in the above ratio we should then obtain the Brake Thermal Efficiency.

EXAMPLE. An engine converts 40 per cent. of the heat supplied to it into mechanical work in the cylinders. What is the thermal efficiency ?

$$\text{Thermal efficiency} = \frac{40}{100} = 40 \text{ per cent.}$$

If the mechanical efficiency of the engine is 86 per cent., what is the brake thermal efficiency ?

$$\text{The brake thermal efficiency} = \frac{0.86 \times 40}{100} = 34.40 \text{ per cent.}$$

This is the percentage of the heat supplied which is absorbed at the brake when the engine is under test.

EXAMPLE. An oil engine uses 0.34 lb. of oil of calorific value 18,000 B.Th.U. per lb. per I.H.P. per hour. The mechanical efficiency of the engine is 85 per cent. Find the indicated and brake thermal efficiencies. Also find the oil consumption per brake-horse-power hour.

Work done in cylinder = 33,000 × 60 ft.-lb. per hr. per horse-power.

$$= \frac{33,000 \times 60}{778} = 2,545 \text{ B.Th.U.}$$

Heat supplied to engine = 0.34 × 18,000 B.Th.U. per hr. per horse-power
= 6,120 B.Th.U.

$$\text{Therefore thermal efficiency} = \frac{2,545}{6,120} = 0.417 \text{ or } 41.7 \text{ per cent.}$$

$$\text{The brake thermal efficiency} = \frac{0.85 \times 2,545}{6,120} = 0.354 \text{ or } 35.4 \text{ per cent.}$$

Oil rate per B.H.P. per hour × B.H.P.
        = Oil rate per I.H.P. per hour × I.H.P.

$$\therefore \text{ Oil rate per B.H.P. per hour} = \frac{0.34 \times 1}{0.85}$$

$$= 0.4 \text{ lb. per B.H.P. per hr.}$$

It will be noted that the actual horse powers are not needed in the solution. Any reasonable horse power values could be used provided that the mechanical efficiency value was 0·85.

EXAMPLE. During a test of a National gas engine working on the four-stroke cycle the following data were recorded :

Gas used, 32·9 cu. ft. in a period of 12 min. Jacket cooling water, 16 lb. per min. Initial temperature of jacket water, 48·2° F. Final temperature of jacket water, 86° F. Revolutions in 5 min., 1,420. Explosions in 5 min., 685. Brake wheel diameter, 37 in. Dead weight on brake, 90 lb. Spring balance, 9·75 lb. Area of indicator diagram, 1·13 sq. in. Length of diagram, 2·65 in. Scale of spring, $\frac{1}{150}$. Calorific value of the gas, 522 B.Th.U. per cu. ft. Cylinder, 6½-in. bore and piston stroke 12 in.

Find from these data :

(1) The mechanical efficiency.
(2) The indicated thermal efficiency.
(3) The brake thermal efficiency.
(4) The percentage of the heat supplied passing to jacket water.

$$\text{Mean effective pressure} = \frac{1\cdot13}{2\cdot65} \times 150 = 64\cdot0 \text{ lb. per sq. in.}$$

$$\text{Area of piston} = 0\cdot7854 \times 6\cdot5 \times 6\cdot5 = 33\cdot18 \text{ sq. in.}$$

$$\text{Firing cycles per minute} = \frac{685}{5} = 137.$$

$$\therefore \text{Indicated horse-power} = \frac{33\cdot18 \times 64\cdot0 \times 137 \times 1}{33,000}$$

$$= 8\cdot82 \text{ horse-power.}$$

$$\text{Revolutions per minute} = \frac{1,420}{5} = 284$$

$$\text{Effective brake load} = 90 - 9\cdot75 = 80\cdot25 \text{ lb.}$$

$$\therefore \text{Brake horse-power} = \frac{80\cdot25 \times 37 \times \pi \times 284}{12 \times 33,000} = 6\cdot7 \text{ horse-power.}$$

$$\therefore \text{Mechanical efficiency} = \frac{6\cdot7}{8\cdot82} = 0\cdot76 \text{ or 76 per cent.}$$

$$\text{Gas taken per hour} = \frac{32\cdot9 \times 60}{12} = 164\cdot5 \text{ cu. ft.}$$

$$\text{Indicated work per hour} = \frac{8\cdot82 \times 33,000 \times 60}{778} \text{ C.H.U.}$$

$$= 22,140 \text{ B.Th.U.}$$

$$\text{Heat supplied per hour} = 164\cdot5 \times 522 = 85,870 \text{ B.Th.U.}$$

$$\therefore \text{Indicated thermal efficiency} = \frac{22,410}{85,870} = 0\cdot261 \text{ or 26·1 per cent.}$$

$$\text{Brake work done per hour} = \frac{6\cdot7 \times 33,000 \times 60}{778} = 17,080 \text{ B.Th.U.}$$

$$\therefore \text{Brake thermal efficiency} = \frac{17,080}{85,870} = 0\cdot1988 \text{ or 19·88 per cent.}$$

Heat carried away per hour by jacket water $= 16 \times (86 - 48 \cdot 2) \times 60$ B.Th.U.
$$= 36{,}288 \text{ B.Th.U.}$$

$\therefore$ Percentage heat carried away by jacket water $= \dfrac{36{,}288}{85{,}870} \times 100$

$$= 42 \cdot 3 \text{ per cent.}$$

EXAMPLES XIX

Section A

1. How would you determine the brake horse power of a small gas engine by means of a rope brake ? Describe the observations needed and give an expression for the brake horse power derived from the data obtained.
                                                                            U.E.I.

2. What do you understand by the " mechanical equivalent of heat " ? An engine is tested and is found to develop 50 B.H.P. How many British Thermal Units per hour does this represent ?

The brake drum of the engine is kept cool by a stream of water entering at 60° F. and leaving at 140° F. Find the number of lb. of water required per hour, assuming that the whole of the heat generated at the brake surface is absorbed by the cooling water.

3. A brake test on an electric motor gave the following results : Pull in tight and slack sides of band, 41 and 18 lb. respectively. Diameter of brake drum, 4 in. Revolutions per minute, 1,200. Current taken, $9\frac{1}{2}$ amp. at a pressure of 100 volts. Calculate the efficiency of the motor.
                                                                            U.E.I.

4. A gas engine working on the four-stroke cycle has a cylinder 8 in. in diameter and a stroke of 15 in. The mean effective pressure in the engine cylinder is 90 lb. per sq. in. The crank shaft makes 200 r.p.m. and there are 10 miss-fires per min. Calculate (*a*) the total effective force on the engine piston, (*b*) the work done during the working stroke, (*c*) the indicated horse-power of the engine.   U.E.I.

5. What do you understand by " mean effective pressure " as applied to a steam engine ? What information should be given with an indicator diagram in order that the indicated horse power may be calculated ? Explain how the calculation would be made if the engine were double-acting.
                                                                            U.E.I.

6. Trace the transformation of the heat units in the coal as fired to a boiler into energy given out by an engine run from the steam generated. How do you account for the large percentage loss ?   U.E.I.

7. Describe the cycle of operations in an oil engine working on the four-stroke cycle. An engine uses 12 lb. of oil per hour, converting 30 per cent. of the heat available into useful work. If 1 lb. of the oil used gives out 20,000 B.Th.U., calculate the brake horse-power of the engine.   U.E.I.

8. An oil engine uses 20 lb. of oil per hour. If the heat liberated by the complete burning of 1 lb. of oil is 21,000 B.Th.U., how much heat is supplied per hour ? If the brake horse-power of the engine is 18, what percentage of the heat supplied is converted into useful work ? 778 ft.-lb. of work must be done to raise the temperature of 1 lb. of water 1° F. U.E.I.

9. Explain *carefully* the cycle of operations in : (*a*) a steam engine, and (*b*) an internal combustion engine working on the four-stroke cycle. U.E.I.

10. A double-acting steam engine has a cylinder diameter of 6 in. and the stroke of the piston is 10 in.   The mean effective pressure of the steam in the cylinder is 40 lb. per sq. in.   At what speed, in revolutions per minute, should the engine run in order to develop 20 H.P. ?   U.L.C.I.

11. Explain the " four-stroke cycle " for an internal combustion engine. An internal combustion engine working on the four-stroke cycle has an explosion every cycle.   The cylinder diameter is 8 in. and the piston stroke is 11 in.   Find the I.H.P. of the engine when the mean effective pressure during the working stroke is 55 lb. per sq. in. and the speed is 220 r.p.m.
U.L.C.I.

12. Make an outline sketch of a brake suitable for determining the B.H.P. of a small engine of about 10 H.P., and indicate the method of cooling the brake drum.   In an engine test a net load of 260 lb. was measured at the end of the brake arm, which was 2 ft. 3 in. long, and the speed was 130 r.p.m. Find the brake horse-power of the engine.   U.L.C.I.

13. Describe the four-stroke cycle of operations of a gas engine, and make a sketch of a typical indicator diagram.   The length and area of a gas-engine indicator diagram were respectively 3·4 in. and 1·15 sq. in.   The diameter of the cylinder was 10 in. and the length of the stroke was 16 in. The number of revolutions and explosions per minute were respectively 180 and 75 and the strength of the spring was 160 lb. per in. movement of the indicator pencil.   Find the indicated horse-power of the engine.   U.L.C.I.

14. An engine develops 70 H.P.   Calculate in B.Th.U. the heat equivalent of the work done in 2 hr.   N.C.T.E.C.

15. An engine is specified to give 25 B.H.P.   Calculate the rate at which heat is produced in British Thermal Units per minute if the power is absorbed by means of a friction brake.   N.C.T.E.C.

16. One lb. of an oil when completely burned gives out 20,000 B.Th.U. and an oil engine converts 30 per cent. of this heat into work.   If the engine consumes 10 lb. of oil per hour, calculate (a) the work done per hour, (b) the horse-power of the engine.   One British Thermal Unit = 778 ft.-lb.
N.C.T.E.C.

17. The burning of an oil fuel generates 18,000 B.Th.U. per lb., and 58 lb. require 1 cu. ft. storage capacity.   Express in foot-tons the energy which can be stored in a tank of 1,000 cu. ft. capacity.   N.C.T.E.C.

Section B

18. In a gas engine trial the following observations and calculations were made :   Diameter of cylinder 6·5 in., stroke 12 in., mean effective pressure obtained from indicator card 90 lb. per sq. in., revolutions per minute 280, explosions per minute 120, diameter of rope brake wheel 3 ft., difference in pull in tight and slack sides of rope 108 lb.
Calculate the mechanical efficiency of the engine.   U.E.I.

19. In a test of a four-stroke gas engine the following figures were recorded :   Diameter of cylinder 8½ in., length of stroke 18 in., area of indicator diagram 0·545 sq. in., length of diagram 1·8 in., scale of spring $\frac{1}{300}$, explosions per minute 90.
Calculate the indicated horse-power of the engine.   If the mechanical efficiency is 0·79, what would be the brake horse-power ?   U.E.I.

20. Describe any experiment with which you are familiar to ascertain the relationship between the heat unit and its equivalent in foot-pounds of work done.

A gas engine uses 10 cu. ft. of gas in 5 min. The calorific value of the gas is 520 B.Th.U. State the equivalent energy in foot-pounds per minute. U.E.I.

21. Describe an experiment to determine the mechanical equivalent of heat. A gas engine uses 450 cu. ft. of gas per hour, the brake horse-power being 10. If 1 cu. ft. of gas in burning gives out 531 B.Th.U. (295 C.H.U.), what is the heat efficiency of the engine ? U.E.I.

22. A dynamo gives an output of 100 amp. at 500 volts. Find the horse-power of an engine to drive it assuming the dynamo to have an efficiency of 90 per cent. If the dynamo gives a full load for 6 hr., find the number of Board of Trade units generated. If the engine steam needed 113 lb. of coal per hour of calorific value 12,000 B.Th.U. per lb., calculate the overall efficiency of the plant. U.E.I.

23. Distinguish between a surface condenser and a jet condenser.

The exhaust from an engine of 1,200 I.H.P., using steam at the rate of 14 lb. per horse-power hour, enters a surface condenser. Assuming a hot-well temperature of 104° F., calculate the supply of condensing water required for a rise of temperature of 14·4° F., if the exhaust steam has a dry-ness fraction of 0·75 and its temperature is 140° F.

Latent heat of dry steam at 140° F. = 1,014 B.Th.U. per lb. N.C.T.E.C.

24. In the working of a steam engine and boiler explain briefly the functions of the following : slide valve, governor, flywheel, condenser, air pump, and circulating pump. N.C.T.E.C.

25. Exhaust steam, dryness fraction 0·8, enters a jet condenser at temperature 122° F. The condensing water enters at 70° F. and the mixture of condensed steam and condensing water leaves at 95·2° F. Estimate the amount of condensing water supplied for each lb. of steam.

Latent heat of dry steam at 122° F. = 1,024 B.Th.U. per lb. N.C.T.E.C.

26. Explain the terms, " wet steam " and " total heat of steam."

Steam at the rate of 500 lb. per hr. enters an engine at pressure 115 lb. per sq. in. abs., 0·95 dry, and leaves at 4 lb. per sq. in. abs., 0·6 dry. Calculate the heat lost by the steam in British Thermal Units per hour.

At 115 lb. per sq. in. abs., $h = 309·6$ B.Th.U. per lb. ; $L = 885·6$ B.Th.U. per lb. At 4 lb. per sq. in abs., $h = 120·6$ B.Th.U. per lb., $L = 1,004·4$ B.Th.U. N.C.T.E.C.

27. An indicator reducing gear of the type shown in fig. 146 has the following dimensions : $OP = 30$ in., $OQ = 5$ in. The link C is 8 in. long and the point P is 3 in. below the engine centre line when the link OP is vertical. The other end of the link C is on the engine centre line. The piston stroke is 20 in. and the link OP is vertical when the piston is at the centre of its stroke. Find, by setting down to scale, the travel of the drum and the fractional position in its stroke of a point on the surface of the drum when the piston is at $\frac{1}{8}$, $\frac{1}{4}$, $\frac{1}{2}$, $\frac{3}{4}$, $\frac{7}{8}$, of its stroke.

CHAPTER XX

PROPERTIES OF GASES

216. Properties of Gases. We have seen, art. 158, that, in the case of steam, we use the word " properties " to indicate quantities like heat, volume of 1 lb., temperature, pressure, etc. We use the word in a similar way in connection with gases.

The principal properties of a gas are temperature, pressure, volume of one pound weight, specific heat and heat content. The volume of one pound weight is the " specific volume " of the gas.

217. The State of a Gas. Suppose a quantity of any kind of gas to be placed in a vessel of volume V cubic feet. Let the pressure be P lb. per sq. ft. abs. and the temperature be T° Fahrenheit absolute. If these three quantities are given definite values, the condition or state of the amount of gas is specified. For example, we may say that " the state of a quantity of gas is 1·5 cu. ft. at 2,880 lb. per sq. ft. abs. and at 600° F. absolute." This information could also be stated as follows : " 1·5 cu. ft. at 20 lb. per sq. in. abs. and 140° F. ordinary temperature." To represent all the three quantities P, V, and T would need a

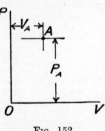

FIG. 152.

diagram in three dimensions which is beyond the scope of the present book. Any two of the three quantities can be represented on a simple diagram. For example, let OV and OP in fig. 152 represent axes of volume and pressure respectively. Then the position of a point A fixes the pressure and the volume of a given weight of the gas.

The volume is V_A and the pressure is P_A, the dimensions being measured as shown in the figure. The point A is called a state point. Similarly the two axes could represent (1) Pressure vertically and Temperature horizontally, or (2) Temperature vertically and Volume horizontally. This method of representing the state of a gas is very largely used to save time in future work.

218. General Properties of Gases. Gases are mostly invisible fluids possessing weight. They are capable of completely filling any space in which they are contained and will exert uniform pressure on all the boundaries of that space.[1] Gases also possess the peculiar property of being able to pass through certain solids. This property is known as diffusion. When different gases are introduced into a container they will " diffuse " amongst each other until each fills the space completely. Each gas will then exert a pressure which would be the same if the other gases were absent. Thus the total pressure exerted by the mixture of gases is the sum of the several pressures exerted by each gas. This is the law of " partial pressures." Each gas exerts its own " part " of the total pressure. We are mainly concerned with total pressure at this stage.

219. Expansion and Compression of a Gas. Suppose a quantity of gas to be shut up in the cylinder represented in fig. 153. Also suppose the right-hand boundary of the gas to be formed by a perfectly fitting piston which prevents leakage of the gas. Then having placed in the cylinder a certain volume of gas, we shall have a definite weight of gas present and this weight will not alter. If the piston is moved towards the right the volume occupied by the quantity of gas is increased. There is a change in volume and the final volume is larger than the

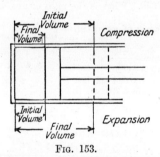

FIG. 153.

initial volume. The gas is said to have expanded. The ratio $\dfrac{\text{Final volume}}{\text{Initial volume}}$ is called the volume ratio of expansion or briefly, the " ratio of expansion." It is always greater than unity.

If the piston is forced to the left the volume occupied by the gas diminishes. The final volume is less than the initial volume

---

[1] This neglects the pressure variation due to the weight of the gas which is generally very small compared with the total pressure exerted.

T

and the gas is said to be compressed. The ratio $\dfrac{\text{Initial volume}}{\text{Final volume}}$ is called the volume ratio of compression. This is also greater than unity.

The engineer is frequently dealing with expansion and compression of gases and in order to show clearly the changes which have taken place it is usual to write the states of the gas at the various times in terms of P, V, and T. This necessitates the use of small letter, or figure suffixes to indicate different state points. Thus if suffix 1 refers to the initial state, then the initial state is denoted P_1, V_1, T_1. Similarly the final state may be denoted P_2, V_2, T_2.

It is possible for P_1 to be equal to P_2, in which case the pressure is constant for the two states. Also T_1 may be equal to T_2, but if expansion or compression is taking place V_1 cannot be equal to V_2. That is, the volume must change if either expansion or compression occurs.

EXAMPLE. Steam is supplied to a cylinder 12 in. diameter and 21 in. stroke until the piston has moved 6 in. It is then shut off and the steam enclosed in the cylinder is expanded behind the piston until the piston moves a further 15 in. What is the ratio of expansion ? (Fig. 154.)

$$\text{Ratio of expansion} = \frac{\text{Final volume}}{\text{Initial volume}}.$$

$$\text{Initial volume} = \frac{\pi D^2}{4} \times 6 \text{ in.} = \frac{\pi \times 12 \times 12}{4} \times 6 \text{ cu. in.}$$

$$= 680 \text{ cu. in.}$$
$$= 0.394 \text{ cu. ft.}$$

$$\text{Final volume} = \frac{\pi \times 12 \times 12}{4} \times 21 = 2,375 \text{ cu. in.}$$

$$= 1.374 \text{ cu. ft.}$$

$$\therefore \text{ Expansion ratio} = \frac{1.374}{0.394} = 3.5.$$

This could have been directly obtained thus :

$$\text{Expansion ratio} = \frac{21 \text{ in.}}{6 \text{ in.}} = 3.5.$$

EXAMPLE. The diameter of a gas engine cylinder is 8 in. and the piston stroke is 14 in. The clearance space (see fig. 142) is 216 cu. in. Find the compression ratio of the engine.

The compression ratio $= \dfrac{\text{Volume at beginning of compression stroke}}{\text{Volume at end of compression stroke}}$ the piston moving towards the clearance end of the cylinder.

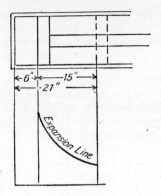

FIG. 154.

Volume at beginning of stroke

$$= \left[\frac{\pi \times 8 \times 8}{4} \times 14 \right] + 216 = 705 + 216 = 921 \text{ cu. in.}$$

Volume at end of stroke = 216 cu. in.

$$\therefore \text{ Compression ratio} = \frac{921}{216} = 4\cdot26.$$

220. Effect of Change of Volume on Pressure. Imagine a cylinder fitted with a weightless piston (fig. 155, a). (If the piston is weightless we can neglect its effect in producing pressure.) Let a quantity of gas be enclosed below the piston and prevent leakage to keep the gas weight constant. Also let the pressure on the gas be created by disc weights which can be removed one by one. The pressure due to the weights will be $\dfrac{\text{Total weight of discs in lb.}}{\text{Area of piston in square inches}}$, and will be in lb. per square inch. In addition to this pressure there will be the pressure of the atmosphere, viz. 14·7 lb. per sq. in., on the piston and weights.

Let p_g = pressure produced by weights in lb. per square inch.

  $p_a =$,,   due to the atmosphere in lb. per square inch.

Then the total pressure on the gas is $p_g + p_a$ lb. per sq. in. This total pressure is known as the " absolute " pressure. It includes the atmospheric pressure. The quantity p_g is the difference between the total pressure on the gas and the pressure of the atmosphere. It is usually measured by a pressure gauge, and is known as the gauge pressure. Pressure gauges always measure the difference between the total, or absolute, pressure and the pressure of the atmosphere. Thus we may write Absolute pressure = Gauge pressure + Atmospheric pressure. This is always true.

Now suppose that the weights are removed one by one. On the removal of a weight the gauge pressure will fall and the absolute pressure will fall. The volume of the gas will increase until the total pressure of the gas has fallen to a value equal to that due to the remaining weights plus atmospheric pressure.

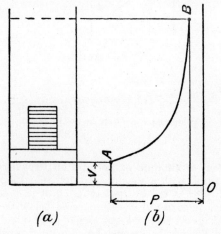

(a)　　　(b)

Fig. 155.

If the operation is repeated by removing further weights it will be found that the volume increases until all the weights are removed. The total pressure of the gas is now equal to atmospheric pressure. To increase the volume further would require a pull upon the piston.

If the absolute pressure is plotted from O, towards the left (fig. 155, b) and if the volume below the piston is plotted above O, for each set of weights, it will be found that the points lie on a smooth curve such as AB. The line AB is called the expansion line, and it is drawn upon a pressure-volume diagram. If weights are added instead of being removed, the volume will decrease and the pressure will rise. If we suppose this addition to take place from atmospheric pressure the starting point on the diagram will be B, and the line BA will be obtained with the same weight of gas. The line will be plotted in the direction from B to A. This is the compression case and the line BA is now known as the compression line.

The important point to notice is that, when the gas weight is constant, increasing volume is accompanied by falling pressure and decreasing volume by rising pressure. There are exceptions to this statement but these must be left until a later stage.

221. Temperature during Expansion or Compression. In the last article the effect of change of volume on pressure was discussed, but no mention was made of the effect on the temperature. The effect of changes of pressure and volume on temperature is of great importance. During the *expansion* described in the last article the temperature may have been

(1) steady at a fixed value.

(2) rising.

(3) falling.

In the case of No. 1 and No. 2 heat must have been supplied, and in No. 3, heat may, or may not, have been supplied. It may have been removed. Similar conditions may hold for the compression case. These cases must be deferred until the student reaches a more advanced stage. The subject is mentioned here to emphasize the importance of the temperature condition in the next article.

222. The Gas Laws. The law of a gas is the relationship between the quantities representing the state of the gas at various times when changes are taking place in those quantities. For example, the law may indicate the relationship between pressure and volume, temperature and volume, or temperature and pressure. The laws are always expressed algebraically.

(1) Boyle's Law. This law states that, *the volume of a given mass of a perfect gas varies inversely as its absolute pressure, provided that the temperature remains constant during the change of pressure.*

Expressed in symbols Boyle's law states that

$$V \propto \frac{1}{P} \text{ when T is constant.}$$

This relationship can be written $V = C \times \frac{1}{P}$ where C is a constant, and transposing P, we get,

$$PV = C.$$

In words, " The product of absolute pressure and total volume of any weight of gas is constant when the temperature is the same at all values of pressure and volume." Suppose that a given weight of gas is existing at a pressure of 200 lb. per sq. in. abs. and that the volume is 0·5 cu. ft. The initial state is denoted by A. Now let the gas expand in such a manner that the temperature remains constant. (The actual temperature is not important.) Then we shall get the following pressures and volumes.

Constant Product.	When pressure is	Volume is
200 × 0·5	200	0·5
,,	100	1·0
,,	66·66	1·5
,,	50	2·0
,,	40	2·5
,,	33·33	3·0
,,	28·57	3·5
,,	25	4·0

When these values of pressure and volume are plotted the curve AB of fig. 156 is obtained. This curve is called a rectangular hyperbola, and the expansion is said to be hyperbolic expansion. The temperature is constant at all points on the

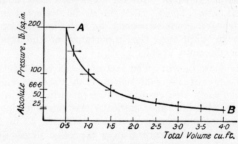

Fig. 156.

curve and for this reason it is also referred to as an isothermal curve and the expansion is known as an isothermal expansion. If compression of a perfect gas occurs with the temperature constant the compression is said to be hyperbolic and isothermal. To use the Boyle's Law equation it is advisable to write it for two states thus:

$$P_1V_1 = P_2V_2$$

where suffix (1) denotes one state and suffix (2) the other.

From this equation $\dfrac{P_1}{P_2} = \dfrac{V_2}{V_1}$

$$\text{or } P_1 = P_2\dfrac{V_2}{V_1}$$

$$\text{or } P_2 = P_1\dfrac{V_1}{V_2}.$$

Alternatively $V_2 = \dfrac{P_1V_1}{P_2}$ and $V_1 = \dfrac{P_2V_2}{P_1}.$

EXAMPLE. A quantity of gas is expanded from 250 lb. per sq. in. abs. and 3 cu. ft. until the volume is 30 cu. ft. What is the pressure at this volume if the temperature is constant ? Also determine the volume when the pressure is 50 lb. per sq. in. absolute under the same temperature conditions.

$$P_1V_1 = P_2V_2 \qquad\qquad P_1 = 250 \text{ lb. per sq. in.}$$
$$\therefore P_2 = \dfrac{P_1V_1}{V_2} \qquad\qquad \begin{array}{l} V_1 = 3 \\ V_2 = 30 \end{array}$$
$$= \dfrac{250 \times 3}{30} \qquad\qquad P_2 = \text{unknown.}$$
$$= 25 \text{ lb. per sq. in. abs.}$$

similarly at 50 lb. per sq. in. $V_2 = \dfrac{P_1V_1}{P_2} = \dfrac{250 \times 3}{50} = 15$ cu. ft.

EXAMPLE. Air is compressed isothermally from 15 lb. per sq. in. abs. and 25 cu. ft. to a volume of 5 cu. ft. Find the pressure when the volume has this value.

$$P_2V_2 = P_1V_1$$
$$\therefore P_2 = \dfrac{P_1V_1}{V_2} = \dfrac{15 \times 25}{5} = 75 \text{ lb. per sq. in. abs.}$$

EXAMPLE. Steam is admitted to an engine cylinder at 150 lb. per sq. in. abs. It is cut off at $\frac{1}{8}$-stroke and the expansion is hyperbolic. Find the pressure at the end of expansion.

In this case the final volume is 8 times the initial volume.
$$\therefore P_1V_1 = P_2V_2$$
and $$P_2 = \dfrac{P_1V_1}{V_2} = \dfrac{150 \times 1}{8} = 18.75 \text{ lb. per sq. in. abs.}$$

223. Charles's Law. This law deals with the relationship between the temperature and the volume of a given quantity of gas when the pressure is constant. The law is as follows:

Equal volumes of different gases expand equally for equal increases of temperature provided that the pressure remains constant during the expansion. It is found by careful experiment that the change in volume per degree Centigrade change of temperature is $\frac{1}{273}$ of the volume of the gas *at* 0° C. when the pressure is constant. Thus 15 cu. ft. of any gas at 0° C. would expand to $15 + (\frac{15}{273} \times$ temp. rise) cu. ft. when the temperature increased to some value above 0° C.

EXAMPLE. A quantity of gas at 0° C. occupies 20 cu. ft. What would its volume be at 400° C. if the pressure is the same at both temperatures ?

$$\text{Increase in volume} = \frac{1}{273} \times 20 \text{ cu. ft. per degree C., rise.}$$

$$\therefore \text{ Total increase in volume} = \left(\frac{1}{273} \times 20 \times 400\right) \text{ cu. ft.}$$

$$= \frac{8,000}{273} = 29\cdot3 \text{ cu. ft.}$$

$$\therefore \text{ Final volume} = 20 + 29\cdot3 = 49\cdot3 \text{ cu. ft.}$$

EXAMPLE. The volume of a given quantity of gas at 500° C. is 30 cu. ft. What would be its volume at 200° C., the pressure remaining the same at both temperatures ?

To solve this example it will be necessary to find the volume at 0° C. Let V = volume at 0° C.

$$\text{Then} \qquad \text{Volume increase} = \left(\frac{1}{273} \times \text{V} \times 500\right) \text{ cu. ft.}$$

$$\text{and, Total volume at } 500° \text{ C.} = \left(\text{V} + \frac{1}{273} \text{ V} \times 500\right)$$

$$= \text{V}\left[1 + \frac{500}{273}\right] = \text{V}\left[\frac{273}{273} + \frac{500}{273}\right]$$

$$= \frac{773}{273}\text{V}$$

$$\text{i.e.} \qquad 30 = \frac{773}{273}\text{V}.$$

$$\therefore \text{ V} = \frac{30 \times 273}{773} = 10\cdot58 \text{ cu. ft.}$$

$$\text{Now,} \qquad \text{Volume at } 200° \text{ C.} = \text{volume at } 0° \text{ C.} + \text{increase in volume}$$

$$= 10\cdot58 + \frac{10\cdot58}{273} \times 200$$

$$= 10\cdot58\left[1 + \frac{200}{273}\right] = 10\cdot58\left[\frac{273}{273} + \frac{200}{273}\right]$$

$$= \frac{10\cdot58 \times 473}{273} = 18\cdot37 \text{ cu. ft.}$$

Note that we could write $\dfrac{30 \times 273}{773}$ for 10·58 in the last term thus :

$$\frac{30 \times 273}{773} \times \frac{473}{273} = 30 \times \frac{473}{773}$$

$$= 18\cdot37 \text{ cu. ft.}$$

This suggests a better method of making this calculation and also suggests a more convenient form of Charles's Law.

224. Working form of Charles's Law. Imagine a long tube of uniform bore, fig. 157, containing a quantity of gas at 0° C. and enclosed by a piston which creates a pressure, p. Let the pressure p remain constant. Let a mark be made opposite the bottom edge of the piston. If now the temperature of the gas is raised by one degree Centigrade the piston will move $\frac{1}{273} \times l$, where l is the length of the core of gas. If raised two degrees in temperature the piston will move $\frac{2}{273}l$.

If the gas is cooled one degree the amount of movement will be the same as when it is heated one degree, but now the gas will reduce in volume. The reduction in volume is $\frac{1}{273} \times$ volume at 0° C. The reduction for 2 degrees would be $\frac{2}{273} \times$ volume at 0° C. Now consider 273 cu. ft. of gas at 0° C. and suppose its temperature to be reduced with the pressure remaining the same throughout. Then we get the following table assuming that the gas follows Charles's Law throughout the whole temperature range.

FIG. 157.

Volume, V, cubic feet.	Temperature.
273	0° C.
272	− 1° C.
270	− 3° C.
200	− 73° C.
100	− 173° C.
10	− 263° C.
0	− 273° C.

[It will be noticed that, if Charles's Law holds throughout, the gas volume has disappeared, which means the destruction of the gas. What actually happens is that Charles's law does not hold in the region of very low temperature because changes in the state of the gas have taken place.]

If now we mark off the length, l, into 273 divisions, each division would represent the effect of one degree change in temperature, and thus the tube could be used as a thermometer, This arrangement is known as the gas thermometer. The zero of this thermometer is at the bottom end of the tube and thus the reading opposite to the original 0° C. would be 273. Thus by adding 273 degrees to the temperatures in the above table we shall get:

Volume, V, cubic feet.	New Temperature.
273	$0 + 273 = 273$
272	$-1 + 273 = 272$
270	$-3 + 273 = 270$
200	$-73 + 273 = 200$
100	$-173 + 273 = 100$
10	$-263 + 273 = 10$
0	$-273 + 273 = 0.$

The new temperature obtained thus, is known as an absolute temperature, and the scale is called the absolute temperature scale.

Similarly the effect of using the new temperatures would be to give volumes proportional to the absolute temperatures. Thus we note that $V \propto T$ where T is absolute temperature. If we divide the volume by the temperature at any corresponding level in the table we get

$$\frac{V}{T} = 1.$$

If any other value of initial volume at 0° Centigrade had been taken the result would be to alter the value of the constant unity. Thus if 273C cu. ft. had been taken where C is any constant multiplier, the equation would have become

$$\frac{V}{T} = C$$

i.e. $V = TC$ or $V \propto T.$

Thus we may state the law of Charles as follows : *The total volume of a given quantity of gas varies directly as the absolute temperature when the pressure is kept constant.* For two different states of gas we should have,

$$\frac{V_1}{T_1} = \frac{V_2}{T_2} \text{ or } \frac{T_1}{T_2} = \frac{V_1}{V_2}$$

where the suffixes 1 and 2 refer to respective states.

EXAMPLE. Ten cubic feet of gas at 100° C. receive heat at constant pressure until the temperature is 400° C. Find the change in volume which takes place during the supply of heat.

Because the pressure is constant Charles's Law is applicable. The pressure-volume diagram for this case is shown in fig. 158.

First the temperatures must be made absolute.

∴ Initial temperature = 100° + 273 = **373° C. abs.**
Final temperature = 400° + 273 = **673° C. „**

now
$$\frac{V_2}{T_2} = \frac{V_1}{T_1}.$$

$$\therefore \ V_2 = V_1\frac{T_2}{T_1} = \frac{10 \times 673}{373}$$

$$= 18\cdot04 \text{ cu. ft.}$$

$\therefore$ Change in volume $= 18\cdot04 - 10 = 8\cdot04$ cu. feet.

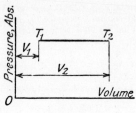

FIG. 158.

225. The Fahrenheit Absolute Scale is obtained in the same way as the Centigrade absolute scale. In the Fahrenheit case the expansion per degree

$$= \frac{1}{273} \times \frac{5}{9} = \frac{1}{491\cdot4}.$$

Since the zero of the Fahrenheit absolute scale is at the same temperature level as the zero of the Centigrade scale, and since 0° C. is equivalent to 32° F. on the ordinary scale, it follows that the zero of the absolute Fahrenheit scale is at $(491\cdot4 - 32) = 459\cdot4^\circ$ below ordinary zero Fahrenheit, see fig. 159.

Thus we get :

Absolute temperature Centigrade $= t^\circ + 273$

    ,,   ,,   Fahrenheit $= t^\circ + 459\cdot4$

where t is the ordinary temperature in both cases.

EXAMPLE. A quantity of gas occupies 3 cu. ft. at 250° F. ordinary temperature. What is its volume when the temperature has risen 300° F. if the pressure is the same at both temperatures ?

Referring to fig. 158,

$$T_1 = 250 + 459.4 \qquad\qquad = \quad 709.4° \text{ F. abs.}$$
$$T_2 = 250 + 300 + 459.4 = 1,009.4° \text{ F.} \quad \text{,,}$$

Now
$$\frac{V_2}{T_2} = \frac{V_1}{T_1}.$$

$$\therefore V_2 = V_1 \cdot \frac{T_2}{T_1} = 3 \times \frac{1,009.4}{709.4} = 4.265 \text{ cu. ft.}$$

EXAMPLE. A gas initially at 600° F. ordinary temperature is reduced in volume by cooling at constant pressure to one-third of its value at the above temperature. Find its final temperature.

Referring to fig. 158,

$$\frac{V_1}{T_1} = \frac{V_2}{T_2}$$

$$\therefore T_1 = \frac{V_1}{V_2} \cdot T_2 \text{ and } T_2 = 1,059.4° \text{ F. abs.}$$

$$= \tfrac{1}{3} \times 1,059.4 = 353.1° \text{ F. abs.,}$$

or $353.1 - 459.4 = -106.3°$ F. below ordinary zero.

that is, at $106.3 + 32 = 138.3°$ F. below ordinary freezing point.

For comparison the working forms of Boyle's Law and Charles's Law are repeated.

Boyle's Law	*Charles's Law*
$\dfrac{P_1}{V_2} = \dfrac{P_2}{V_1}$ or $\dfrac{P_1}{P_2} = \dfrac{V_2}{V_1}$ } Temperature Constant.	$\dfrac{T_1}{T_2} = \dfrac{V_1}{V_2}$ or $\dfrac{V_2}{T_2} = \dfrac{V_1}{T_1}$ } Pressure Constant.

226. Combination of Boyle's and Charles's Laws. The pressure, volume and temperature of a quantity of gas may all change at the same time. When this occurs Charles's Law will not apply because the pressure changes, and Boyle's Law will not apply because the temperature changes. It is possible to imagine this change of state as taking place in two stages, (*a*) by a change according to Boyle's Law, followed by (*b*) a change according to Charles's Law.

Consider a quantity of a perfect gas at pressure P_1, volume V_1 and temperature T_1, in the cylinder A, fig. 160. The same gas is found later to be in the state $P_2 V_2 T_2$ as in the cylinder C. Now imagine an intermediate state such as shown in cylinder B. and note the suffixes carefully.

Then because the temperature is the same in A and B, the change from state A to state B follows Boyle's Law.

Hence $P_1V_1 = P_2V$

$$\therefore V = \frac{P_1V_1}{P_2} \qquad \cdot \quad \cdot \quad \cdot \quad (1)$$

Note that the V denoting volume in the intermediate state has no suffix.

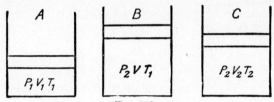

FIG. 160.

In the change from B to C the pressure remains the same whilst the temperature changes; hence Charles's Law applies.

$$\therefore \frac{V}{V_2} = \frac{T_1}{T_2}$$

$$\therefore V = \frac{T_1}{T_2}V_2 \qquad \cdot \quad \cdot \quad \cdot \quad \cdot \quad (2)$$

In equations (1) and (2), the volume V is that in B, and hence is the same quantity.

$$\therefore \frac{P_1}{P_2}V_1 = \frac{T_1}{T_2}V_2 \qquad \cdot \quad \cdot \quad \cdot \quad \cdot \quad (3)$$

$$\therefore \frac{P_1V_1}{T_1} = \frac{P_2V_2}{T_2} \qquad \cdot \quad \cdot \quad \cdot \quad \cdot \quad (4)$$

By similar reasoning, if the gas undergoes a further change of state to P_3, V_3, T_3, the equation (4) could be extended thus:

$$\frac{P_1V_1}{T_1} = \frac{P_2V_2}{T_2} = \frac{P_3V_3}{T_3}.$$

Thus this general equation (4) can be applied to any point on curves such as AB, figs. 155 and 156, and to any points on vertical or horizontal lines on pressure-volume diagrams *when the weight of the gas remains constant.*

This result may be expressed thus: " The product of the absolute pressure and total volume of a quantity of gas divided by its absolute temperature is a constant." This may be written algebraically

$$\frac{PV}{T} = K \quad \text{or} \quad PV = KT \quad . \quad . \quad . \quad (5)$$

where K is constant.

EXAMPLE. A quantity of gas at a pressure of 200 lb. per sq. in. abs. volume 2 cu. ft. and temperature 900° F. abs. expands to a volume of 10 cu. ft. when its pressure is found to be 30 lb. per sq. in. abs. Find its final temperature.

Let suffix (1) refer to initial state and suffix (2) to final state.

Then $\quad \dfrac{P_1 V_1}{T_1} = \dfrac{P_2 V_2}{T_2}$

$$T_2 = \frac{P_2 V_2}{P_1 V_1} \cdot T_1 = \frac{30 \times 10}{200 \times 2} \times 900 = \frac{300}{400} \times 900$$

$$T_2 = 675° \text{ F. abs.}$$

or $\quad\quad t_2 = 675 - 459\cdot4 = 215\cdot6° \text{ F. ordinary temperature.}$

EXAMPLE. A quantity of gas is reduced in temperature from 1,000° C. abs. to 600° C. abs., the pressure falling from 350 lb. per sq. in. abs. to 40 lb. per sq. in. abs. What is the volume ratio of expansion ?

$$\frac{P_1 V_1}{T_1} = \frac{P_2 V_2}{T_2}$$

$$\therefore \frac{V_2}{V_1} = \frac{P_1 T_2}{P_2 T_1}$$

$$\therefore \frac{V_2}{V_1} = \frac{350 \times 600}{40 \times 1,000} = \frac{210}{40} = 5\cdot25.$$

That is, the final volume is 5·25 times the initial volume.

227. Normal Temperature and Pressure. In order to compare quantities of gas it is usual to state the volumes at normal temperature and pressure (N.T.P.). This temperature is 32° F. and the pressure is 14·7 lb. per sq. in. abs., i.e. atmospheric pressure. The equation (4) of the last article is the equation employed in reducing a quantity of gas to N.T.P.

EXAMPLE. A gas engine consumes 360 cu. ft. of gas per hour, the pressure of the gas being 1 lb. per sq. in. above atmospheric pressure and the temperature 50° F. Find the consumption of gas at N.T.P.

To answer this example requires a new volume.

$$\therefore \frac{P_2 V_2}{T_2} = \frac{P_1 V_1}{T_1}$$

$$\therefore V_2 = \frac{P_1}{P_2} \cdot \frac{T_2}{T_1} V_1$$

$$= \frac{15\cdot7}{14\cdot7} \times \frac{491\cdot4}{509\cdot4} \times 360$$

$$371 \text{ cu. ft.}$$

$P_1 = 14\cdot7 + 1$ lb. per sq. in.
$P_2 = 14\cdot7$,, ,, ,, ,,
$V_1 = 360$ cu. ft.
$T_1 = (459\cdot4 + 50)°$ F. abs.
$T_2 = (459\cdot4 + 32)°$ F. abs.

That is 371 cu. ft. at 32° F. and 14·7 lb. per sq. in. are equivalent to 360 cu. ft. at 50° F. and 15·7 lb. per sq. in.

Note that the reduction of pressure increases the volume and that reduction of temperature decreases the volume. In this example the increase due to pressure effect is greater than the decrease due to temperature effects. Also note that the pressures are written as a ratio and the temperatures also. The result is to get a number which multiplies a volume to give a volume as the result.

228. The Characteristic Equation of a Gas. This equation connects the pressure, the specific volume and the temperature of a gas. The specific volume (see also arts. 169 and 216) enables us to calculate the weights of gases which, hitherto, we have not undertaken.

We shall now show that the constant K in equation (5) includes the weight of the gas.

Let V_s = volume of 1 lb. of gas in cubic feet (called the specific volume).

V = Total volume of gas in cubic feet

w = Weight of gas in lb. $= \dfrac{V}{V_s}$; $\therefore V = wV_s$.

P = Pressure in lb. per square foot absolute.

T = Temperature in degrees absolute.

R = Characteristic constant for the gas.

Then equation (5), art. 226 is $PV = KT$

i.e. $PwV_s = KT$

Now $PV_s = \dfrac{K}{w}T$ where $\dfrac{K}{w}$ is a new constant which we denote R.

Thus the equation (5) now becomes

$$PV_s = RT \quad . \quad . \quad . \quad . \quad (6).$$

This equation is known as the *characteristic* equation and the constant R is known as the *characteristic constant*. It has one value for each gas. For air $R = 96$ when T is in degrees Centigrade and it has the value 53·2 when T is in degrees Fahrenheit.

EXAMPLE. A cylinder contains 25 cu. ft. of air at a pressure of 100 lb. per sq. in. abs. and at 80° C. ordinary. Find the *weight* of air in the cylinder taking R to be 96.

First find the specific volume

$PV_s = RT$ $R = 96$

$V_s = \dfrac{RT}{P}$ $T = 80 + 273$

           $P = 100 \times 144$

$\therefore V_s = \dfrac{96 \times 353}{100 \times 144}$

$= 2·35$ cu. ft. per lb. of air.

$$\therefore \text{ Weight of air in cylinder} = \frac{\text{Total volume}}{\text{Specific volume}}$$

$$= \frac{25}{2 \cdot 35} = 10 \cdot 63 \text{ lb.}$$

The corresponding temperature in degrees F. is 176° ordinary, and the corresponding value of R is 53·2.

$$\therefore \text{ The specific volume is } \frac{53 \cdot 2 \times 637 \cdot 4}{100 \times 144} = 2 \cdot 35 \text{ cu. ft. per lb.}$$

The meaning of R is important. Suppose 1 lb. of gas at absolute temperature T_1 and pressure P lb. per sq. ft., occupying V_1 cu. ft., is placed in a cylinder fitted with a piston whose area is A sq. ft. Let L_1 be the length of cylinder occupied,

$$\text{then } V_1 = AL_1.$$

Now increase the temperature to T_2 so that the volume becomes V_2 and the occupied length L_2, the pressure remaining constant at P,

$$\text{then } V_2 = AL_2.$$

Then work done on piston = Force on piston × Distance
moved

$$= PA \times (L_2 - L_1)$$
$$= PAL_2 - PAL_1$$
$$= PV_2 - PV_1$$
$$= RT_2 - RT_1 = R(T_2 - T_1)$$

$$\therefore R(T_2 - T_1) = \text{Work done on piston}$$

$$\therefore R = \frac{\text{Work done on piston}}{T_2 - T_1} = \begin{array}{l} \text{Work done in foot-pounds per} \\ \text{degree rise in temperature} \\ \text{per lb. of gas.} \end{array}$$

Thus the figure 53·2 or 96 is not merely a number, it is a quantity of energy. The units of the quantities involved in the characteristic equation must be carefully noted.

229. Specific Heats of Gases. All gases have two specific heats, (1) a value when the heat is added at constant volume and denoted Cv, and (2), a value when the heat is added at constant pressure denoted Cp. The latter value is always greater than the former and the difference between these values is the value of R. For example, the specific heat of air at constant pressure is 0·2375 heat units per lb. per degree, and the specific heat at constant volume is 0·1691 heat units per lb. per degree.

Thus R = 0·2375 − 0·1691.

$$= 0 \cdot 0684 \text{ heat units per lb. per degree.}$$

i.e. = 0·0684 × 778 = 53·2ft.-lb. per lb. per degree F.

or   = 0·0684 × 1400 = 96   ,,   ,,   ,,   ,,   ,,   ,,   C.

EXAMPLE. The two specific heats of a certain gas are 0·238 and 0·169 respectively. Find the volume of a cylinder to hold 3 lb. of this gas at 200 lb. per square inch absolute and at 104° F.

First find the characteristic constant.

$$R = 0·238 - 0·169$$
$$= 0·069 \text{ B.Th.U. per degree F. per lb.}$$

Since the temperature is in degrees F. use Joule's equivalent for B.Th.U.

Thus $R = 0·069 \times 778$ ft.-lb. per lb. per degree F.
$$= 53·5 \text{ ft.-lb. per lb. per degree C.}$$

$$\therefore \text{ Volume of 1 lb.} = \frac{RT}{P} = \frac{53·5 \times 563·4}{200 \times 144}$$

$$= 1·048 \text{ cu. ft. per lb.}$$
$$\therefore \text{ Volume of cylinder} = 3 \times 1·048 = 3·144 \text{ cu. ft.}$$

230. General Law to Expansion or Compression Curves.
Let the line 1–2, fig. 161, represent an expansion or compression line. Then the relationship between pressures and volumes at all points between 1 and 2 is such that $P \times V^n$ is constant. This is the general law to an expansion or compression line.

Thus $$PV^n = C.$$

The value of n usually varies from 0·9 to about 1·6, but it

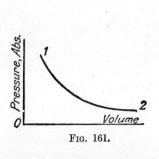

FIG. 161.

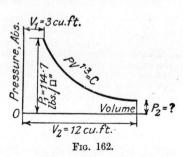

FIG. 162.

may have values outside this range. We have already dealt with the special case of this law when n is unity (i.e. Boyle's Law).

Using the suffixes we can write

$$P_1V_1^n = C$$

and $$P_2V_2^n = C$$

and therefore $P_1V_1^n = P_2V_2^n$. This is the usual working form of the equation, the actual value of the constant C being rarely required.

The following examples will show how this equation is used.

U

EXAMPLE. The pressure of a quantity of gas enclosed in a cylinder is 100 lb. per sq. in. by gauge and the volume occupied by the gas is 3 cu. ft. The gas expands according to the law $PV^{1\cdot3} = C$ until the volume is 12 cu. ft. Find the final pressure.

Draw and dimension the $P - V$ diagram as in fig. 162. Pressure given is by gauge, but the pressure used in the equation is always absolute.

$$\therefore \; P_1 = 100 + 14\cdot7 = 114\cdot7 \text{ lb. per sq. in.}$$
$$P_1 V_1^{1\cdot3} = P_2 V_2^{1\cdot3}$$

and since P_2 is required

$$P_2 = P_1 \left(\frac{V_1}{V_2}\right)^{1\cdot3}$$

$$= 114\cdot7 \times \left(\frac{3}{12}\right)^{1\cdot3} = \frac{114\cdot7}{4^{1\cdot3}}$$

Note that the figure 4 is the expansion ratio, a mere number. Taking logs. for the denominator only

$$1\cdot3 \times \log_{10} 4 = 1\cdot3 \times 0\cdot6021 = 0\cdot7827.$$

The antilog. of this figure is 6·063

$$\therefore \; 4^{1\cdot3} = 6\cdot063$$

$$\therefore \; P_2 = \frac{114\cdot7}{6\cdot063} = 18\cdot9 \text{ lb. per sq. in. abs.}$$

or

$$= 18\cdot9 - 14\cdot7$$
$$= 4\cdot2 \text{ lb. per sq. in. gauge.}$$

EXAMPLE. The pressure of the gases just after the commencement of the expansion stroke in a gas-engine cylinder is 290 lb. per sq. in. gauge and the volume is 0·32 cu. ft. Find the volume when the pressure is 48 lb. per sq. in. gauge if the expansion law is $PV^{1\cdot32} = C$.

Draw the curve as in fig. 163 and dimension it to suit this problem.

Then

$$P_1 V_1^{1\cdot32} = P_2 V_2^{1\cdot32} \qquad\qquad P_1 = 290 + 14\cdot7 = 304\cdot7$$

$$V_2^{1\cdot32} = \frac{P_1}{P_2} V_1^{1\cdot32} \qquad\qquad P_2 = \;\; 48 + 14\cdot7 = \;\; 62\cdot7$$

$$V_2^{1\cdot32} = \frac{304\cdot7}{62\cdot7} \times 0\cdot32^{1\cdot32} = 4\cdot87 \times 0\cdot32^{1\cdot32}$$

Logarize the equation.

$$\begin{aligned}
1\cdot32 \log V_2 &= \log 4\cdot87 + 1\cdot32 \times \log 0\cdot32 \\
&= 0\cdot6875 + 1\cdot32 \times \bar{1}\cdot5051 \\
&= 0\cdot6875 + 1\cdot32 \times (-\;0\cdot4949) \\
&= 0\cdot6875 + (-\;0\cdot6532) \\
&= 0\cdot0343
\end{aligned}$$

$$\therefore \; \log V_2 = \frac{0\cdot0343}{1\cdot32}$$

$$= 0\cdot026$$

Delogarizing $V_2 = 1\cdot062$ cu. ft. answer.

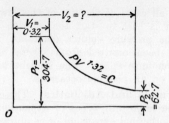

FIG. 163.

EXAMPLE. The pressure at the beginning of compression in an oil-engine cylinder is 14 lb. per sq. in. abs. and the volume ratio of compression is 13. Find the pressure at the end of compression if the law is $PV^{1.4} = C$. Also find the pressure when the volume has been reduced to one-third of the initial value.

Let suffix 1 refer to the initial state and 2 to the final state.

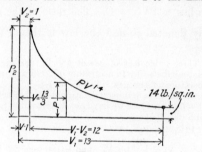

FIG. 164.

Then

$$P_2 V_2^{1.4} = P_1 V_1^{1.4}$$

$$\therefore P_2 = P_1 \left(\frac{V_1}{V_2}\right)^{1.4}$$

$$= 14 \times \left(\frac{13}{1}\right)^{1.4}$$

$$= 14 \times 13^{1.4}$$

$$= 14 \times 36.25$$

$$= 507.5 \text{ lb. per sq. in. abs.}$$

Log 13 = 1·1139
1·4 × log 13 = 1·5594
Antilog 1·5594 = 36·25

Similar work is required for the second part.

$$P_2 V_2^{1.4} = P_1 V_1^{1.4}$$

$$\therefore P_2 = P_1 \left(\frac{V_1}{V_2}\right)^{1.4}$$

$$= 14 \times \left(\frac{3}{1}\right)^{1.4}$$

$$= 14 \times 3^{1.4}$$

$$= 14 \times 4.655$$

$$= 65.17 \text{ lb. per sq. in. abs.}$$

Log 3 = 0·4771
1·4 × log 3 = 0·6679
Antilog 0·6679 = 4·655.

Note that in all cases of the use of this law, logarithms are required, and it is best to start the solution by drawing and dimensioning the pressure volume diagrams. Pressure-volume diagrams have been omitted from several of the foregoing exercises to economize space. The student is advised to use these diagrams on all possible occasions.

231. Isothermals and Adiabatics. These two names are used to describe important types of expansion or compression of gases. An isothermal expansion or compression is one which takes place with the temperature of the gas remaining the same throughout. Thus Boyle's Law expansion or compression is isothermal. In all cases of isothermal operation on perfect gases the law will be $PV = C$.

An adiabatic expansion or compression is one which takes place without heat entering or leaving the gas during the process. In this case the law is $PV^{\frac{C_p}{C_v}} = C$. The ratio of the specific heats, $\dfrac{C_p}{C_v}$, is usually denoted γ, and the law is then $PV^\gamma = C$

EXAMPLE. Three cubic feet of gas at 180 lb. per sq. in. abs. and at 1,400° C. expand adiabatically to a pressure of 20 lb. per sq. in. abs. Find the final temperature of the gas. Take $\gamma = 1.4$.

It will be noted that the temperature cannot be obtained without calculating the final volume because we have not described the pressure-temperature relationship (fig. 165).

Thus $P_1 V_1^{1.4} = P_2 V_2^{1.4}$

$\therefore V_2 = \left(\dfrac{P_1}{P_2}\right)^{\frac{1}{1.4}} V_1$ and extracting the 1.4th root

$\qquad = \left(\dfrac{180}{20}\right)^{0.715} \times 3$

$\qquad = 9^{0.715} \times 3$ $\qquad\qquad$ log 9 = 0.9542

$\qquad = 4.81 \times 3$ $\qquad\qquad$ 0.715 log 9 = 0.6822

$\qquad = 14.43$ cu. ft. $\qquad\qquad$ antilog. = 4.81

Now $\dfrac{P_1 V_1}{T_1} = \dfrac{P_2 V_2}{T_2}$

$\therefore T_2 = \dfrac{P_2 V_2}{P_1 V_1}.T_1$

$\quad T_2 = \dfrac{20}{180} \times \dfrac{14.43}{3} \times 1,673$

$\qquad = \dfrac{4.81}{9} \times 1,673$

$\qquad = 896°$ C. absolute.

or $\qquad = 623°$ C. ordinary temperature.

Alternatively, using Fahrenheit degrees.
1,400° C. = 2,552° F. = 3,011·4° F. absolute.

$$T_2 = \frac{20}{180} \times \frac{14\cdot43}{3} \times 3011\cdot4$$

$$= 1,613° \text{ F. absolute}$$
$$= 1,153° \text{ F. ordinary temperature.}$$

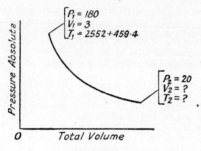

Fɪɢ. 165.

The temperature always falls during an adiabatic expansion although no heat has left the gas. The explanation is that work has been done during the expansion and because no heat, as such, has been supplied to the gas, the energy in the gas itself has been converted into work. This conversion of the gas energy into work has caused the fall in temperature. The student will later apply the principle of the conservation of energy to this important case and he will then learn that the change in the energy of the gas is exactly equal to the work done by the gas during the expansion.

In an adiabatic compression the work expended on the gas increases the temperature of the gas.

Now consider the isothermal expansion. If the temperature is to be kept at the initial value heat must be supplied during the expansion, and the amount of heat supplied in this case is equal to the work done. Similarly in the compression of a gas isothermally heat must be removed by an amount equal to the work done in compression.

In all cases of gas calculations use absolute pressures, absolute temperatures and total volume of gas as indicated in the worked examples.

EXAMPLES XX

Section A

1. What are the quantities known as the properties of a gas ?

2. Explain how the state of a quantity of gas can be represented on a diagram.

3. A quantity of gas has its volume increased from 4 cu. ft. to 30 cu. ft. What is its expansion ratio ?

4. 36 cu. ft. of air are compressed through a ratio of 8 : 1, what is the final volume ?

5. The clearance space of a gas engine measures 400 cu. in. and the volume swept by the piston (i.e. product of area of piston × stroke) is 1,200 cu. in. What is the compression ratio of the engine ?

6. A pressure gauge reads 56·2 lb. per sq. in. What is the absolute pressure ?

7. A vacuum gauge reads 10 lb. per sq. in. What is the absolute pressure ? If 30 in. of mercury is equal to 15 lb. per sq. in. and if a vacuum gauge reads 28 in. of mercury, what is then the absolute pressure ?

8. State Boyle's Law and Charles's Law.

9. A quantity of gas expands from volume 1·2 cu. ft. to a volume of 6 cu. ft. according to Boyle's Law. The final pressure is found to be 40 lb. per sq. in. abs. What was the initial pressure ?

10. 2,000 cu. ft. of air are compressed from 15 lb. per sq. in. abs. according to Boyle's Law. The delivery valve opens when the pressure is 75 lb. per sq. in. abs. What is the volume when the valve opens ?

11. Steam is supplied to a cylinder at 120 lb. per sq. in. abs. and then cut off at ⅓-stroke. The expansion is hyperbolic. Find the pressure at the end of the stroke.

12. A quantity of gas is heated at constant pressure until its final volume is 1·3 times the initial volume. The final ordinary temperature is found to be 1,603° F. Find its initial temperature ?

13. The initial state of a gas is : Pressure 200 lb. per sq. in. abs., Volume 0·4 cu. ft., and Temperature 1,652° F. ordinary. The gas expands until the volume is 2 cu. ft., when the pressure is found to be 75 lb. per sq. in. abs. What is the final temperature ? If the final pressure had been 60 lb. per sq. in. abs., what would the temperature have been ?

14. If the final temperature in the last example was 752° F. ordinary, what would be the pressure at 2 cu. ft. volume ?

15. What do you understand by Charles's Law ? 10 cu. ft. of air are heated from 50° to 60·8° F., the pressure remaining constant. Find the final volume. U.E.I.

16. State Boyle's Law and Charles's Law.

Steam at 100 lb. per sq. in. abs. is admitted to an engine cylinder, and cut-off takes place at ¾-stroke, after which expansion may be assumed to take place according to Boyle's Law. Draw a curve showing the pressure of the steam throughout the stroke. What is the pressure at the end of the stroke ? U.E.I.

17. In a gas-engine trial it is found that 450 cu. ft. of gas are used per hour at a pressure of 4 in. of water. What would be the gas consumption at atmospheric pressure, i.e. at 15 lb. per sq. in. abs. without variation in temperature ? You may assume that atmospheric pressure will support a column of water 34 ft. high. If this gas consumption was at a temperature

of 64·4° F., what would be the gas consumption at atmospheric pressure and at a temperature of 32° F. ?   U.E.I.

18. What do you understand by absolute pressure and absolute temperature ?   1·5 cu. ft. of gas at a pressure of 15 lb. per sq. in. abs. are contained in a cylinder. The gas is compressed at constant temperature until its pressure is 90 lb. per sq. in. abs. What is then the volume of the gas ? If after compression the temperature of the gas was raised from 68° F. to 140° F., the pressure being kept constant, what would then be the volume of the gas ?   U.E.I.

SECTION B

19. What is meant by standard temperature and pressure ?   Reduce 3 cu. ft. at 64° F. and $1\frac{1}{2}$ lb. per sq. in. gauge to standard volume at N.T.P.

20. The characteristic constant for a certain gas is 53·9 ft.-lb. per lb. per degree F. What is the specific volume of this gas at 172·6° F. and at 100 lb. per sq. in. abs. ?

21. What would be the specific volume in the last example if reduced to N.T.P. ?

22. An air compressor takes in per minute 2,000 cu. ft. of air at 14·7 lb. per sq. in. and at 59° F. If the characteristic constant is 53·3, find the weight of air taken in per minute.

23. 4 cu. ft. of gas at 150 lb. per sq. in. abs. expand until the volume is 16 cu. ft. according to the law $PV^{1\cdot25} = C$. Find the final pressure.

24. State exactly the meaning of each letter, and the unit in which it is expressed, in the equation $PV = RT$, as applied to a perfect gas.

A gas engine when using 24 cu. ft. of gas has a suction pressure as measured by means of a manometer of 12·5 lb. per sq. in. abs., and the temperature is observed to be 60° F. What will the gas consumption be at a pressure of 15 lb. per sq. in. abs. and a temperature of 32° F.   U.E.I.

25. A quantity of gas has its volume doubled at constant pressure whilst its temperature is raised by 500° F. Find the initial and final temperatures.

26. The temperature and pressure at the end of the compression stroke in a gas engine cylinder are 179° C. and 63 lb. per sq. in. abs. Heat is then supplied at constant volume until the temperature is 832° C. ordinary scale. Find the pressure attained at constant volume.

27. A tank of 120 cu. ft. capacity contains air at a gauge pressure of 100 lb. per sq. in. and at a temperature of 84° F. Water is then forced into the tank until the gauge pressure is 125 lb. per sq. in. and at the same time the temperature is raised to 65° C. Determine the reduction in volume of the air.   U.L.C.I.

28. A receiver of 280 cu. ft. capacity contains air at an absolute pressure of 120 lb. per sq. in. and at a temperature of 84° F. Find the weight of air in the receiver having given that 1 cu. ft. of air at 32° F. and at an absolute pressure of 14·7 lb. per sq. in. weighs 0·0807 lb.   U.L.C.I.

29. A gas-propelled bus runs 100 miles per day, and uses 46 cu. ft. of gas, at atmospheric pressure, per mile. The gas used for the day is carried in a gas-container under a pressure of 200 atmospheres. Calculate the capacity of the container. What would be the cost of the gas used in a day's run if the gas were supplied at 10d. per 1,000 cu. ft. and it cost $7\frac{1}{2}d.$ per 1,000 cu. ft. for compression ? Assume constant temperature throughout the operations.   U.L.C.I.

30. Air at pressure 500 lb. per sq. in. abs., temperature 80·6° F., flows

through a heater which causes the pressure and temperature to increase to 600 lb. per sq. in. and 392° F. respectively. Calculate the percentage increase in volume of the air.   N.C.T.E.C.

31. A closed cylinder is filled with air at temperature 70° F. and pressure 60 lb. per sq. in. above the atmospheric pressure of 15 lb. per sq. in. If the temperature is raised to 1,500° F., calculate the pressure in the cylinder.
        N.C.T.E.C.

32. Before compression, the volume, pressure and temperature of a gas are 10 cu. ft., 15 lb. per sq. in. abs., and 302° F. respectively. Find the temperature after compression to a volume of 4 cu. ft., the pressure then being 190 lb. per sq. in. abs.   N.C.T.E.C.

33. Air at pressure 14·7 lb. per sq. in. abs. and temperature 54° F. is compressed into a reservoir of 20 cu. ft. capacity to a pressure of 350 lb. per sq. in. abs. If the temperature after compressing is 104° F., calculate the volume of the air before compressing.

What will be the pressure in the reservoir if the temperature of the air subsequently falls to the original value ?   N.C.T.E.C.

34. Establish the relationship between pressure, volume and temperature of a gas and hence state the law connecting pressure volume and temperature of one pound of air at atmospheric pressure and 32° F. If the pressure is increased to $2\frac{1}{2}$ atmospheres and the temperature to 266° F., what is its volume ? (Volume of 1 lb. of air at atmospheric pressure and 32° F. = 12·39 cu. ft.)   N.C.T.E.C

CHAPTER XXI

CYCLIC ACTIONS IN ENGINE CYLINDERS

232. The Slide Valve. This valve is so called because it slides on a working face prepared for it. It is of box form and a sectional pictorial view of the valve and the cylinder ports is shown in fig. 166. The valve V slides with a to and fro motion on the valve face F and alternatively uncovers the port P_1 and the port P_2. The steam is supplied to the chest space C and is said to be " outside " the valve. The space E is the exhaust port to which the exhaust pipe is connected. The steam is exhausted from the cylinder through the ports by which it is admitted, and passes through the inside of the valve. Exhaust is shown taking place for the right-hand side of the piston whilst steam supply is taking place on the left-hand side. The valve is really four valves in one. The edge (1), admits and cuts off the steam to the left side of the piston whilst the edge (2), releases the steam and cuts off the exhaust from the left side of the piston. Similar functions for the right-hand side of the piston are performed by the valve edges (4), and (3) respectively.

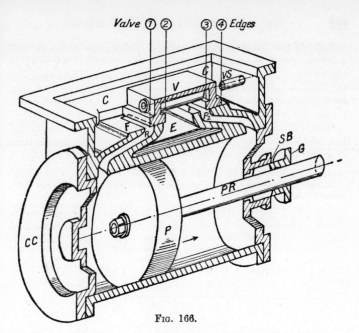

Valve ① ② ③ ④ Edges

FIG. 166.

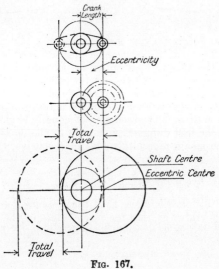

Crank Length

Eccentricity

Total Travel

Shaft Centre

Eccentric Centre

Total Travel

FIG. 167.

233. Valve Drive. The valve is driven by a crank and connecting-rod mechanism in which the crank is very short compared to the length of its connecting rod. The crank pin of this arrangement is enlarged so as to include the shaft within its section and is then known as an eccentric. The centre diagram of fig. 167 shows successive enlargements of the crank pin.

The crank length is the distance between the shaft centre and the crank pin or eccentric centre. It is called the eccentricity and the total travel of the valve is twice this distance.

∴ Eccentricity = Half valve travel.

EXAMPLE.—The eccentricity of an eccentric is $1\frac{3}{4}$ in. What is the valve travel ? Answer $3\frac{1}{2}$ in.

234. The Valve Dimensions. The figure 168 shows the plane section of valve and cylinder ports in the direction of

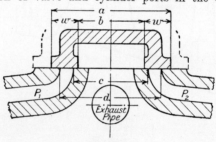

FIG. 168.

motion of the valve. It is important to note that the valve is shown in its central position and that the eccentric centre line will be vertical. It will be noted that the length a of the valve is greater than the extreme distance d across the outer edges of the steam ports. This difference is equally divided over the edges and the half difference is known as the outside " lap " or because the steam passes this edge of the valve, the " steam " lap.

Thus the steam lap $= \dfrac{a - d}{2}$.

Also the distance b is less than the distance c and the inside edges of the valve overlap the inside edges of the ports. This amount of lap is the inside or exhaust lap. Thus exhaust lap $= \dfrac{c - b}{2}$.

These laps can only be measured when the valve is in its central position.

The steam lap of a slide valve is the amount by which the steam edges of the valve overlap the outside edges of the steam ports when the valve is in its central position. Similarly the exhaust lap is the amount of overlap of exhaust edge relative to the inside edges of the steam port. It will be noted that the width w of each valve face is equal to steam lap + port width + exhaust lap. Sometimes the exhaust lap is zero and sometimes it is negative. In the latter case b is greater than c, and in the former $b = c$.

235. Relationship between Travel, Lap, and Port Opening. Referring to fig. 169 let T = valve travel from extreme to extreme. Then $\dfrac{T}{2}$ = eccentricity.

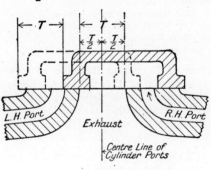

L.H. Port   Exhaust   R.H. Port

Centre Line of
Cylinder Ports

Fig. 169.

Now when the valve has moved its full half-travel from its central position say towards the right, the left-hand edge (1) will have uncovered the left-hand port. The amount of opening will be equal to $\left(\dfrac{T}{2} - \text{steam lap}\right)$. Similarly the right-hand port will have been opened to exhaust by an amount equal to $\left(\dfrac{T}{2} - \text{exhaust lap}\right)$.

Thus movement available for opening ports = (half travel — lap). The movement available for opening ports may not be exactly equal to the port width. If it is greater the valve overruns the ports, and if less the valve travels too little to uncover the ports completely.

EXAMPLE. The travel of a slide valve is $3\frac{3}{4}$ in. The outside or steam lap is $\frac{3}{4}$ in. and the inside lap is $\frac{3}{8}$ in. What is the maximum port opening (a) to supply steam, (b) to discharge exhaust ?

(a) Maximum opening to steam $= \dfrac{3\frac{3}{4}''}{2} - \frac{3}{4}'' = 1\frac{1}{8}$ in.

(b) ,, ,, ,, exhaust $= \dfrac{3\frac{3}{4}''}{2} - \frac{3}{8}'' = 1\frac{1}{2}$ in.

A port width of $1\frac{1}{2}$ in. would therefore be sufficient to give full opening to exhaust. It would only give $1\frac{1}{8}$ opening to steam since the steam edge would not travel the full width of the port.

EXAMPLE. The width of the ports in a cylinder casting is $1\frac{3}{4}$ in. and the lap to steam is 1 in. whilst the exhaust lap is $\frac{1}{2}$ in. What travel will be required to give full exhaust opening and what will be the steam port opening at this travel ?

Half travel $= 1\frac{3}{4}$ in. $+ \frac{1}{2}$ in. $= 2\frac{1}{4}$ in.
∴ Full travel $= 2 \times 2\frac{1}{4} = 4\frac{1}{2}$ in.

Since the steam lap is 1 in.,

Steam port opening $= 2\frac{1}{4}$ in. $- 1$ in. $= 1\frac{1}{4}$ in.

236. Position of Eccentric Relative to Crank. Imagine the engine crank OA, see fig. 171, to be in the horizontal position. Then the piston will be at the left-hand end of its travel. If the valve is in its central position, as shown in the lay-out diagram, fig. 170, then the eccentric centre line OE must be either vertically upwards or vertically downwards. In either case no steam can

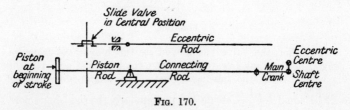

FIG. 170.

be admitted if the valve has lap. Now imagine the eccentric centre line to be moved to OE_1, fig. 171, with the engine crank and piston remaining in the same position as before. Then the valve will have moved from its central position an amount OM. When OM is equal to the steam lap the valve will commence to admit steam, and if the engine is to continue to receive steam further movement of OE_1 must increase the opening.   Thus while the eccentric centre moves from E_1 to E_2, the valve is opening the port wider and wider, and from E_2 to E_3 it is gradually closing it again.   Thus if the eccentric is keyed in the position OE_1 the crank remaining at OA, then the engine will run in the clockwise sense.   If it is keyed at OE_3, then E_3 would be the commencement of opening and the engine would run in the anti-clockwise sense.   Actually the eccentric is carried slightly farther forward than OE_1 to give a projector OM_1 on the line of travel when the piston is at the beginning of its stroke.   This causes the port to open before the crank actually reaches the position

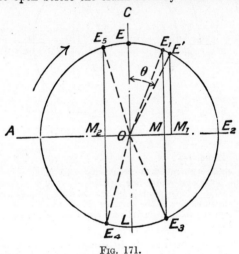

Fig. 171.

OA, when rotation is in the clockwise sense.   The amount of opening of the admission port when the crank is at OA is MM_1 and is known as the " lead."   The eccentric is finally secured in the position OE' when the crank is in the position OA.

By similar reasoning it will be found that, when OM_2 is the exhaust lap, E_4 is the position of the eccentric centre when the left-hand exhaust commences and E_5 is the position when this exhaust ceases.   Also the total distance MM_2 is equal to the sum of the steam and exhaust laps.

The angle θ is called the " angle of advance " of the eccentric. The total fixed angle between the main crank and the eccentric is $90° + \theta$ and is sometimes called the "angular advance" of the eccentric.

EXAMPLE. The travel of a slide valve is $4\frac{3}{4}$ in. and the outside lap is $\frac{7}{8}$ in. and the lead is $\frac{3}{16}$ in. Find the angle of advance and also state the total angle between crank and eccentric centre lines.

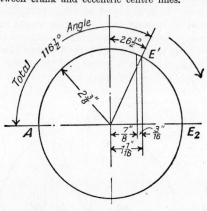

FIG. 172.

Referring to fig. 172:
Draw a circle with radius = eccentricity = $2\frac{3}{8}$ in.
Draw the horizontal centre line AOE_2.
Mark out OM_1 = lap + lead = $1\frac{1}{16}$ in. Erect a perpendicular from M_1 to cut the circumference of the circle in E'. Join OE'. Then θ is found to be $26\frac{1}{2}°$ and the total angle between crank and eccentric centre lines is therefore $116\frac{1}{2}°$.

237. Position of Piston in Stroke when Chief Events Occur. We have seen, art. 236, that E_1, E_3, E_4 and E_5 represent supply, cut off, release, and cessation of exhaust respectively for one side of the piston only. To find where the piston is, when these events take place, it will be necessary to measure from each line, OE_1, OE_3, OE_4 and OE_5, an angle $90° + \theta$, when each crank position will be found. From the crank positions, the piston positions can be found by drawing the centre lines of the crank-connecting rod mechanism to scale.

To simplify this process, imagine all the lines with the exception of the line OA to be rotated anti-clockwise an amount $90° + \theta$. Then the lines OE_1, etc., will fall on corresponding engine-crank positions, and the diagram becomes as shown in fig. 173.

The line AO continued is the line of stroke and E′B represents the piston stroke to scale.

To find the fraction of stroke at any event, say cut-off, draw a perpendicular from that crank-pin centre on to the stroke

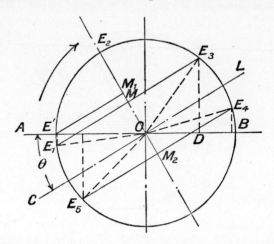

line E′B. Such a line is E_3D. Then the fraction of the stroke at cut-off is $\dfrac{E′D}{E′B}$.

Note that two events for one side of the piston occur on each stroke, namely *cut-off* and *release* on the forward stroke, and *compression* and *admission* on the backward stroke. The word compression is used to denote the end of the exhaust period. The above method neglects the effect of the connecting rod on piston position.

EXAMPLE.   The travel of a slide valve is $4\frac{1}{2}$ in., outside lap $1\frac{1}{8}$ in., exhaust lap $\frac{3}{16}$ in, lead $\frac{1}{8}$ in.   Find the angular advance of the eccentric and the position of the crank at cut-off, release, compression, and admission.

U.E.I.

Draw a circle $4\frac{1}{2}$ in. diameter, fig. 174.

Draw the horizontal centre line, OB.

With B as centre, draw an arc of radius $\frac{1}{8}$ in. to fix the lead.

With O as centre, draw an arc with radius $1\frac{1}{8}$ in. to represent the outside lap, and on the opposite side draw an arc with O as centre and with radius equal to $\tfrac{3}{16}$ in.   Draw the internal tangent AE between the lead and outside lap arcs.   Produce it to cut the travel circle.   Join these cutting points to the centre O.

Then OA is the position of the crank at admission and OE is the position of the crank at cut-off.

Draw the centre line LL′ parallel to the internal tangent.   This centre

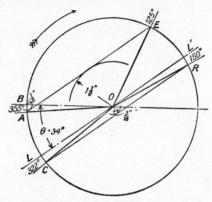

Fig. 174.

line makes an angle θ with the line of centres OB and θ is the angle of advance.   This angle is found to be 34°.   On the opposite side of the centre line draw a line tangential to the arc denoting exhaust lap and parallel to the centre line LL′.   Produce this to cut the travel circle.   Join O to the cutting points and then OR is the position of the crank at release and OC is the position of the crank at compression.   The crank positions required are Cut-off 125°, Release 150°, Compression 322° and Admission 355°, all measured clockwise from OB.

238. Hypothetical Indicator Diagram for Steam Engine. This diagram is the one which would be traced out by the pencil of an indicator if the engine worked in accordance with certain assumptions or hypotheses.   It is for this reason that it is called the hypothetical diagram.

Such a diagram is shown in fig. 175.   The following are the assumptions made in setting out the diagram:

(1) There is no clearance space in the cylinder when piston is at beginning of the stroke.

(2) Steam is supplied to the cylinder at a constant pressure equal to boiler pressure.   In fig. 175 the length OA scales the absolute boiler pressure and the line AB is the admission line at constant pressure.

(3) Cut-off is instantaneous, thus giving a sharp change of direction of diagram at B. This point is known as the Cut-off point. This is the point at which the admission valve closes.

(4) The expansion BC is hyperbolic (not isothermal, because as the pressure falls the steam temperature will fall, art. 159). The expansion law is thus $PV = C$.

(5) Expansion is carried to the end of the stroke.

(6) Release of the steam takes place at the end of the stroke and pressure falls instantly to exhaust pressure. This is denoted by the vertical line CD. The vertical distance OE scales the back pressure or exhaust pressure.

(7) Exhaust takes place at constant pressure and continues throughout the whole stroke.

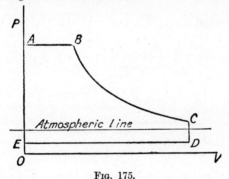

Fig. 175.

Exhaust pressures are assumed to be the designed condenser pressure in a condensing engine and to be from 2 to 3 lb. per sq. in. above atmospheric pressure in a non-condensing engine.

In actual engines the hypothetical conditions are departed from in the following manner, fig. 176.

(1) All engines have clearance space for mechanical reasons.

(2) Steam is supplied at a pressure which rapidly rises, but is finally less than boiler pressure (line fa). The pressure then falls slightly as the piston moves, due to inertia and friction in pipes and passages. This is shown by the line ab. The whole line fb is called the admission line of the diagram.

(3) At cut-off point b the valve action is not instantaneous and the rounded corner results.

(4) The expansion line *bc* is not hyperbolic but falls below and to the left of the hyperbolic expansion line. This is due to condensation in the cylinder and to heat exchange between the steam and the cylinder.

(5) The exhaust valve opens and expansion is stopped before the end of the stroke, in order to allow the pressure to drop before the piston begins its return stroke. The actual release point is marked *c*.

(6) Even with early release the fall of pressure is not completed at the end of the stroke. This is shown by the curved portion or toe of the diagram, marked *cd*.

(7) The exhaust line *de* of the diagram often lies above the assumed back pressure line.

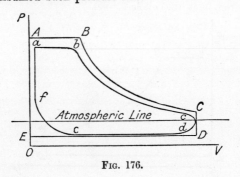

Fig. 176.

(8) The exhaust is not continued to the end of the back stroke. It is stopped at a point *e* where the exhaust valve edge closes the port, and from this point the remaining steam is compressed until the next admission.

Compare the inner diagram of fig. 176 with the valve diagram of fig. 173. We then note that f corresponds to E_1, b to E_3, c to E_4, and e to E_5. We also note that the four processes are as follows:

(1) f to b or E_1 to E_3 Steam supply. fb is the admission line.
(2) b to c or E_3 to E_4 Expansion. bc is the expansion line.
(3) c to e or E_4 to E_5 Exhaust. ce is the exhaust line.
(4) e to f or E_5 to E_1 Compression. ef is the compression line.

The four principal events are therefore

(1) Admission, f or E_1.   (3) Release, c or E_4.
(2) Cut-off, b or E_3.   (4) Compression, e or E_5.

239. Mean Effective Pressure from Hypothetical Diagram. This may be obtained by the methods indicated in art. 207. It may be shown that the mean effective pressure of the hypothetical indicator diagram is given by

$$p_m = \frac{p_1(1 + \log_e r)}{r} - p_b.$$

where p_m = hypothetical mean effective pressure in lb. per square inch.

p_1 = boiler pressure of supply in lb. per square inch absolute.

e = base of Naperian logs = $2\cdot718$.

r = volume ratio of expansion = $\dfrac{1}{\text{cut-off fraction}}$.

p_b = back pressure or exhaust pressure in lb. per square inch absolute.

In all cases, however, the mid-ordinate method can be applied which dispenses with the need for this equation. The mid-ordinate method is, however, fairly lengthy, and this formula is frequently required and for this reason must be included.

EXAMPLE. Find the mean effective pressure from a hypothetical indicator diagram to which the following particulars relate. Boiler pressure, 120 lb. per sq. in. gauge. Back pressure, 3 lb. per sq. in. gauge. Cut-off at $\frac{1}{4}$ stroke.

$$p_m = \frac{p_1(1 + \log_e r)}{r} - p_b \qquad\qquad r = \frac{1}{\frac{1}{4}} = 4.$$
$$\log_e r = 2\cdot3026 \log_{10} r$$
$$= 2\cdot3026 \log_{10} 4.$$

$$\therefore \; p_m = \frac{134\cdot7(1 + 2\cdot3026 \log_{10} 4)}{4} - 17\cdot7$$

$$= \frac{134\cdot7(1 + 2\cdot3026 \times 0\cdot6021)}{4} - 17\cdot7$$

$$= \frac{134\cdot7(1 + 1\cdot386)}{4} - 17\cdot7$$

$$= 33\cdot675 \times 2\cdot386 - 17\cdot7$$
$$= 80\cdot34 - 17\cdot7$$
$$= 62\cdot64 \text{ lb. per sq. in.}$$

Note that absolute pressures must be used in the equation and that the mean effective pressure is a pressure difference.

240. Diagram Factor. Examination of fig. 176 will lead to the conclusion that the mean height of the probable indicator diagram *abcdef* is less than the mean height of the hypothetical diagram. Thus the mean effective pressure actually obtained is less than the hypothetical mean effective pressure.

x*

The ratio $\dfrac{\text{actual mean effective pressure}}{\text{hypothetical mean effective pressure}}$ is equal to the

ratio $\dfrac{\text{area of actual indicator diagram}}{\text{area of hypothetical indicator diagrams}}$, when both are set

down to the same scales of pressure and volume and when they are based on the same length of stroke. The latter ratio is known as the "Diagram Factor." Thus the actual mean effective pressure can be obtained if we know the diagram factor and the hypothetical mean effective pressure.

Thus, actual mean effective pressure = hypothetical mean effective pressure × diagram factor.

EXAMPLE. If the diagram factor for the last example is 0·6, find the actual or probable mean effective pressure.

$$\text{Actual M.E.P.} = 62\cdot64 \times 0\cdot6.$$
$$= 37\cdot584 \text{ lb. per sq. in.}$$

Note that the factor is always applied to the problem as the last step in the evaluation.

EXAMPLE. Find the bore and stroke of a double-acting steam engine to develop 120 H.P. at a speed of 80 r.p.m. Supply pressure 150 lb. per sq. in. gauge, cut off at $\frac{1}{3}$ stroke, back pressure 5 lb. per sq. in. gauge. Assume hyperbolic expansion and take a diagram factor of 0·72. The stroke is $1\frac{1}{2}$ times the cylinder bore.

The first step is to find the hypothetical M.E.P.

$$p_m = \frac{p_1(1 + \log_e r)}{r} - p_b$$

$$= \frac{164\cdot7(1 + 2\cdot3026 \log_{10}3)}{3} - 19\cdot7$$

$$= \frac{164\cdot7(1 + 2\cdot3026 \times 0\cdot4771)}{3} - 19\cdot7$$

$$= \frac{164\cdot7(1 + 1\cdot098)}{3} - 19\cdot7$$

$$= 115\cdot1 - 19\cdot7 = 95\cdot4 \text{ lb. per sq. in.}$$

∴ Probable M.E.P. $= 0\cdot72 \times 95\cdot4 = 68\cdot7$ lb. per sq. in.

Work to be done per minute $= 120 \times 33,000$ ft.-lb.

∴ Work to be done per stroke $= \dfrac{120 \times 33,000}{2 \times 80}$ ft.-lb.

$$= 24,750 \text{ ft.-lb.}$$

Let D = diameter of cylinder in inches. Then stroke $= 1\frac{1}{2} \times \dfrac{D}{12}$ ft.

Mean effective force on piston $= \dfrac{\pi D^2}{4} \times 68\cdot7$ lb. $= 54 D^2$ lb.

∴ Work done per stroke = force × stroke length in feet.

$$= 54D^2 \times \frac{1 \cdot 5D}{12} = \frac{81}{12}D^3 \text{ ft.-lb.}$$

$$\therefore \frac{81}{12}D^3 = 24,780$$

$$D^3 = \frac{12 \times 24,750}{81} = 3,667$$

$$\therefore D = \sqrt[3]{3,667} = 15 \cdot 43 \text{ in.}$$

$$\therefore \text{Stroke} = 1 \cdot 5 \times 15 \cdot 43 = 23 \cdot 145 \text{ in.}$$

Note that if the piston speed had been given instead of the stroke/bore ratio, the problem would have been simplified. Suppose the piston speed had been 360 ft. per min. (i.e. stroke $2\frac{1}{4}$ ft.). [The piston speed is the product : length of stroke × number of working strokes per minute.]

$$\text{Then force on piston} = \frac{120 \times 33,000}{360}$$

$$= 11,000 \text{ lb.}$$

$$\therefore 54D^2 = 11,000$$

$$D = \sqrt{\frac{11,000}{54}} = 14 \cdot 28 \text{ in.}$$

241. Actual Indicator Diagrams from Steam Engine. Typical indicator diagrams from double-acting steam engines are illustrated in figs. 177 and 178. It will be noted that two diagrams are shown, one in full line, the other in dotted line.

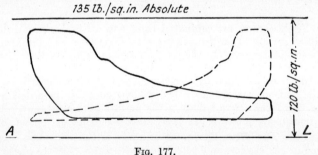

FIG. 177.

Each diagram corresponds to the action on one side of the piston. The mean effective pressure is found for each side and then the average of the two values may be taken in calculating the indicated horse power. When this average is used the average area of piston, allowing for piston rods, etc., must be employed (see art. 208). The M.E.P.s for fig. 177 are 43·2 lb. per sq. in. for full line diagram and 32·2 lb. per sq. in. for dotted line diagram, giving 37·7 lb. per sq. in. as the average value. The values for fig. 178 are 16·3 lb. per sq. in. and 18·21 lb. per sq. in. respectively, giving 17·25 as the average.

It will be noted that the whole of both diagrams in fig. 177 lies above the atmospheric line AL. This shows that the engine is non-condensing and diagrams from such engines always show this feature. Similarly it will be observed that the exhaust lines of the diagrams in fig. 178 lie below the atmospheric line. This shows that the engine exhausts into a vacuum and that it is a condensing engine. The position of the atmospheric line relative to the diagram shows whether the engine is a condensing or a non-condensing engine.

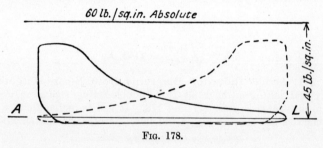

60 lb./sq.in. Absolute

45 lb./sq.in.

Fig. 178.

The diagrams are calibrated by means of the horizontal lines above them. The distance between these lines and the atmospheric line represents the gauge pressure corresponding to the absolute value shown on the upper line. Thus the "spring scale" can be found by measuring the vertical distance between the two horizontal lines. The student may use these diagrams to check the above values of the mean effective pressure. The atmospheric pressure has been taken as 15 lb. per sq. in. abs.

242. The Otto Cycle. This cycle is the one upon which many gas engines and petrol engines operate. It is sometimes called the Beau-de-Rochas cycle and also the "four-stroke" cycle. The latter name arises from the fact that four strokes of the piston are necessary to carry out the whole series of operations comprising the cycle. The indicator diagram is shown in fig. 179. The line AL is the atmospheric line. The point O is the zero point for both volume and pressure scales.

The Volume V_C is the clearance volume, V_S is the volume swept by piston $\left(\text{i.e. } \dfrac{\pi D^2}{4} \times L\right)$ and V_T is the total volume enclosed when the piston is at the extreme right. The length V_S is proportional to the length of the piston stroke. The cycle is carried out as follows, starting with the piston at the left-hand end of the cylinder. The first stroke is outwards from the clearance space.

(1) The piston draws in a charge of gas and air, the pressure of the charge being slightly less than that of the atmosphere. This process is shown by the line 1–2, which is known as the suction or induction line and is below the atmospheric line

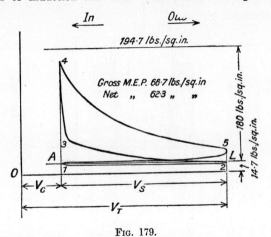

Fig. 179.

During this stroke air and gas valves are open. Fig. 180 shows the suction stroke taking place.

(2) The air and gas valves close at the end of the first stroke and the piston returns to the clearance end of the cylinder compressing the charge as shown by the line 2–3. This compression is according to a law of the form $PV^n = C$. The line 2–3 is called the compression line.

(3) Between the points 3–4 the heat is supplied. This is done while the piston is practically stationary at the end of the second stroke. The heat supply commences on passage of the igniting spark.

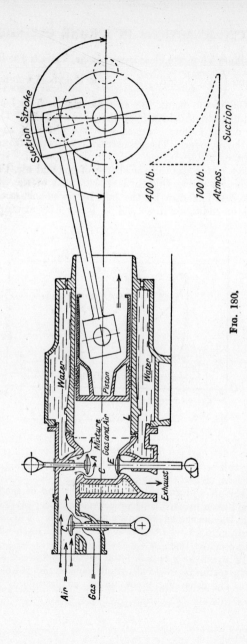

FIG. 180.

(4) The third stroke now commences and the high temperature gases expand and thrust the piston forward. This is the " power " or " working " stroke and is shown by the line 4–5. This line is called the expansion line. Its law is again of the form $PV^n = C$. During this stroke all the valves are closed as in the second stroke.

(5) At the end of the third stroke the exhaust valve opens and the piston again returns to the clearance end of the cylinder. This is the fourth stroke or exhaust stroke. The line 5–1 indicates this stroke and is known as the exhaust line. The exhaust valve closes at or near the end of this stroke. This stroke com-

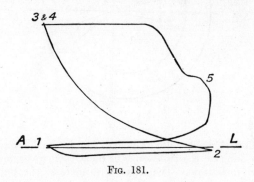

Fig. 181.

pletes the cycle, and the next out stroke commences a new set of the same processes in the same order.

It will be noted that the diagram comprises two loops. The upper and larger one is known as the positive loop and the lower and smaller one is the negative loop. Where the negative loop is clearly defined its M.E.P. should be obtained and subtracted from that of the positive loop in order to obtain the net indicated horse power. If the M.E.P. from the positive loop is used alone, then the gross indicated horse power will be obtained. The fig. 181 shows the negative loop indicated with a lighter spring than that used when fig. 179 was indicated. This has the effect of opening out the negative loop.

243. Valve Timing. We have already pointed out that three valves control the action of the Otto cycle. To show the actual sequence of operation a " timing " diagram is used. This is composed of four semicircles each representing a stroke.

x*

From a convenient point near the centre of this diagram, radial
lines are drawn to represent the engine crank positions when
the various valves open and close. Fig. 182 shows a typical
timing diagram for a four-stroke gas engine.

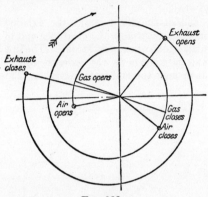

FIG. 182.

244. The Two-stroke Cycle. An internal combustion
engine working on the two-stroke or Clerk cycle gives one power
stroke per revolution. The effect is to increase the work done
per unit time by an engine of given size. A diagram of such an
engine is shown in fig. 183 whilst a typical indicator diagram
from a two-stroke engine is shown in fig. 184.

The action of the engine is as follows : Air and fuel are drawn
into the crank case through a spring-operated inlet valve at I
on the inward stroke of the piston. On the outward stroke the
mixture is slightly compressed in the crank case on the right hand
of the piston. Towards the end of this out-stroke the piston
uncovers the inlet port IP and also the exhaust port EP, when
the gas and air charge in the crank case sweeps into the cylinder
driving the exhaust gases of the previous working stroke before
it through the exhaust port. This process is known as the
scavenging process. The piston now returns and for a short
portion of the stroke, shown by line AB on indicator diagram,
the scavenging process continues. When the exhaust port is
closed by the piston (at B) scavenging ceases and compression
commences. Compression continues for the remainder of the

inward stroke (line BC on diagram). At C the spark is passed
and the pressure rises to its maximum value. The piston now

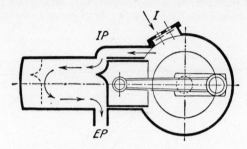

FIG. 183.

moves to the right and this stroke is the working stroke. It is
shown by the line DE on the diagram. The point E indicates

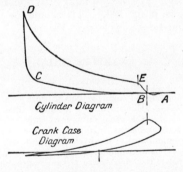

FIG. 184.

the point in the stroke where the exhaust and the scavenging
part of the cycle commences. At the point A the stroke is
completed.

The lines on the diagram are classified as follows:

From E to B (through A). Exhaust and scavenging.

,, B to C. Compression of the charge.

,, C to D. Supply of heat for which no stroke is needed.

,, D to E. Expansion of the working substance.

It will be noted that the piston head is formed in such a manner as to deflect the fresh charge into the cylinder and to prevent it from passing straight across into the exhaust passage. Such an occurrence would waste the fuel and diminish the

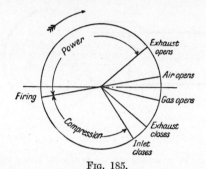

FIG. 185.

thermal efficiency. The valve-timing diagram for a two-stroke oil engine is shown in fig. 185. This should be compared with that for the four-stroke cycle, fig. 182.

EXAMPLES XXI

SECTION A

1. An internal combustion engine is said to work on the "four-stroke" or "two-stroke" cycle. Explain what is meant by these terms. Describe carefully the four-stroke cycle of operations and show by means of diagrams the positions of valves and crank at important points in the cycle.   U.E.I.

2. Explain diagrammatically, the cycle of operations of a single-acting internal combustion engine running on gaseous fuel. Why does such an engine need no piston rod, and where is the connecting rod fastened?
     N.C.T.E.C.

3. Name the chief working parts of a simple steam engine and show by an outline sketch how the reciprocating motion of the piston is converted into the rotary motion of the crank shaft.   U.L.C.I.

4. The cylinder of an engine is 7 in. in diameter and the piston stroke is 11 in. The mean effective pressure of the steam in the cylinder is 40 lb. per sq. in. Find the speed of the engine in revolutions per minute in order that it may develop 16 I.H.P.   U.L.C.I.

5. A double-acting steam engine has a cylinder diameter of 6 in. and the stroke of the piston is 10 in. The mean effective pressure of the steam in the cylinder is 40 lb. per sq. in. At what speed, in revolutions per minute, should the engine be run in order to develop 20 H.P.?   U.L.C.I.

6. Steam at an absolute pressure of 80 lb. per sq. in. is admitted to the

cylinder of an engine and is cut off at 0·4 stroke, the back pressure being 17 lb. per sq. in.   Draw, to scale, the hypothetical indicator diagram (in which expansion follows the law $pv =$ constant) and determine the mean effective pressure of the steam during a stroke.   U.L.C.I.

7. The diameter of the cylinder of a double-acting steam engine is 9 in., and the length of the piston stroke is 15 in.   Find what mean effective pressure of the steam would develop 15 H.P. at a speed of 125 r.p.m.
                                                                    U.L.C.I.

8. The cylinder of a steam engine is 10 in. diameter and the length of the piston stroke is 18 in.   What is the horse-power when the number of effective strokes is 2·5 per sec. and the mean effective pressure is 40 lb. per sq. in. ?   C.G.L.I.

9. The diameter of an engine cylinder is 16 in. and the length of stroke is 26 in.   The work done per stroke is 26,130 ft.-lb.   Find the mean effective pressure.   C.G.L.I.

SECTION B

10. Steam enters the cylinder of an engine at a pressure of 80 lb. per sq. in. abs. and is cut off at 0·5 stroke.   Assuming a back pressure of 17 lb. per sq. in., draw to scale a hypothetical diagram for one stroke, and find the theoretical mean effective pressure of the steam.

Indicate by dotted lines how the theoretical diagram would be modified in practice.   U.L.C.I.

11. Sketch in outline, an eccentric and describe briefly how the slide valve of a steam engine is operated.   U.L.C.I.

12. Explain the cycle of events that occur in a gas engine working on the " Otto " cycle.

Find the indicated horse-power of a four-stroke gas engine running at 240 r.p.m., if the mean effective pressure during the working stroke is 70 lb. per sq. in., the diameter of the cylinder 8 in., and the stroke 15 in. Assume an explosion to be missed in every six cycles.   U.L.C.I.

13. The travel of a slide valve is 5 in.   What is the eccentricity of the eccentric ?   The steam lap is $1\frac{1}{8}$ in. and the lead is $\frac{1}{8}$ in.   Find the angle of advance of the eccentric.

14. If the inside lap in example 13 is $\frac{1}{2}$ in. find the crank positions relative to the horizontal centre line, when the events of cut-off, release, compression, and admission occur.

15. The following particulars relate to a double-acting steam engine : Piston area 19·6 sq. in., stroke 20 in., revolutions per minute 180, initial steam pressure 100 lb. per sq. in. abs., exhaust pressure 10 lb. per sq. in. abs., cut off 0·5 stroke.

Draw the hypothetical indicator diagram to scale and use it to find the hypothetical mean effective pressure.   Thence determine the I.H.P. of the engine if the actual mean effective pressure is 0·8 of the hypothetical value.
                                                                  N.C.T.E.C.

16. For a single-cylinder double-acting steam engine, the mean effective pressure found from the hypothetical diagram is 72 lb. per sq. in. and the actual value may be taken as 0·9 of this.   Determine the cylinder diameter required to develop 100 I.H.P.   Stroke 24 in., revolutions per minute 150. If you use a formula it must be deduced.   N.C.T.E.C.

17. The mean effective pressure of steam on a piston is 40 lb. per sq. in. ; the area of the piston is 150 sq. in. ; the length of the crank is 1·3 ft. ; what is the work done in one stroke ? If there are 300 working strokes per minute, what is the horse-power ?

If the steam is cut off at $\frac{1}{3}$ of the stroke and the entering steam has a volume of 5 cu. ft. per lb., find the steam consumption, neglecting clearance and condensation.   N.C.T.E.C.

18. Steam is admitted to an engine cylinder at a pressure of 60 lb. per sq. in. abs. Taking a back pressure of 5 lb. per sq. in. abs. and cut-off at $\frac{1}{3}$ stroke, construct the hypothetical indicator diagram and from it find the mean effective pressure.

If the area of the piston is 126 sq. in. and the crank is 11 in. long, how much work is done in one stroke ?   N.C.T.E.C.

19. Sketch the type of indicator diagram obtained from a steam engine, and write on the diagram the most important features. The cylinder diameter of a double-acting steam engine is 18 in. and the stroke 27 in. The mean effective pressure at 120 r.p.m. is 43 lb. per sq. in. Calculate the indicated horse-power.   N.C.T.E.C.

20. Consider the following cases :

(a) Steam is admitted to a cylinder of an engine at 80 lb. per sq. in. abs. for the full stroke of 24 in.

(b) Steam is admitted at 80 lb. per sq. in. abs. to the same cylinder but is cut off at 0·6 of the stroke. The steam then expands during the remainder of the stroke, the law of expansion being assumed to be $pv = $ constant.

If the piston area is 100 sq. in. and the back pressure 15 lb. per sq. in. abs., find the work done during one stroke per cubic foot of steam. What do you learn from this problem ?   N.C.T.E.C.

21. A double-acting steam engine has cylinder diameter 12 in. and stroke 2 ft. If the cut-off is at $\frac{1}{3}$-stroke and the steam has a volume of 2·2 cu. ft. per lb., calculate the probable steam consumption in lb. per hour at 120 r.p.m. Compare the work done per lb. of steam if the steam had been used non-expansively, assuming the ratio of mean effective pressures to be 2.   N.C.T.E.C.

22. Given the boiler pressure to be 135 lb. per sq. in. gauge, back pressure 17 lb. per sq. in. abs., cut-off at 0·6 stroke, expansion according to Boyle's Law, draw to scale the theoretical indicator diagram for the engine.

Find, in any way you please, the mean effective pressure on the piston. Denote on the diagram, using dotted lines, the indicator diagram such as might be expected from a non-condensing steam engine, fitted with a slide valve, and describe what each part of the diagram means.   U.E.I.

23. From the initial steam pressure, back pressure and point of cut off, the mean effective pressure in a proposed engine cylinder is calculated to be 70 lb. per sq. in. The calculation assumes that expansion of the steam takes place according to Boyle's Law, and that clearance and other losses are neglected. Find the dimensions of such a double-acting steam engine cylinder (bore and stroke) to develop 40 H.P. with a piston speed of 600 ft. per min., the diagram factor being 0·7 and revolutions of the engine crank shaft 120 per min.   U.E.I.

24. The dimensions across the outside edges of the steam ports in a slide valve engine are $8\frac{1}{4}$ in. and the ports are $1\frac{1}{4}$ in. wide in the direction of motion. The outside edges of the valve measure 10 in. and the inside edges

$4\frac{1}{2}$ in. Determine the steam and exhaust laps. What travel would be required to open the exhaust port fully and what would be the corresponding steam port opening ?

25. If the valve in exercise 24 is to open the steam port to its full extent, what should be the travel ? If this travel is adopted, by how much does the inside edges of the valve overrun the outside edges of the ports ?

TABLE V

Properties of Steam

Pressure. Lb./sq. in. Absolute.	Tempera-ture. ° F.	Specific Volume. Cu. ft./lb.	Total Heat of Liquid. B.Th.U.	Latent Heat. B.Th.U.	Total Heat of Steam. B.Th.U.
p	t	V_s	λ	L	H
0·5	79·6	643·0	47·6	1048·5	1096·1
0·6	85·3	540·6	53·2	1045·4	1098·6
0·8	94·4	411·7	62·4	1040·3	1102·7
1·0	101·7	334·0	69·7	1036·1	1105·8
2	126·1	173·7	94·0	1022·2	1116·2
4	153·0	90·63	121·0	1006·7	1127·7
6	170·1	61·98	138·1	996·6	1134·7
8	182·9	47·35	151·0	988·5	1139·5
10	193·2	38·42	161·3	982·5	1143·8
14·7	212·0	26·80	180·1	970·6	1150·7
16	216·3	24·74	184·5	967·9	1152·4
18	222·4	22·17	190·6	964·0	1154·6
20	228·0	20·09	196·3	960·4	1156·7
25	240·1	16·30	208·6	952·5	1161·1
30	250·3	13·73	219 0	945·6	1164·6
35	259·3	11·89	228·0	939·6	1167·6
40	267·2	10·50	236·1	934·4	1170·5
50	281·0	8·516	250·2	924·6	1174·8
60	292·7	7·175	262·2	916·2	1178·4
70	302·9	6·206	272·7	908·7	1181·4
80	312·0	5·472	282·1	901·9	1184·0
90	320·3	4·896	290·7	895·5	1186·2
100	327·8	4·434	298·5	889·7	1188·2
110	334·8	4·046	305·7	884·2	1189·9
120	341·3	3·729	312·5	878·9	1191·4
130	347·3	3·456	318·8	874·0	1192·8
140	353·0	3·222	324·9	869·1	1194·0
150	358·4	3·015	330·6	864·5	1195·1
160	363·6	2·835	336·0	860·1	1196·1
170	368·4	2·677	341·2	855·9	1197·1
180	373·1	2·534	346·1	851·9	1198·0
190	377·5	2·407	350·9	847·9	1198·8
200	381·8	2·290	355·5	844·0	1199·5
220	389·9	2·089	364·2	836·5	1200·7
240	397·4	1·918	372·3	829·4	1201·7
250	401·0	1·844	376·1	826·0	1202·1
260	404·4	1·775	379·9	822·6	1202·5
280	411·1	1·651	387·1	816·1	1203·2
300	417·3	1·543	394·0	809·8	1203·8
350	431·7	1·326	409·9	795·0	1204·9
400	444·6	1·161	424·2	781·3	1205·5

ANSWERS

1. 16 lb. **2.** 8,300 lb. **3.** 0·28 in. **4.** 8·97 tons per sq. in. **5.** 9·43 tons.
6. 88·1 lb. per sq. in. **7.** 2,880 lb. **8.** 4·53 tons per sq. in. **9.** 47,500 lb.
10. 14,320, 0·000,474 in. **11.** 27,600 lb. per sq. in., 0·00112 in. **12.** 84 lb.,
16 in.

1. 16,000 lb. per sq. in., 0·0000625, 256 × 10⁶. **2.** 2·315 tons per sq. in.
3. 800 lb. per sq. in., 0·0000533, 15 × 10⁶. **4.** 25,150 lb. **5.** 29·6 × 10⁶.
6. 11·4 tons per sq. in. **7.** 30·1 × 10⁶. **8.** 4 tons per sq. in., 0·00237.
9. 8·85 tons, 0·0448 in. **10.** 0·0318 in. **11.** 0·0328 in. **12.** 0·0551°.
13. 0·00522 in., 5·66 tons per sq. in., 2·34 tons per sq. in. **14.** 56,470 tons
per sq. in. **15.** 196·5 lb., 8·727 in. **16.** 666·7 lb. per sq. in.

1. 10·38 cwt. **2.** 18 cwt. **3.** 40 lb., 30 lb. **4.** 451 lb. at 32½° to
240 lb. force. **5.** 4·61 lb., 4 lb. **6.** 4·92 tons, 0·868 tons. **7.** 5·77 lb.
8. (*a*) 75 lb., 130 lb.; (*b*) 100 lb., 141 lb. **9.** 19·3 tons, 14·1 tons.
10. 42·4 lb. **11.** 11,120 lb., 11,380 lb., 1,970 lb. **12.** 11·52 lb., 10·34 lb.
13. 18 lb., 21·9 lb., 34° to BC. **14.** 8·7 lb. perp. to ladder, 46 lb. at 11°
to vertical. **15.** 61·1 lb., 53·8 lb. at 40° to horizontal. **16.** 0·373 tons,
0·762 tons at 71° to horizontal. **17.** 2·5 tons, 10·61 tons. **18.** 1·98 lb.,
6° W. of N. **19.** 9·62 tons, 55·6 tons, both tension. **20.** 30·6 lb., 51·5 lb.
at 55° to horizontal. **21.** 24·1 lb. **22.** 28·95 lb. at 17° W. of S.
23. 17·35 lb. **24.** 364·9 lb., 360 lb.

1. 3½ lb., 7½ in. from thick end. **2.** 2,883 lb., 4,377 lb. **3.** 23·3 lb.,
36·67 lb. **4.** (*a*) At mid-point, (*b*) 1·5 ft. from each leg. **5.** 12·78 ft. from
one end. **7.** 3·39 tons, 3·61 tons. **8.** 3·5 ft. from fulcrum, 1,820 lb.
9. 4·23 in. from open end. **10.** 0·375 in. from centre of disc. **11.** 0·3 in.
from centre of square. **12.** 11·23 in. from end of rod. **13.** 4·8 in. from
end of middle limb. **14.** 6·32 ft. from thick end. **15.** 19·5 lb., 9·5 lb.
16. 1·875 tons. **17.** 1·115 ft. from 8 lb. wt. **18.** 6⅔ lb. **19.** 5·96 in.
from round end. **20.** 19·46 lb. **21.** 50 lb. **22.** 36 ft.

1. 6,790 lb. at 19½° to vertical, 1,250 lb., 6,664 lb. **2.** 4,070 lb., 705 lb.,
20,000 lb.-in. **3.** 6,040 lb., 7,970 lb. **4.** 10·05 tons, 6·95 tons. **5.** 60·8 lb.
per sq. in. **6.** 7·28 tons, 4·47 tons, 78·86 ton-ft., 3·03 tons. **8.** 42·9 lb.,
57·1 lb. **9.** AC tie 5 tons, CD strut 7·07 tons, DA tie 7·07 tons,
BD strut 10 tons. **10.** B.M.s 1,205, 2,192, 1,796, S.F. 241, 141, 99, 449.
11. 52 lb. **12.** BD tie 8 tons, CD strut 11·3 tons, AC strut 16 tons,
BC tie 11·3 tons. **13.** 38 ton-ft. **14.** 8·3 ton-ft. **15.** 50 in. **16.** 20 ton-in.
17. 1,680 lb.-in.

EXAMPLES VI (*page* 73)

1. 84·5 lb., 181·2 lb. **2.** 672,000 ft.-lb., 27·1 H.P. **3.** 3,600 ft.-tons.
4. 512. **5.** 118,000 ft.-lb., 0·119 H.P. **6.** 100. **7.** 0·2885 H.P.
8. 516,000 ft.-lb., average H.P. 3·13. **9.** 6,000 watts, 9·35 H.P.
11. 38,675 ft.-lb. **12.** (*a*) 1·6 H.P., (*b*) 10·13 H.P. **13.** 40 in.-lb.
14. 2,550 ft.-lb., 0·193 H.P. **15.** 4,000 lb., 2,350 lb. **16.** (*a*) 62·5, (*b*) 21·8.
17. 210 lb.-ft. **18.** 7,480 lb., 598·4 H.P. **19.** 1,332 lb. **20.** 268 H.P.
21. 21·2 H.P., 13,600 watts, yes. **22.** 252 lb., 480·9 lb., 1·603 sq. in.
23. 19·8 H.P., 32·9 amps. **24.** 14·9*d*. **25.** 6·03. **26.** 2·095. **27.** 464.

EXAMPLES VII (*page* 83)

1. 4 lb. **2.** 116·7 lb., 0·6. **3.** 212 ft.-lb. **4.** 1·99 lb. per sq. in.
5. 300 lb., 159 lb. **6.** 11·5 lb., 13°. **7.** 1·003 B.Th.U. **8.** 82,000 ft.-lb.,
105·4 .BTh.U. **9.** 161·4 lb., 361 lb. **10.** 9 tons, 1 in 79. **11.** 2·3 H.P.
12. 0·2.

EXAMPLES VIII (*page* 101)

1. 50, 0·48. **2.** 70, 3·06 lb. **5.** 616 r.p.m., 78·6 r.p.m. **6.** 20 r.p.m.
7. 330 lb. **8.** 3·14 tons. **9.** 18 in., 6 in. **10.** 444·4 lb. **11.** 11·14 lb.
12. 100. **13.** E = 0·046L + 0·24, 0·588. **16.** 19·5 lb., 57·5 per cent.
17. 96 per cent.

EXAMPLES IX (*page* 117)

1. 78·4. **2.** 6·28. **3.** 62·5 sec. **4.** 102·5, 0·0347, 0·417. **5.** 8·33.
2,222, 152·5. **6.** 6 ft. per sec. **7.** 2·4 ft. per sec.^{2} **8.** 5 ft. per sec^2.
9. 34 ft. per sec., 26 ft. per sec., 208 ft. **10.** 43·8 ft. per sec. **11.** 7·21 ft.
per sec. 56° to hor. **12.** 2·81 ft. per sec.,^{2} 6·903 in. **13.** 17½° W. of S.
14. (*a*) 1·21 ft. per sec.^{2}, (*b*) 17·6 rad. per sec., 0·969 rad. per sec.^{2}
15. (*a*) 4·03 ft. per sec.^{2}, (*b*) 5·46 sec., (*c*) 4·03 rad. per sec. **17.** 0·644 rad.
per sec.^{2}, 28 sec. **18.** 36·6, 23, 27 miles. **19.** 1,100 yd. **20.** 17·4 sec.
21. 2 ft. per sec.^{2}, 44·7 sec.

EXAMPLES X (*page* 133)

1. 2·33. **2.** 258 lb. **3.** 0·61. **4.** 4,250 dynes. **5.** 200. **6.** 3,450 lb.
per sq. in. **7.** 3,850 lb. **8.** 1·9 sec., 34·8 ft. **10.** 32·7 lb. bisects AOB.
11. 0·977 ft. per sec.^{2}, 48·8 ft. **12.** 4,650, 775 lb. **13.** 83·2 lb., 6,800 lb.,
6,637 lb. **14.** 7·6 ft. per sec., 1·2 ft. per sec.^{2} **15.** 20,940 lb. **16.** 9·94 ft.

EXAMPLES XI (*page* 142)

1. 25,120,000 ft.-lb., 152 H.P. **2.** 55,700 ft.-lb. **3.** 20,870 ft.-lb.
4. 14 ft.-lb. **5.** 17,920 C.H.U., 32,300 B.Th.U. **6.** 1,296 × 10^7 ergs,
1,296 joules. **7.** 59·68. **8.** 13,450 ft.-lb., 224·7 ft. **9.** 12·7 ft. per sec.,
18 in. **10.** 9,020 ft.-lb., 820, 142 lb. **11.** 69,600 ft.-lb., 3·55 ft.
12. 2,930,000 ft.-lb. **13.** 116·5 ft.-lb., 1·97 ft. **14.** 4 ft. per sec.,
33,400 ft.-lb. **15.** 5·87 ft. per sec. **16.** 341·4 r.p.m. **17.** 22·62 ft. per
sec. **18.** 38·58 rev.

EXAMPLES XII (*page* 153)

1. 0·0361. **2.** 56·25, 0·0325. **3.** 32,000, 222. **4.** 0·181. **5.** 1,995.
6. 124·8 lb. per sq. ft., 1,995. **7.** 1,740 lb. **8.** 0·332 lb. per sq. in.
9. 864,000 lb., 1,664 lb. per sq. ft. **10.** 2,560 lb. per sq. ft., 18,100 lb.
11. 9·74.

EXAMPLES XIII (*page* 159)

1. 25·4 ft. per sec. **2.** 12 ft.-lb. per lb. **3.** 0·406 cu. ft. **4.** 348 lb.
5. 1·94 gall. **6.** 0·905 in. **7.** 86 ft. per sec., 13,430 ft.-lb., 24·5 H.P.
8. 342 lb. **9.** 0·768 lb., 0·86, 0·86 lb. **10.** 4·32 lb., 1·34, No. 1·34 lb.

EXAMPLES XIV (*page* 175)

7. 160° C. **8.** 356° F. **9.** 1° R = 1·25° C. = 2·25° F. **10.** 167° F. and
75° C. **11.** 2·834 in. **12.** Vol. = 41·3884 cu. in. and density = 0·254 lb.
/cu. in. **13.** 0·126 in. **14.** 1·6524 in. **15.** 0·0726 in. **16.** − 12·2° C.,
88·8° C., − 4° F. and 140° F. **18.** 1·53 in.

EXAMPLES XV (*page* 185)

3. 72° F. **4.** 5,452 gr.-cals. **5.** 1,875 B.Th.U. **6.** 0·413 tons,
4·913 tons. **8.** 126,000 C.H.U., 10,500 lb. **9.** 0·409. **10.** 19,712 B.Th.U.
11. 64·5° F. **12.** 277·6° F. **13.** 360° F. **14.** 0·12. **15.** 37·8 B.Th.U.,
76·2° F. **16.** 340,200 B.Th.U., 3,780 lb. /hr. or 378 gall. /hr.
18. 6,240,000 B.Th.U. **19.** 716·7 B.Th.U., 92·6° F.

EXAMPLES XVI (*page* 200)

3. 1,334·5 B.Th.U. **4.** (*a*) 1,059·5 B.Th.U., (*b*) 1,017·3 B.Th.U.
5. (*a*) 45·47 B.Th.U., (*b*) 88·33 B.Th.U. **6.** 1,261·7 B.Th.U.
7. 1,081·7 B.Th.U. **8.** 826·0 B.Th.U. **9.** 11·2 lb. **10.** 103·7° F.
11. 140·4° F. **12.** From left to right, 26·3, 491·7 and 653·6, 3,185·5 C.H.U.
13. 899 B.Th.U. **14.** 11,052 B.Th.U., 6,140 C.H.U. **15.** 111,300 B.Th.U.
331 cu. ft. **16.** 394 B.Th.U. **17.** 11,751, 8,260 latent, 3,491 sensible.
18. 44·4 B.Th.U. **19.** 0·0774 lb. **20.** 936 B.Th.U., 963 B.Th.U.
21. 1,062·85 B.Th.U., 1,125·4 B.Th.U. **22.** 19,420 lb. **24.** 8·41 lb.

EXAMPLES XVII (*page* 217)

3. O_2 23 per cent., N_2 77 per cent. by wt., O_2 21 per cent., N_2 79 per cent.
by vol. **5.** 11·57 lb., 34·8 lb., 4·35 lb. **6.** 0·23478 lb. **7.** 21,150 B.Th.U.,
19,840 B.Th.U. **8.** 14·7 lb. **9.** (Higher) 20,490 B.Th.U., 18·06 lb.
10. 10·68 lb., 15 lb. **11.** 2,357 B.Th.U. and 3,018 B.Th.U.
12. 13,390 B.Th.U. **13.** 11·23 lb. **14.** 46·35, 18·64, 46·35 lb.
15. 11·58 lb. **16.** 11·25 lb., CO_2 3·258 lb., H_2O 0·279 lb., O_2 1·293 lb.,
N_2 12·99 lb. **17.** 8,449 C.H.U. and 15,208 B.Th.U. **18.** 11·57 and 34·8 lb.,
14·59 lb., 1·17 lb. steam and 3·184 lb. CO_2.

EXAMPLES XVIII (*page* 247)

1. 2,545 B.Th.U. or 1,414 C.H.U. **2.** 3·53 lb. **3.** 205·6 B.Th.U.
4. 8,940 lb. **5.** 37·4 per cent. **6.** 8·6 per cent. **7.** 14·95 per cent.
9. 6,900 ft.-lb., 8·86 B.Th.U. **10.** 0·568 lb. **11.** 1,190,000 ft.-lb.
12. 59,400 B.Th.U. 46·2 × 10⁶ ft.-lb., 23·3 H.P. **14.** 2,169 B.Th.U.,
43·9 per cent. **15.** 2,830 lb. **16.** 1,413·7 lb. **19.** 0·775. **20.** 558 lb.
21. 10·34 lb. **25.** 23·6, 21·38, 9 lb. and 9·08 lb. **26.** 22,562,000 ft.-lb.,
34·2 min. **27.** 3,124·8 B.Th.U., 17·45 lb. **28.** 123·4° F.

EXAMPLES XIX (*page* 269)

2. 127,250 B.Th.U. per hr., 1,590·6 lb. per hr. **3.** 69 per cent.
4. (*a*) 4,518 lb., (*b*) 5,647·5 ft.-lb., (*c*) 15·38 H.P. **7.** 28·3 B.H.P.

324 ANSWERS

8. 420,000 B.Th.U. and 10·9 per cent. **10.** 349 r.p.m. **11.** 8·46 I.H.P.
12. 14·47 B.H.P. **13.** 12·85 I.H.P. **14.** 356,330 B.Th.U.
15. 1,060 B.Th.U. **16.** 46,680,000 ft.-lb., 23·57 H.P. **17.** 362,500,000 ft.-
tons. **18.** 79·6 per cent. **19.** 21·06 I.H.P., 16·66 B.H.P.
20. 809,120 ft.-lb. per min. **21.** 10·65 per cent. **22.** 74·5 H.P., 300 kw.
hours, 12·57 per cent. **23.** 927,150 lb. per hr. **25.** 33·53 lb. per lb. of
steam. **26.** 213,840 B.Th.U. per hr. **27.** 3·404 in., 0·1472, 0·2822, 0·527,
0·77, 0·886 of its full travel from right.

EXAMPLES XX (*page* 294)

3. 7·5. **4.** 4·5. **5.** 4. **6.** 70·9 lb. per sq. in. **7.** 4·7 lb. per sq. in. and
0·7 lb. per sq. in. **9.** 200 lb. per sq. in. abs. **10.** 400 cu. ft. **11.** 40 lb.
per sq. in. abs. **12.** 1.127° F. **13.** 3,958° F. abs., and 3,168° F. abs.
14. 22·9 lb. per sq. in. abs. **15.** 10·21 cu. ft. **16.** 75 lb. per sq. in. abs.
17. 454 cu. ft., 426 cu. ft. **18.** 0·25 cu. ft., 0·284 cu. ft. **19.** 3·105 cu. ft.
20. 2·36 cu. ft. **21.** 12·5 cu. ft./lb. **22.** 153·4 lb. **23.** 26·5 lb. per
sq. in. abs. **24.** 18·94 cu. ft. **25.** 500° C. and 1,000° F. abs.
26. 157·5 lb. per sq. in. **27.** 9·7 cu. ft. **28.** 167 lb. **29.** 23 cu. ft. and
6/8½. **30.** 31·4 per cent. **31.** 262 lb. per sq. in. gauge. **32.** 3,400° F.
ordinary. **33.** 433 cu. ft., 318 lb. per sq. in. abs. **34.** PV = 53·2T ;
7·3 cu. ft.

EXAMPLES XXI (*page* 316)

4. 187 r.p.m. double acting. **5.** 350 r.p.m. **6.** 44·32 lb. per sq. in.
7. 24·95 lb. per sq. in. **8.** 21·42 lb. per sq. in. **9.** 59·8 lb. per sq. in.
10. 50·72 lb. per sq. in. **12.** 13·32 H.P. **13.** 2·5 in. and 30°. **14.** Cut-
off 122·3°, Rel. 160·5°, Comp. 318°, Adm. 356·5°. **15.** M.E.P. 74·8 lb. per
sq. in., 21·3 H.P. **16.** 10·38 in. **17.** 15,600 ft.-lb., 141·8 H.P., 3,258 lb.
per hr. **18.** 36·8 lb. per sq. in., 8,500 ft.-lb. **19.** 179 H.P.
20. (a) 9,360 ft.-lb., (b) 13, 847 ft.-lb. **21.** 3,433 ft.-lb., 3 : 2. **22.** 119 lb.
per sq. in. **23.** 7·57 in. dia. 30 in. str. **24.** ⅞ in., ⅝ in., 3¾ in., 1 in.
25. 4¼ in., ¼ in.